Married to Albert

❦

To Angie
with love
& laughter

Anne Waller
x x x

Annie Waller lives in Wiltshire with her son (and now-doting husband). She wrote the book to avoid a dawning realisation that once darling child hit school age, part-time labour would be her destiny. Now she can look forward to her dream of affording a psychotherapist and hours of talking about herself.

Married to Albert

A turbulent tale of marriage, mayhem and the military

Annie Waller

Boltneck Publications

Published by Boltneck Publications 2004

First published in Great Britain in 2004 by
Boltneck Publications
The Media Centre
Abbey Wood Park
Emma-Chris Way
Filton
Bristol BS34 7JU

Boltneck Publications Limited Reg. No. 91093290

A CIP catalogue record for this book is available from the British Library

ISBN 0 9546399 0 1

Typeset in Palatino by Ark Creative, Norwich, Norfolk
Printed and bound in Great Britain by Bookmarque Ltd, Croydon, Surrey

For Trevor
And women who wait

Preface

Life is too funny to forget. Even as a kid I could make people laugh with my weird anecdotes. And I've always thought that everyone should put their memoirs down on paper at some point in their lives, mainly because ordinary people often have more interesting stories of love, sorrow and courage than any public figure I've ever read about. For years my grandparents would tell me how they grew up in poverty and survived a world war, and I would listen to stories about them cuddling a shoe because they were too poor to afford a doll or about what it was really like to be the youngest in a family of fourteen. But I could never be bothered to spare the time to capture these fabulous true accounts – there was always tomorrow.

When they died within a few years of each other, it was like taking a reality pill regarding my own mortality. We're here on this planet for such a short time, and I honestly believe that it's not what you leave behind, but what you don't leave behind that counts. And this thought drove me to write a story about being married to someone who's already married…to his job.

Betrothed to the 'sport of angels' before I met him, my husband is totally in love with his career as a pilot, and I accepted my position in his life, determined to bide my time and eventually take precedence. Unfortunately, I failed miserably, destined to play second fiddle to forty tonnes of metal called Fat Albert, and set about writing for women who suffer the same fate, not only in the Air Force but in all areas of life where work comes first.

Days, months and years pass so quickly, the only way to cope with a career junkie is to know what you're getting into, accept defeat ungracefully and laugh all the way to retirement together.

ONE

"Good morning…"

"Fuck off."

Charles lounges in reception with impregnable cool, engrossed in the *Yorkshire Post*, and gives the same answer to every cheery greeting offered. I sneak in late, as usual, and tiptoe past, convinced I can hear him growling.

Bolting up the stairs, I glance back to see his piercing black eyes looking at me over the top of an imaginary pair of spectacles. (God I'm scared of him.) The only good thing about being in the presence of our managing director is my metabolism shoots sky-high, threatening visible neck rash and verbal babbling syndrome. But at least I'm in calorific overdrive, and that's never a bad thing.

Piers Portman, the other director, rolls in five minutes after me, carefully leaning his folding bicycle against a cupboard door. Siobhan says he looks like a paraplegic Postman Pat, which raises a few laughs in the office and a hurt glance from Piers. Immensely talented but communicatively inept, Piers sails through life blissfully unaware of the chaos he generates around him. My job is to smooth the way before and after he gets there. We always have our best rows in public, tempting nearly every member of staff to wander slowly past our door.

Finally at my desk, I flick on my computer and start organising a topping-out ceremony for a large housing developer. At 9.15 in the morning, it's hard to muster any enthusiasm for the new suburb of little boxes awaiting human habitation, and I wonder how on earth they can commercialise the ancient pagan customs of blessing the highest stone on a building or ritually placing a sod of grass on a roof. It seems so shallow to turn it all into a sales pitch. Oh well, best get on with it; I'm not paid to think.

Looking across the brightly lit office, I notice Jimbo staring back, deliberately focusing left of my gaze. It amazes me how he can hold such an inane expression without laughing and I giggle loudly, making eye contact. Seconds later, he jumps up awkwardly, throws paper at a filing cabinet, coughs repeatedly and says, "Hello?" into a switched-off mobile phone.

"Broken any New Year's resolutions yet?" I enquire.

"Nope," he replies, asking what mine are.

"Same as last year of course…to be more selfish, conceited and glamorous."

There's a commotion going on outside across the road – someone's having a heart attack…it's an old lady, she's collapsed on the pavement sending her groceries spewing into the traffic. We all clamber around the window to watch and become instant medical experts over our bacon sandwiches and cups of tea.

"Ooh look, there's Dawn," Maggie says.

Lauren squeezes in between our shoulders asking, "What's she doing?" as we watch the managing director's secretary run across the road, get down on her knees and start cardiopulmonary resuscitation.

"Bloody hell, she's giving mouth-to-mouth!"

"Good God, I could only do that to someone I really loved," exclaims Jimbo.

"I've done it to my dog," Camp Carl blithely informs us.

"Exactly," mutters Jimbo.

Seconds later, an ambulance appears and the poor old dear gets carted off unceremoniously (our breakfast suddenly loses its appeal).

Dawn returns to a hero's welcome and brushes aside compliments, saying, "Anyone would've done the same." (True, but none of us did.)

Charles calls me into his office and I wonder what I've done wrong (reluctant to go in, I loiter by the doorway).

"Don't worry, I'm not going to bite," he purrs, oozing charm.

"I'm still not coming in any further," I say, warily.

"Wondered if you'd like to take the Jag at lunchtime, that's all," he offers, knowing we all drive into York for a one-hour mad dash of shopping and coffee.

"Are you sure…thanks, that's great," I reply, honoured to be allowed to borrow his pride and joy.

"Good, then you can give me a lift too," he grins, knowing I can't refuse.

Shit, shit, shit, I think, catching his keys and walking away. I hate driving anyone other than my friends, especially someone as terrifying as him. He thinks it's really funny to shout "Go woman!" at every amber traffic light while a car-load of women scream "Stop!" from the backseat.

Lunchtime, and with sweating palms I abandon the prized vehicle across two parking spaces in Castle car park and emerge to find a microphone shoved in my face. The others, including Charles, disappear.

"Hi there, gorgeous. We're roving reporters taking the doorstep challenge into major towns and I just bet my cameraman ten pounds that a busy lady like you uses Jade washing powder." My interrogator shows his pearly white teeth to the camera and breathes impatiently, waiting for an answer.

Somewhat flustered from the drive, I try to think fast in this surreal situation and become increasingly aware of the camera.

I flick back my non-existent long hair and say, "Well then, you just lost it, sunshine," batting my eyelashes at his mate with the lens. "I most certainly do not use a product which depicts women as having nothing better to do than stay indoors, striving to get their old man's underpants a divine shade of white."

The C-list celebrity starts backing away, giving throat-cutting signals to a bloke beside me, but I grab his microphone and lick my lips, pouting, "Let me tell you what women really want, and it isn't a large multinational stereotyping women as bleach-craving socio-economic D-groups. Oh no…they want wild parties, choice, an intelligent approach to domestic drudgery and a perfect orgasm every night." And with that I blow a kiss towards the camera and ask them to carefully move their equipment away from my beautiful car.

I stride confidently away but realise minutes later that I've forgotten to buy a parking ticket. I return sheepishly, hoping they don't notice me.

Getting home after 7pm, I don't even bother trying to share my day's events with mum and dad because the opening bars of *Coronation Street* are playing so loudly that I'm forced out of the lounge into the kitchen.

Hattie, serial sandwich-maker and mother of our sometimes-happy family, sprawls across a comfy chair holding hands with dad who's laid out on the sofa. Both of them are glued to the telly, ready for today's gospel episode.

"Catherine, put the kettle on and hurry up – you're missing *Coro*," Mum shouts, oblivious to my absence (only mum and dad call me Catherine; every one else calls me Kate).

Placing mugs of strong, sweet tea beside them, I announce, "I have no intention of ever living in a terraced house…so therefore I have no desire to watch people who do, thank you."

Tom, my rarely seen and lanky nineteen-year-old brother, sniggers as I walk past him.

Aaargh! I have to get away from this parent-dominated lifestyle, but limited funds have bound me to this extended sentence of childhood. Will it ever end? Society tells me I should be embarrassing children of my own by now and living in marital bliss. But no knight in shining armour has remained long enough at "Si-thee", No. 4 White Rose Drive, before dad says, "Are you just trying to get into my daughter's knickers?" They always leave faster than their turbo-charged, alloy-shod steeds can take them.

Much as I adore my parents, they need to sail down the waist-widening, mind-narrowing passage of old age without me. I shouldn't be here anymore, play-acting to please them and reliving times when dad was a hero and mum was always right.

Think I'll kill myself.

*

Another day, another expletive. Someone should challenge our Tourette's-afflicted boss.

I finish boxing up the last of the Christmas decorations and feel quite empty inside now that the festive season's over. Manage to rid myself of the feeling with an enormous bar of chocolate and work through my lunch hour to catch up on the amount of skiving I've done this morning.

Notice an editorial mistake in the topping-out ceremony press release and reissue it, replacing 'throw the old sod off' with 'throws off the grass sod'. Make a New Year's resolution to start concentrating more.

Annabel, our new graduate trainee, begs to be relieved from reception duty as she keeps cutting people off and I'm given the dubious task of training her to use the fax.

"You've got a degree, right?" I ask.

Annabel nods and takes a fax header from me like it's made of precious silk.

"Simple as dial, insert, send," I say, my fingers dancing across the buttons, and then we go back to photocopying.

An hour later, "Anyone seen Annabel?" I ask a room full of vacant expressions.

"Looking for me?" Annabel breezes in happily.

"Yeah, could I have that fax you sent for Piers?"

"Er, no."

"Why?"

"'Cos it's gone."

"Gone where?"

"Down the thing, eaten up and sent, I suppose." Annabel makes whooshing noises and gesticulates that the machine has eaten the paper, digested my fax and is electronically transporting it to the 'other side'. (I bang my head on the table.)

I really want to yell "Idiot!" at her but she's so incredibly nice, I don't have the heart to knock her enthusiasm.

Jimbo's telephone has never been known to ring; in fact, I sometimes wander over to check it still works. Suddenly, to my utter astonishment, it starts to ring. Jimbo picks it up, opens a drawer and throws it inside, shouting, "Leave me alone, damn you."

Irritated as usual, Siobhan asks, "Why don't you fuckin' answer?"

"Because of the little voices – they make me do things I don't want to do," he whispers insanely.

"Time to go to the pub, girls and boys," Pippa shouts, and most of us grab our coats to leave.

Jimbo's phone is still ringing in the drawer.

A crowd of us squeeze round a table and review the week's events. Christian from graphic design tells me the building opposite his office is a girl's dormitory and provides hours of pervy viewing for him and his sidekick, Spyder. Spyder grins. Disgusted, I turn away to hear the usually calm Pippa laying into our resident office bully – Eleanor.

"She's such a cow. I didn't sleep a wink last night worrying about seeing her today."

"You and everyone else in her team," adds Siobhan.

Pippa (normally shy) continues, fired up by two vodkas. "I'm not kidding, I want to smack her one. She might be good at her job, thin and attractive, but treating her staff with contempt is not man management. I mean, who does she think she is?"

Jimbo disagrees. "You think she's attractive? I think she has the kind of face that only a mother could love."

Lauren, our bubbly junior account manager, adds, "I submitted a news release for approval yesterday and she just wrote 'crap' in big red letters right across it."

"See, what did I tell you?" seethes Pippa. "No constructive criticism, no advice or encouragement – just bullying."

Bored by listening to our bitching, Spyder starts telling

Christian how his 'ex' once drew a face on the end of his knob with a biro. We all stop and stare at him for a moment, then carry on talking and eyeing up potential heart-throbs arriving at the bar.

I suddenly realise I've missed my train home.

"Never mind, you can stay at mine," Maggie offers.

Halfway down the Micklegate run (lots of pubs in one street), we drunkenly totter along the pavement discussing the shortcomings of parental home life.

"I love them desperately but feel utterly oppressed. Mum's sole ambition is to teach me the art of home-made gravy and dad keeps stroking my hair – I'm twenty-six, not six!"

Siobhan thinks for a second, then says dreamily, "But Hattie does make the best onion gravy in the world."

"Shiv…!" I whinge.

"Okay, okay. Tell you what, I'm sick of sharing a house with my big bro, so why don't we look for somewhere together?"

"Yippee!" I yell, and give her a big kiss.

*

"Mum, I'm moving out," I say, looking through the property section of the *Yorkshire Evening Press*.

"What, again dear?"

"Yes, but this time I'm not coming back."

"Whatever you say, dear."

*

"I can't believe I'm doing this," I tell Siobhan, shining a torch around a narrow hallway.

"What? Looking around a house without any electricity?"

"No, contemplating living here in Coronation Street."

Siobhan drinks like a fish and has the sharpest tongue I've ever come across. She's sexy, quite short, and Irish through and through. Her hair changes colour with her moods and she has absolutely no self-control (doesn't give a toss about anyone's opinion of her). We are going to be perfect housemates.

No. 222 Ouse Terrace is squashed behind the train station

and obviously housed families working on the railway many years ago. Today, over a century later, it's prospective home to a pair of self-professed socialites. Broken armchairs flank a flea-bitten sofa and psychedelic wallpaper complements brown window frames throughout. The kitchen is cold and damp with exposed electric wiring and cracked tiles, while the bathroom plumbing wobbles alarmingly. As there is no blind on the bathroom window, we have a panoramic view of the backyard-cum-builders tip, and I don't think the toilet has been cleaned since installed. One bedroom is divided off with a piece of plasterboard to make it into two (neither half offering wardrobes nor any other furniture).

I think of my large, en suite bedroom, fully stocked kitchen and cosy lounge with roaring log fire waiting for me at home.

"We'll take it," I say to the agent.

*

John Wayne (or rather Max), Siobhan's current boyfriend, screws coloured light bulbs into each room ready for our Hollywood-theme house-warming party. I bake a tray of frozen sausage rolls and place bowls of crisps around the kitchen next to crates of beer before going upstairs to get ready.

Siobhan appears dressed as Dorothy from *The Wizard of Oz* and her five-foot-four frame lends an impish touch to the outfit. She's even managed to make her shoulder-length plaits curl upwards by pushing wire coat hangers through them. I, subtle as ever, am ready for the operating theatre in silk pyjamas, with 'Implant', 'Tuck', 'Nip' and 'Lift' written over various parts of my body.

Siobhan's brother, Danny, turns up in a Zorro outfit, carrying the four large bags of clothes she left at his place.

"Glad to get rid of the little sponger," he teases Siobhan, accepting a beer. I stand on tiptoes to kiss him hello and he hugs me for a split second too long (the charmer).

Cowboys and Indians mix with Madonna, Dracula, Cher and a gorilla. Soon our horrid little home is buzzing with over thirty people drinking and dancing to cheesy eighties music.

The gorilla refuses to reveal his real identity and causes havoc in the kitchen.

Spyder arrives with his flatmate, Luke, who makes a very good Rambo, and I laugh when he asks me if there is somewhere he can store his shotgun. Unfortunately, Luke doesn't see the joke and explains with a straight face that, actually, he's not kidding. He went out shooting rabbits earlier this morning and this is the real thing.

I punch Spyder for bringing such a stupid idiot, and not only that, but a stupid idiot with a gun. Wrapping it in a bath towel, I place it carefully in the airing cupboard and hope my fingerprints aren't on it.

"Why is Superwoman wearing Max's ten-gallon hat and gun holster?" Pippa asks Maggie, who shakes her head, equally confused.

Annabel introduces me to her fiancé, Jason, and, after directing him into the kitchen for a drink, whispers to me, "He's perfect, isn't he? Forty-forty, you know."

I raise my eyebrows in bewilderment and she answers, "Under forty years old, earning over forty thousand." (It seems our Annabel isn't so much green-as-cabbage-looking after all.)

Siobhan's talking to a very authentic-looking policeman, tapping her heels together. "…But Officer, there's no place like home," she says.

"I don't care, turn the noise down," he shouts, and leaves soon after we placate him with a burst of Pavarotti.

"Was he a real copper?" I ask, painfully aware of the contents of my airing cupboard (Lauren nods nervously).

I find Danny carefully placing a solitary sausage roll in the middle of our spare-room floor and intend to ask why but am interrupted by a compelling need to wee. Pushing past snogging rock stars on the stairs, I join the queue behind Julius Caesar.

Minnie Mouse and Darth Vader fall giggling out of our spare room as John Wayne and Superwoman sneak into Siobhan's bedroom.

Four good-looking blokes gatecrash downstairs and try to blend in but end up looking like a bunch of film extras. Pippa's eagerly telling one of them about her five-point plan: husband, enamel bath, iron bed, Belfast sink, babies (he's sitting opposite, petrified).

"The night is young and so are we. I'm off to find my future love and plastic surgeon," I tell Danny and invite gatecrasher number two to dance. Siobhan and Max are having a row in the kitchen while Superwoman scoffs crisps with Elvis. I step outside for a bit of fresh air and see smoke coming out of the gorilla's nostrils.

"Want some?" it grunts, holding out a spliff.

"No thanks, Christian," I say, and return indoors.

*

The house looks like a celebrity sleepover; bodies lie haphazardly around the floor and I've been woken by an annoying static noise coming from the CD player. My head hurts as I stand on people in sleeping bags, trying to open the window. Siobhan saunters downstairs with PC Plod in tow.

"I hate you for not getting hangovers," I say, wincing. "And where's Max?"

"Collecting bastard kryptonite for all I care," she answers, violently breaking eggs into a pan. "Anyway, this is Roger, my new, er, friend…"

"I'm called Nick," new friend interrupts. "I kept telling you last night, 'roger' is what I have to say into this radio," and he points to a walkie-talkie clipped to his shirt.

"Pleased to meet you, Nick," I yawn. "Are you going home now? No need for a shower here or anything?" Siobhan looks confused at my twittering when Christian, still in his gorilla outfit, bids us a hasty goodbye, obviously not wanting Nick to meet him or his marijuana.

"Suits him – should wear it more often," Siobhan mumbles to his departing figure.

"Ex," I explain to Nick in a single word.

*

Budgie, my yellow Ford Fiesta, is no longer with us, dear diary. He left us this morning, as I have realised that rent and bills will inevitably force me to sell him anyway, in order to stay party-solvent. I will now ride a bicycle to work, which is much healthier and better for the environment.

Siobhan and I wear black armbands and hold a vodka martini wake for him.

*

Big important client meeting today. I must get there early, I tell myself, battling through traffic jams and overtaking Piers on his ridiculous folding contraption. A car pulls up next to me at the traffic lights and an anonymous figure inside ejects a cigarette packet onto the road. Litter louts really piss me off, so I bend down, pick it up and throw it back through the open passenger window, saying, "You dropped this by mistake," and peddle off.

It's a gloriously bright, sunny morning and I can't help feeling great, even though I'm breathing in exhaust fumes. I love York with its city walls, history and architecture. I love working at Panache, too, and think about the people there – twenty weird individuals thrown together in a Georgian three-story building, all overtly creative. In fact, today I love everybody. Of course, all jobs have their boring side but we have a laugh whenever possible. So, all in all, life is good.

"Morning…" I say, going through the front door.

"Fuck off."

"Get me the latest news clippings on the Wetlands Trust, and file this lot before lunchtime," Eleanor barks, dumping an armful of paper on me before I even get through reception.

"May I at least take my bicycle helmet off first?" I hiss acidly, annoyed she's just burst my happy bubble.

I work like crazy all morning, arranging cuttings, collating news releases and generally getting things ready for this afternoon's client meeting. Piers doesn't say a word (even when spoken to), preferring to raise an eyebrow at me instead. Luckily, I am fluent in eyebrow and retaliate by stamping around loudly.

Determined to grab a lunch hour, I leave the office in a hurry to seek solace in retail therapy. I stand in Coppergate Square and drool over diamond rings in the jeweller's window, trying to choose a new favourite. But the same old green emerald jumps up and down on card 107, silently shouting, "Me, me…I'm the one."

Summer (Panache's hippy artist) and Lauren are inside and I wander in to browse with them. As Summer chooses a bangle, I tell Lauren and the assistant, "If a man ever comes in and buys that ring over there on card 107, can you make sure it's for me – Kate Ashcroft – size 'N' for 'no'?" The assistant smiles politely at us and promises to remember.

Stuffing a sandwich into my mouth, I notice a beautiful ball gown in the window of Phoenix, an exclusive designer dress shop. Always a Cinderella, I try it on and hear the assistant saying, "It's half price this week, love – only two hundred pounds."

When would I ever wear it? My weight fluctuates from fattish to thinish so often I forget which diet I'm supposed to be on. How could I possibly afford it? But it's gorgeous – black halter-neck velvet bodice and full-length duchess satin skirt. Financial common sense pisses off and leaves me alone with it in the changing room: I buy it.

Returning to the office in shock, I show it off to the graphic design team. Camp Carl thinks it's fabulous and Summer insists I put it on. Christian and Spyder are startled (and a bit frightened) but they look at my tits anyway.

Charles comes out of the conference room and sees me wearing my new purchase.

"Can we have six white coffees, please," he asks Angel, our attractive blonde receptionist. "And Kate," he says, winking at me, "I dare you to bring them in wearing that."

Accepting his challenge, I sweep into the midst of their meeting in my gorgeous gown, quietly place the tray of drinks on a nearby table, thank the three open-mouthed prospective clients, and swish out. Charles, oozing charm, carries on discussing business as if I always bring in coffee wearing such garb.

*

I can think of better ways to spend my Wednesday evening

than working late for Eleanor but it's Siobhan's turn to cook dinner tonight. Fantastic – I wonder what she'll create?

"Why is it that I'm the one stuffing press releases into envelopes and she's buggered-off home?" I ask a pot plant in amazement.

"Another leadership gem from Eleanor Morrell," Maggie replies, looking up from proof-reading.

"If I had her job I'd stay behind and help, since I created the work," I decide.

"Yeah right, course you would," she drawls sarcastically.

"There – done, finished, finito…food here I come."

At home, two plates are on the table complete with knife, fork and spoon. I see no sign of meat or vegetables, just a can of beer on each plate.

Siobhan's draped on the sofa in moleskin jeans and a cashmere sweater. "Dinner's ready," she shrugs.

Danny calls round to check we're okay and ends up altering the water pressure, as we can't understand why it takes over an hour to fill the bath.

"Bastardly tight landlord trick," he tells me in his soft Irish accent. "Now then, ladies, while I'm here…". he adds, wandering off into the spare room. "Aha! See! Yer a dirty little scrubber," he says to Siobhan, holding up a fast-decomposing party-size sausage roll, proving we are a long way short of house-proud. He insists he doesn't miss her one bit.

"And you're nothing but a bollocks," she snaps back at him.

After sharing our beer dinner, he hugs us both goodbye, ruffling Siobhan's hair and winking suggestively at me.

Halfway through *Emmerdale*, the telephone rings and I ignore it, amazed someone has the audacity to disrupt my one thousand eight hundred seconds of escapism. Siobhan shouts loudly from upstairs. "Kate – that'll be the phone!"

Screening our calls, I wait for the answering machine to inform whoever's calling that "Kate and Siobhan can't come to the phone right now because they're upstairs with 'me'…But if they can walk when I've finished with them, they'll get right back to you…"

Oh my God, Christian must've recorded this message at the party! I make a mental note to kill him, race to the phone and speak to my unamused father. Summoned to Sunday lunch, I agree to remind myself of what they look like – and yes, I do love them; no, I won't get into debt; and of course I'm looking after myself.

The phone rings again almost immediately and I drag myself off the sofa to hear Max for the fourth time this week. Siobhan will not talk to him, answer his calls or acknowledge his existence. And I refuse to cover for her – I've never been able to tell lies; she can do her own dirty work.

"Hi Max, how are you?" I ask, signalling to Siobhan erratically. Siobhan runs straight to the front door and stands outside in the rain.

"Hi Kate, I'm after Siobhan…"

"Sorry, she's not in," I say (not a lie).

"Any idea when she'll be back?"

"Oh, very soon." (Siobhan is barefoot and freezing cold.)

"Where's she gone?"

"Outside the front door."

Fuming, Siobhan steps inside and takes the phone from me.

*

A few of us from the office are going to see an evangelist and queue up at the Town Hall to buy a programme. I'm apprehensive at gatherings like these due to my staunch, high Church of England background, but it should make for an interesting evening.

Standing near the front, we watch a trendy young band sing 'Amazing Grace' and I look around for a hymnbook until a nudge in the ribs directs me to the overhead projector. People start raising their hands to the ceiling. It's more like a concert than a church, and, enjoying the soul-type rhythm, I move self-consciously with the ecstatic worshippers. Two songs later, I'm shocked to see that I am the only person with my hands still in my pockets; everyone else is almost touching the roof. (I wonder if it's me that's weird and them that's normal.)

"Praise the Lord," booms a loudspeaker as our host arrives on stage with open arms.

"Amen," the audience chants. Siobhan looks bored and Spyder asks what time the group sex starts.

Sitting shoulder to shoulder on uncomfortable chairs, we listen to a tall Dutch man with a Texan accent tell us his life story and how God saved him at the ripe old age of fifty. I must admit he's extremely convincing (mainly because of his charisma and good grooming), so I drift along, enjoying the show, surprised to hear the meaning of life is not chocolate.

Thirty minutes later, Siobhan instructs us, "Come on, we're off up," as the audience gets invited onto the stage. Curiosity gets the better of me and I line up with the rest of the flock. Christian wants to know if anyone's taking their clothes off backstage. Young and old wait to meet 'Mr Preacher', moving slowly along the queue while bouncers catch each person as they're filled with the Holy Spirit. I can't wait to sample a bit of this and get into the swing of things, daring to show my palms (Pippa's already touching the fluorescent lights above).

"The only way to heaven is through me," booms the loudspeaker. (Spyder disagrees, saying he's already shown three young ladies another route.)

One down, two to go, I think to myself, watching old dears throw away their inhibitions (and zimmer frames) as he approaches. Two bouncers quietly stand behind me, waiting for my inevitable healing; but incensed at the fact that they think I need two to catch me, I'm determined to stand my ground.

"What's missing in your life, little lady?" our parson queries in a southern drawl, and I stare into a pair of deep chestnut-brown eyes.

"Aga, free-standing kitchen, stone-flagged floor, underfloor heating, Welsh dresser, big garden, en suite bathroom and a four-wheel drive," I blurt out, getting the giggles.

"Aah see you are filled with laughter," he smiles, waiting for me to tell him more.

"Er, well, Siobhan's Uncle Fucker died last week – shall we pray for him?" I suggest into the microphone. Siobhan quickly

15

takes the mike off me and informs the audience his name's Fiachra (it's Irish). Our priest, visibly amused by my babbling, tells Siobhan they'll pray together in a moment and calmly waits for my answer.

"Actually, I'm very happy and shouldn't be here on stage, but please could you pray for one of my dearest friends who suffers from excruciating back pain?" I ask him.

"Sure…but nothing at all for you?"

By this time I'm totally in love with 'Mr Too-much-hair-dye-and-pearly-white-teeth', utterly committed to leaving Britain behind and going around America with him in a camper van, preaching to sinners.

"Oh go on, then. Can I have some of that, please?" I ask, pointing to the old lady holding her spectacles while twitching on the floor. "I've always wanted to experience the Holy Spirit."

He steps closer and places one hand on my head, the other on my shoulder. I look down and see my reflection in his shiny shoes. He whispers hot, unintelligible words in my right ear and I feel an electric chemistry fizzle between us. I scrutinize the expensive weave of his shirt and smell his fake tan, waiting to be thrown backwards, healed, happy and whole.

He's speaking in tongues and I try to understand, listening intently. "Sharabang, sharabang" is all I can make out and I wonder why he's talking about a seven-seater bus used to take Victorian holiday-makers to the beach.

"Your friend is in my prayers…and honey, I know you're already filled with the spirit," and with that he moves away.

"Can't work out why you bother with all that faith stuff," Siobhan says when we get outside.

"You think it's all nonsense, don't you," I reply.

"No, but I have my doubts. Had it for breakfast, lunch and dinner all my life. Suppose I'm just a bit full."

Encouraged from the evening's teaching, I spout, "I think of religion as an eternal war – dark versus light, fought by an army of old ladies wearing hats, singing hymns."

(Siobhan just looks at me like I'm bonkers.)

"One thing I do want to know is how come they can hear him, you know...God," I ask.

"Apparently, you can if you fast and pray for ages," she replies.

"Suppose I'll never know, then," I sigh, thinking how impossible it is to miss breakfast even once.

*

Usual day of late deadlines and critical tea-making. Drift through work not really focused, starting one job and doing another before finishing the first.

Siobhan's away at a conference this weekend, so I'm going clubbing with a bunch of old school friends.

Becky, still tanned from her travels, looks long and lean next to Megan's hourglass figure, and Zoë's incredibly slim waist supports huge boobs that can turn a man's head from across the street. The three of them wait for me in Parliament Square. We link arms and head off to the nearest pub, shivering in our skimpy clothes.

My favourite riverside haunt, The King's Arms, is bustling with locals and tourists. I immediately notice a tall, good-looking blond bloke standing at the bar, laughing. Catching up with events and gossip from home, I keep looking across to see him return my glance and excitedly inform the girls.

"Do you like him?" Megan asks.

"Like him? He's gorgeous!"

"Right, then. Next time he looks at you, hold his gaze for four seconds. That tells him your interested."

We giggle like teenagers, but sure enough I manage to do the deed, and to my amazement he starts moving towards me.

"Hi," he says, smiling.

"H..." I manage, smiling back at his gorgeous blue eyes.

"I couldn't help noticing that you're not wearing very much," he adds dryly.

I try to cover up my boosted breasts, realising we're dressed for hardcore clubbing, not pie-and-pint pubbing.

"Zis is an enormous amount of clothing for where I come from," I tell him in a foreign accent.

"And where might that be?"

"Planet Strip – you really must visit sometime," I tease, and we continue flirting for a couple of minutes.

"The name's Guy...Guy Willesley," he says eventually, offering his hand.

"Kate Ashcroft," I reply, accepting his firm grip before introducing the others. "Well, Guy, nice to meet you, but we're off for a boogie at Silvers nightclub next to the fire station, so if you're a bright boy we'll see you in there later."

Waving goodbye, we leave the steaming pub behind, heading towards a long queue of twenty-somethings outside the nightclub.

At midnight, I'm convinced he's not coming and console myself with a bag of cheese-and-onion crisps.

It's customary, when drunk, for me and Becky to swap outfits on the dance floor during bouts of dry ice – she dons my catsuit and I wear her hot pants, heels and black jacket. Practising my chat up lines on handsome men, Becky and Megan (alias Luscious and Blossom on Friday nights) just laugh at my awful attempts:

"I'll cook your tea for you while you watch football"; or

"I can almost make real gravy."

It doesn't help that Zoë tells them how I used to drag my right leg as a nine-year-old...Then, standing alone by a table watching people dance, I notice someone staring at me. It's him! But he's looking confused and starts to walk past me. Maybe he's not interested anymore.

"Er, Kate?" he asks. "I could've sworn I saw you seconds earlier on the dance floor necking a black man."

"Oh, I'm sorry. We changed clothes," I explain.

Megan is dancing like a mad thing and Becky seems to be enjoying herself in the arms of a bouncer, so I try conversing with Guy over the deafening dance music.

He tells me he drives a small vehicle that sweeps pebbles off the runway at RAF Linton-on-Ouse, and although not normally my type (I like dark hair), he makes me laugh.

Tired of forever playing the politically correct mating game with ideal breeding specimens (saying what they want to hear in order to keep them, such as "I'm only looking for a bit of fun"), I decide to kill him with the acid test.

"If you want to marry me, my ring's in Coppergate Jeweller's, card 107."

"Pardon?" he shouts, unsure of what he just heard.

"Never mind," I sigh, thinking, oh what the hell, I may as well put the effort in for no reward again. I'm pushing thirty with not a man in sight ('cos every time I reveal marriage and motherhood are a priority, they run a mile). I agree to go to a 'bad taste' party with him tomorrow night (he writes my phone number on a piece of chewing-gum paper).

"Pick you up at eight, then," he says, kissing my hand and walking away to join his friends. I'm dumbstruck: no one has ever done that before – I expected a good snog at least (was it the cheese-and-onion crisps?). Oh well, tomorrow should be interesting.

Zoë, Megan and I catch a taxi home. To my horror, I realise I've lost my keys, and Siobhan's away – help, what will we do? Keeping the meter running, we each take turns trying to karate kick the front door but the knackered old thing holds fast. Becky's long since gone off with her bouncer bloke, so we scramble back into the taxi.

"Can you take us to the police station, please?" I ask the gormless driver.

When we get there we roll in, still seeing the funny side of things, to face two tired-looking policemen, one of whom I recognise from our Hollywood party.

"'Ello Nick, in the nick," I chortle drunkenly.

"Okay ladies, which one of you got mugged?" he asks, slightly amused.

"None of us," we reply indignantly. Noticing how dishevelled we look after a night on the town, we explain our circumstances.

Nick drives us back to the house with a big plastic box full of keys and we painfully try each one until Megan bursts into tears. I have a brainwave and phone Danny. At 3am he's less than pleased to hear my voice, but when I burst into tears too he agrees to let us stay overnight. Nick refuses to let us walk across town at this time of the morning "without any clothes on" and drops us off outside Danny's front door. We all thank him for being a very nice man (a very *very* nice man) and promise to get Siobhan to ring him soon.

Danny makes us coffee and throws a quilt on the sofa. "You girls can have my bed," he informs us. "Now sod off and let me get some sleep."

We kiss and hug him for being so wonderful and pile into his bedroom, noting the trendy minimalist decoration. Being immensely tired, conversation dries up quickly, and once we're all curled up together, we fall nosily asleep.

*

Mid-morning, Danny walks in with fresh coffee. Wide-eyed at the three women in his bed, he declares, "Jeysus Mary and Joseph, this is my best fantasy ever."

I absolutely refuse to wear last night's clothes again and take a shower before borrowing Danny's rugby strip. Zoë looks almost respectable in her sparkly jeans and cropped top but Megan, however, doesn't care and stays in her minidress, smelling of cigarette smoke, sweat and perfume.

Cuddling him goodbye, we giggle, "That was so kind of you Danny, how can we possibly thank you?"

"Ah well now, I'm sure I can think of something..." he winks, before kissing me briefly on the lips.

Slightly stunned, I walk away, but get distracted by the girls discussing how clean and tidy his bathroom is.

After sleeping peacefully all afternoon, the phone rings and Siobhan answers it first for a change. Seconds later, she demands to know exactly who the hell Guy is. I quickly fill her in on the essential missed gossip, mouthing, "Pulled him last night," while giving directions to Guy and feeling sick with excitement about tonight. What on earth should I wear to a bad taste party?

Siobhan is useless, suggesting things like nuclear waste or facial hair, so I ring my big sister for ideas. Isobel's slightly more helpful and tells me she went to some fantastic Air Force parties back in her student-nurse days. Bingo! I'll go as a nurse.

At ten past eight I hear a horn beep outside and look out of our front window to see a shiny new sports car.

"Bit flash for a runway sweeper," I comment, and Siobhan worries I'm dating a drug dealer.

Now it's Guy's turn to be speechless and he almost trips over himself looking at my sexy nurse's outfit complete with stethoscope. He holds open the car door as I get in and I can't help feeling ladylike when he closes it behind me. During the drive we discuss our jobs and I tell him about the agency, Siobhan, my family and my ambitions. He tells me about all the little buttons he gets to push on his sweeper machine. When we arrive at the base, Guy parks the car in order to clear my details with the entry-gate official. Once sorted, Guy returns to the car, showing the official his own identity card. My suspicions are confirmed when he salutes Guy and says, "Thank you, sir."

"I thought so," I say amused. "You're no runway sweeper are you?"

"Apparently not, my dear Moneypenny," Guy says in a James Bond accent, and he goes on to tell me rather pompously that he's a Commissioned Officer in Her Majesty's Royal Air Force (flying her planes because he can't afford one of his own).

Guy's room is No. 74, a twelve-foot-square box packed to the rafters with Air Force paraphernalia, bed, desk, armchair and a small sink (he tells me there are two types of Officer, those who pee in the sink and those who don't).

"And I hope you're the latter," I comment.

Most of the doors along his corridor have some sort of aviation cartoon emblazoned across them, revealing an aspect of the character in residence. Guy's just has a business card that reads 'Aeroplane driver/car redesigner'. (Apparently, he's been through a few cars.) Inside, ordnance survey maps of the local area act as makeshift wallpaper.

Someone puts a sign on my back exclaiming 'Nurse – Shag Me' just before I walk into the Officers' Mess and I receive a round of applause from the boys at the bar. Unfortunately, I don't go down so well with the seventeen student nurses bussed in from York District Hospital.

In the Ladies Powder Room I defend my costume to two furious nurses. "Don't you get it? It's meant to be bad taste...that's the whole point – if you don't like it, go home."

One bloke is dressed as the boss's dog, which got run over earlier today. He's wearing a sheepskin coat inside out with tyre tracks across his chest and 'Rex' written on his forehead (now that really is bad taste!).

The DJ's wearing a pink latex body stocking and plays fantastic dance tracks giving everyone itchy feet for a boogie. He fits in perfectly with the theme, yet bears a solemn expression adjusted only to swallow beer (Guy informs me 'NODI' always does Mess discos and wears pink latex regularly).

We dance most of the night away, but each time I'm asked exactly who my escort is, Guy's nowhere to be seen (so I just point at the nearest bloke). He reappears after the third time this happens to tell me I've just killed that particular chap's career.

"How on earth have I managed that?"

"The boss's wife is not impressed with your outfit because she trained as a nurse at York District Hospital. Apparently, she wants your blood but will settle for nagging her husband to end your boyfriend's career instead," he grins, before adding cheekily, "I, however, think you're fantastic."

Around midnight, I jump onto the minibus returning a few of the uglier nurses back to their accommodation and beg a lift into town before telling Guy what a great time I've had. He stops me mid-sentence by kissing me and promises to see me again soon, if I agree. Agree! I almost faint. Men like him just don't exist, but I play calm and confident, saying, "Okay, that would be great. But don't leave it too long, though, or I might get snapped up by some sweet-talking rugby player."

Walking in through the door, I yell at Siobhan to wake up, run into her bedroom and climb into bed with her.

"Shiv, I've met the man I'm going to marry," I tell her, and I go on to explain my night.

Siobhan sits up and listens intently to my description of a military base full of gorgeous men in uniform. "I've died and gone to heaven – get me in there woman!" she says, quickly waking up.

*

Head fuzzy from last night, I laze around reading the Sunday papers and think about getting a train to my mum's for lunch when Guy calls by unexpectedly.

"Wondered if you fancied a drive out into the country?" he asks casually before I get a chance to tell him of my plans.

"Of course I do," I say and run upstairs to get changed, thinking, hmm, if he is the one for me then I suppose I'd better put him through the parent test early and get it over with.

Guy's totally at ease with the thought of meeting my folks but that's because he doesn't know what he's letting himself in for. I phone mum and tell her I'm bringing a friend with me, a male friend, a boyfriend – my boyfriend!

"Ey up, son. You our Katie's latest?" dad says, shaking Guy's hand firmly. Mum, meanwhile, drops her 'h's trying to make him comfortable and baby brother grunts a few short noises before burying himself again in his computer screen.

"So then, lad, how can you afford a car like that?" dad asks, and I die a thousand deaths watching Guy give as good as he gets. Dad's a six-foot-four gentle giant of few words, and when he does speak, his deep Yorkshire accent drowns out passing traffic, but strangely enough he's convinced he talks softly, much to our amusement. Mum's a midget in comparison – she just about comes up to his chest and has to stand on the stairs to kiss him. What I love about them is that they're completely devoted to each other (while being constantly at odds).

Leaving Guy and dad in the lounge, I walk into the kitchen and help myself to a handful of freshly podded peas when mum says, "I'm making onion gravy, love – want to watch?"

"What for?" I ask, thinking the instant type is so much easier.

"Because you'll have to learn how to look after 'im," she says, pointing her head in Guy's direction.

(Aaargh!) "Mum, some men are known to cook nowadays," I start to spout, but I give up: arguing is futile.

Mum and dad adore him; they're utterly absorbed by his charm, wit and enormous appetite. I cringe as Guy looks through family photo albums showing me at various stages of childhood through to spotty teenager. Scrutinising one picture of me at ten months old, he asks what it is that I'm sucking. "Bacon rind, dear," mum informs him. "She loved the stuff."

Horrified to find out I was tortured at ten months by these imbeciles entrusted with my life, I demand to know why I didn't suck a dummy like normal babies.

Dad defends Hattie's maniac child-rearing abilities saying, "'Sup wi' yer? You grew up on lard and it never did you any harm."

We leave after stuffing ourselves silly on home cooking but not before Hattie offers to give Guy the recipe for 'granddad's gravy' next time he visits.

Back home at my place, the evening floats by as we lounge around upstairs in my room, dangerously close to the unmade bed. Guy leans over and blows up my nose, saying it's an old trick he learnt from Barbara Woodhouse on how to seduce women. I scream and hit him, remembering the famous old bag is a dog trainer. We wrestle each other round the room before ending up in that terrible cliché of a clinch – arms entwined, breathless and gazing into each other's eyes. Suddenly, the silly games are over and we are facing our first serious decision.

"You sure?" he asks, knowing full well I'm begging for him (just as Mrs Woodhouse knew I would be). We start to have slow, fantastic sex and I feel on top of the world.

Sometime later, Siobhan knocks on my bedroom wall, shouting, "Will you two stop shagging! I'm jealous."

Guy shouts back, "In a minute, you're next…"

TWO

At 6am, Guy gets up to leave and I murmur, "Thank you for having me," like a polite six-year-old, before going back to sleep for an hour. When I wake up again, I wonder if the weekend did actually happen – or was it just a wonderful dream? No, I really have met the most delicious man and I'm on a roller coaster to ecstasy.

I go into work as usual with an extra bright "Morning" on my lips.

"Fuck off," comes the normal reply, only this time it's weird because everything's changed. Neither man nor beast, not even Eleanor Morrell for that matter, can quash my happy hormones and I make cups of tea for everyone in the office, leaving them wondering what's got into me (or who, as Charles quips).

At lunchtime, a few of us dash into town to catch up on grocery shopping and we stop off in a coffee bar for a bite to eat. Siobhan makes me the sole discussion point and proceeds to update the girls on all the gory details of my love life.

Back at the office, Ms Morrell is on the rampage over some minor amendments to a launch-party guest list and I avoid her by concentrating on Camp Carl's training session. Sitting on Siobhan's desk, I feign interest in the company website as Carl talks us through his 'exciting new sales tool'.

"Now, you must police this continually and make sure all query hits are answered." Siobhan and I snigger at the word 'police'. Carl rolls his eyes and continues monotonously.

"Carl, you have such nice skin," says Siobhan, distracting him.

"Cleanse, tone, moisturise – day and night, darling," he replies without looking at her. "Now, listen hard because you're both a bit thick at computers."

He explains another aspect of cyber-selling when he suddenly howls, "Arrrgh! No, no, no!"

We jump off the desk and run around to the other side to get a better view of a now completely blank screen.

"Wha…what's happened?" whispers Siobhan.

"I was altering a hot link but it seems to have crashed."

Siobhan lets out a muffled wail and is about to throw up over the loss of work as Carl tries to restore today's data and frantically taps away, offering apologies. "Sorry, so sorry. 'Fraid that was me being a bit of a clever dick."

"Why bother with the adjective," seethes Siobhan angrily.

Lesson temporarily over, I return to my own desk to find a box of name badges for tomorrow's product launch and check off each one against the guest list. Noticing there isn't one for me, I call into the design office to ask Summer if she's forgotten mine (after all, Piers did promise I could go).

Spyder and Christian want to know if I've come to get my kit off again and I give them the kind of smile that leaves them slightly uneasy, wondering what I might do next.

Various clear and coloured crystals hang from the ceiling around Summer as she works. Trying to gain her attention, I walk straight into a long, jagged rose quartz. (Apparently, these artefacts encourage creative energy, but Spyder insists they're used to ward him and Christian away from her biscuits.)

"No, babe, your name's not down on my job sheet," she tells me gently. "Looks like you're not going."

Confused, I ask Eleanor what's going on, as I've spent weeks working on this launch. It's only going to be a morning of standing around greeting clients, but I still want to go.

"You can't possibly go," she says. "You're just a secretary. Lauren's going instead."

I'm stunned by her arrogance and lack of insight into exactly what her subordinates do all day. Secretaries in this day and age are not all tweed, twills and typing – we handle, manage, organise and execute high-profile accounts without being seen. Often, I hold more client discussions than the allocated manager and become the key contact.

With my blood boiling at her stuck-up superiority, I walk calmly away, unsure of how someone so blatantly insensitive can be in her job.

Hurt from being left behind and out of the campaign completely, I escape into the kitchen for a few minutes, trying to regain my composure.

Resentment boils inside me as I make myself a cup of tea and relive her audacity. I can't help thinking to myself angrily, be careful with your assumptions about people's capabilities you cow…every secretary, personal assistant or sidekick has hidden talents. The difficult part is developing them when the bills need paying. I sob for a minute or two then pull myself together, confident in the knowledge that I'm worth ten of her.

Taking my cup of tea back to my desk, Maggie, our office manager (and mother hen), sits quietly back in her chair after surreptitiously witnessing the whole scene.

At home, I have a large pizza and then settle into a relaxing candlelit bath with a good book and a bottle of wine. Danny's rugby kit lays strewn on the bathroom floor, still waiting to be washed and returned. Suddenly, Siobhan bursts in excitedly, holding the phone. "Its gorgeous Guy," she breathes and I immediately sit bolt upright to reach for the receiver, forcing cascades of bubbly water over the side.

"What's going on? You're echoing and I can hear water – you're not in the bath are you?"

"Uh-huh," I giggle seductively.

"Phwar! The agony of knowing you're naked and wet is killing me. Can I come round and scrub your back?"

"No."

"Suppose a soapy-tit wank's out of the question then?"

"Eh, a what? Look, Guy, it's a school night and way past my bedtime. I'm off to bed in a minute."

"Even better!"

"Guy!" I protest.

"Okay, okay, but come to the base on Friday night. It's a belated Burns Supper."

"Burns Night was ages ago," I think aloud.

"Yeah, we were going to have it the first week of January but some nutter poured lighter fluid on the floor which meant the whole Mess needed recarpeting."

"Oh no!" I laugh. "Did they catch who did it?"

"Yup. The stupid idiot wrote his initials."

I giggle and agree to go with him, asking what the dress code is (and am delighted to hear that I can wear my new black ball gown).

"And bring Siobhan if she wants to come," he adds.

*

"Piers is leaving."

The gossip hits me as soon as I arrive at the office, not even time for a "Fuck off". Everyone's talking about his impending move to a television company.

I feel sad, because even though we struggle to communicate, I like Piers. I like working for him much more than I like working for Eleanor. Men are so much easier to look after than women – there's no bitchiness or visible social climbing. I'm going to miss him; we could've been great friends if only he'd let me get close enough.

"What's this I hear about you getting Richard Whiteley's job?" I tease, taking my coat off.

"Don't tell me you're surprised, Kate. It's been on the cards for a while." He looks drawn, older than his thirty years.

"Suppose Eleanor will get your job?" I ask, and notice a hush develop across the room.

"Actually, no. My role is to be dissolved and Charles has hired a woman executive."

"Oh…right. When do you go, then?"

"These things are always untidy, Kate, and because of my position, I have to clear off this morning – so I'm packing up now. Want my stapler?"

"What! You can't go now, I'm in shock," I cry, accepting the stapler.

"Oh, and I have a little something for you." He reaches into his suit pocket and hands me a small velvet case. I open it to see a beautiful gold bracelet and burst into tears at the suddenness of it all.

"Piers, you can't go…I fear change," I plead (thinking better the devil you know).

"Be good," he sighs as he carries his folded-up bicycle downstairs. I turn to see a room full of staring eyes awaiting my next emotion and, right on cue, I blub into Carl's immaculate kipper tie.

Piers is talking to Charles in the car park and I watch him shake Charles's hand as he prepares to peddle away. Maggie calls me into Charles's office and asks Angel to bring us two coffees before explaining that I am to be 'floating around' until my new boss arrives next week.

"Starting this morning with a trip to the printer's," she suggests, knowing I need a breath of fresh air.

I return from Oaksons to find Lauren in the kitchen discussing Frozen Fayre's product launch (the one I missed out on) and try to eavesdrop, genuinely interested to hear how my clients are.

"It was so boring. I stood around all morning directing people around the site. Might've helped if I'd known who the client was, but since I've never worked on the account I couldn't really do much."

I continue to make my lunch, thinking gleefully, zilch productivity for you there, Eleanor.

"There's something for you in reception," Angel tells me knowingly, and I wander through with a mouthful of sandwich. I'm stunned to see two-dozen red roses and one white rose laid across her keyboard.

Reading the card over my shoulder, Angel informs all around us, "'Kate, hope these will remind you of me until Friday. All my love, Guy'," and swoons dramatically over her in-tray. "Wow, those fly boys really can charm the pants off a girl," she says rather unangelically.

(I feel sick with excitement and totally silly for the rest of the afternoon, looking at the bouquet and fiddling with my new bracelet.)

My sister yells across the street to me and Siobhan as we walk into town together. We stop to see her running breathlessly towards us.

"I've been waiting ages for you two," she complains. "Honestly, Katie, you're useless. I've been stood outside your house for ever but got fed up and came into town – I had fresh cream cakes for you both as well."

Isobel's in bossy big sister mode and I try to explain that I don't finish work until 5.30pm. It's now 5.45pm and I'm halfway home.

"The cakes, Izzy – where are they?" I ask.

"I threw them in the bin 'cos you don't deserve them anymore."

We walk home in silence until Siobhan ventures, "Er, Isobel, which bin did you put them in?"

"Oh, I don't know. The one beside the railway station entrance I think."

Back at home, I put the kettle on and answer her quick-fire questions about the flowers.

"I'm warning you, sis, it's hard work being involved with someone in the military. You'll never come first, his career will."

Isobel's husband Hugh is an OBE-honoured Lieutenant Colonel and hardly ever at home. I listen to her love lecture but choose to ignore most of it, thinking what a know-all she is – how could she possibly discourage me?

She says, "When I did my nursing training we went to lots of parties at Linton and I soon learnt to identify his type from ten paces. The watch gives them away – velcro strap, chronograph, dark face, lots of dials including GMT and local time – standard issue to trainee aircrew. I'm not kidding, sis, be careful. These blokes are stuffed full of testosterone, wear designer shirts and have hair so short you could light a match on it. Don't approach unless you're prepared to tolerate second place – to flying. In fact, third place, because the priorities among his species are flying, beer and women. In that order."

"Well thanks very much, but I like him, he's wonderful," I

state, adamantly wearing rose-tinted glasses regarding my love life.

Siobhan bursts in triumphantly, shouting, "Found them," and holds up a soggy bag of squashed cream cakes.

*

"Kate, you're overseeing the brochure shoot at Venus this lunchtime so please make sure the photographer is still on schedule." Maggie briefs me on the situation, explaining that I'm taking more responsibility than normal because of Piers's departure.

Good old Piers, I think as I skip to my desk, constantly interrupted by thoughts of what to wear on Friday night. What does one wear to a Burns Night? Will my new ball gown be too much? I can't bear the thought of a tartan sash, but Siobhan has already designed her wedding dress which funnily enough sports exactly that.

I pick up the phone and dial Carl's number. "Green or black?" I ask without stating my reason.

"Oh black every time, darling," he answers before hanging up.

Right, back to work. I can concentrate on the job in hand now that's sorted. Of course, I should've known – black it is.

Venus, 'the plush new health hall specialising in balancing mind and body', opens next month and Panache is handling the publicity. Piers had almost finished the literature design with Summer and I was enjoying the role of co-ordinator. Looks like I'll have to keep things ticking over until the new boss arrives (but I want to prove that I can handle it myself).

I go over the outline plan with ideas for today's shoot while holding a small lump of hematite at Summer's insistence (to counteract my headstrong ways).

"Everyone booked and ready to go?" she asks me.

"Yup. The client's apparently organised her own models, so it's just a question of turning up and getting on with it."

We arrive at the venue looking ever so PR (immaculate and a

bit too trendy). 'Matron' checks us in, treating us like new clientele until she realises we're trade and dismisses us to the plush sofa area with a wave of her neatly manicured hand.

Ned, the tall, unshaven photographer, asks for help unloading his van and we carry two tripods, four flashes and three large umbrellas through to the Zen room. Bonnie, the owner and our new client (ahem…*my* new client) is really nice, greeting us in a cloud of perfume. I suspect she's a bit too fair and forty for her grey and gracious years, but I like her anyway. In the Zen room, I collapse onto an enormous sky-blue 'water sofa' and start feeling a bit sea sick watching Ned set up the equipment. We're all intrigued and a little intimidated by this incredibly peaceful room. Bonnie describes each expensive treatment.

"'Counselling Corner'," she says, pointing to a pair of overstuffed chairs. "Where shattered people pour their troubles away – they talk, I listen."

Then she moves to an elevated bed under a deep-blue, star-studded ceiling. "We call this 'Universal Exposure' – it restores celestial balance to the soul."

Ned leans over and mumbles in my ear. "I don't know what language she's talking but it sounds like bollocks."

Bonnie answers her bleeper by switching it off on her pink belt and picks up a nearby telephone. Turning to us three vacant twits, she says, "Please excuse me a moment," and goes into conversation with a troubled therapist.

Summer is busy trying out everything around her but I'm listening to Bonnie's priceless advice. "Yes, yes, dear…Look, I'm a bit busy at the moment – people to convince etc. Just tell him he's a dolphin swimming with sharks and that'll calm him down. I'll be out soon. Bye bye."

An overwhelming urge to flop and relax comes over us as we arrange the picture set. When we're done, I ask Bonnie for our first model.

"I thought you were organising them," she snaps at me suddenly.

"Er, no. We were told you were."

"Look, sweetie, I'm not paying for half a service." Bonnie tenses up fast (and in the Zen room of all places).

"Summer?" I plead, thinking this is her thing, she's definitely going to play along – but she disagrees, saying, "Bog off, I'm not having Jo Public think I'm some sort of nutter needing 'Comfy Counselling'."

"'Counselling Corner'," Bonnie corrects.

Hoping someone would jump at a modelling job, I ask, "Can we borrow a member of staff?"

"Can't spare anyone today…you'll just have to do it," she says. Her sweet smile is beginning to stick a little and her manner is proving fake, like her image.

I sigh loudly and sit back in one of the oversized chairs, resigned to my new career as a model. Bonnie's caring smile suddenly reappears for the camera and she places a cold hand on my forehead, feigning reassurance.

"Great shot," clicks Ned, and he takes a few more.

Before I know it, I'm laid out on the daybed, being manoeuvred closer to the ceiling. It's a weird feeling but quite nice – a bit like being in the dentist's chair without the uncontrollable fear. The curved ceiling makes me feel as though I'm in space but in reality I'm not actually that far off the floor. I try to find Orion in a synthetic galaxy while the others position camera flashes about me…

"Wake up, Kate, time for the next room." Ned shakes me roughly and I'm brought back from my indoor space odyssey far too abruptly.

Next, I'm in a large, sage-green room flickering with candlelight, which makes me feel as though I'm walking into a mossy clearing. In the centre stands a normal-sized, sage-coloured bath with two steps built all around (like a throne gone wrong). It's full of slimy brown mud, and oddly enough the bath is carpeted right up to the rim on all four sides with the same stuff that's covering the floor.

"A bit kitsch," Summer decides. "What's this all about?"

"You will notice, my darlings, that it's impossible to feel oppressed in here," Bonnie says. "Nothing too close on all sides of one's being. Because your body is a vessel, you can either sail roughly through life in a battered old boat or glide on a yacht enjoying the ride."

"Well, I'm shipwrecked if she's the skipper," Ned says of Bonnie.

I pad across the deep carpet in a pair of flannels made into slippers and a soft, thick dressing gown. "Turn around all of you," I order, not wanting to be watched getting into a bath full of warm mud wearing a borrowed white bikini on my pale-blue flesh.

"The object is to relax," Bonnie tells me, slightly frayed.

"Ooh," I moan, totally relaxed. "That I can do."

Summer turns to Ned and teases, "What've you got if you have Kate up to her neck in shite?"

"Don't know."

"Not enough shite!"

The mud's cooling fast and I startle as Bonnie grabs my shoulders, shoving me in deeper. Ned takes a few more photos and decides to call it a day. I wonder how to get out without dripping green and brown slime everywhere and eventually slip across the floor on three tiny towels that Bonnie has laid out for me. I shower, get dressed and go home to relax properly with a large gin and tonic.

*

After yesterday's weird antics work seems rather mundane today. Although, I do help Maggie with an enormous mail shot, sitting through my lunch hour stuffing envelopes that have been spread neatly over the conference table. Halfway through, I realise that there's a personally dictated letter to each client and that I've mixed up eight hundred pre-printed letters with individually addressed envelopes (oops!).

Hiding under the huge walnut table for an hour, I watch Maggie's angry feet prowl back and forth asking for my head on a plate. Poor Maggie – she's still there now, sorting it out.

We're having a sex-aid party tonight with the girls from work and I walk into the lounge to see a 'middle-aged mother of four'-type woman introducing herself as Tallulah from Cunni-

Linguists International. Intrigued, I take my seat at the back of the room and notice how prudishly we're all acting. Tallulah hands each of us a piece of paper and a pen, telling us to place it on our heads with one hand and draw a penis on it with the other. Not my idea of fun, and my pathetic attempt couldn't roger a rodent; Siobhan's, however, is perfect (funny that...). I decline the next 'ice-breaking' activity, preferring to sort the drinks out instead.

An hour later, Maggie arrives to find us laughing at strange objects I never knew existed. Siobhan hands her a cup of rum punch and some love eggs, sniggering loudly.

"And *what* am I meant to do with these?" she asks soberly.

"They go up your fluffy, dear," Tallulah explains, so deadpan she could be selling insurance.

Flicking through the mail-order catalogue, I realise it's upside down but keep turning it through 180 degrees anyway, just to be sure. The girls are in hysterics at Tallulah's suitcase full of baby-doll nighties and sexy French maids' outfits. We run through the alphabet really fast using obscenities for each letter, and if anyone pauses, they have to drink a glass of punch.

"'A' is for anal," shouts Lauren.

"'B' is for blow jobs," adds Pippa.

"I'm Sally and I like sucking," interrupts Pippa's enthusiastic, thirty-something friend. (Tallulah tells her to sit down as it's not her turn yet.)

"'C' is for Cunni-Linguists International," Tallulah continues.

"'D' is for dildo."

"I'm Sally and I really like sucking!" persists Sally drunkenly, right through the alphabet (until Pippa decides at the letter 'R' to take her home).

Siobhan crashes into the lounge wearing a very expensive black PVC maid's outfit, fishnet stockings, suspenders and split-crotch knickers.

"Do you think this is a bit tacky?" she asks our gawping faces.

By the end of the evening, most of us have felt, fondled and handed back an astonishing assortment of vibrators, but

Summer (being last in line) has amassed a large pile of them and places one at each of our feet.

"Okay girls, when I say go, switch on your vibrators," she slurs. "First one into the kitchen wins this," she adds, holding up her just-purchased tub of chocolate body paint.

We get ready for the race of the night and fall over each other laughing, trying to aim plastic penises towards the kitchen.

"Steady, aim…GO!"

Spilt punch and shrieking accompanies the race as our fake willies jump and buzz their way across the floor.

"Hooray," yells Lauren as hers crosses the carpet-rod finish line first.

"That's not fair," Maggie argues. "Yours has a little thumb on it pushing it along."

"We all need a little help sometimes," winks Summer as she gets up to leave, clutching a catalogue tightly.

Tallulah thanks us for giving her a new party game idea and packs up the severed members before folding up a few completed order forms.

*

It's cold and raining, so when Siobhan offers to give me a lift to work in her new company car I accept gratefully, not wanting to get soaked to the skin and catch flu before my date tonight with Guy. She does have some odd mannerisms, though, and I flinch as she spits out of the window saying "Magpie" to me as if that makes it all right.

"Old Irish custom," she explains, saluting another. "'Fraid I was dragged up. Can't cross someone on the stairs or put shoes on a table."

She drives into a petrol station on the wrong side, blocking any cars waiting to exit. Becoming flustered, she attempts to do a seven-point turn and approach the garage from the correct side.

A cute petrol pump attendant watches us closely from his kiosk window as Siobhan eventually swings the car out into the road and drives back again through the one-way filter system. Pulling up next to pump no. 4, she swears loudly – the filler cap is on the other side.

"Never mind," I tell her, cringing in the passenger seat. "The hose will stretch over the roof and down the side of the window."

Unused to new cars, Siobhan can't work out how to open the petrol cap and flicks at it with her fingers until I lean across and pull the lever from underneath the steering wheel. Sensing a long, slow refuelling process, I decide to wander into the shop, leaving her to her fate.

While studying a celebrity magazine, I notice her struggle with the petrol cap and then hold it up in triumph like some sort of trophy – she's pulled the bloody thing right off! I head back outside towards the car but our good-looking assistant gets there before me.

"What on earth's going on?" I ask, as Mr Cute begins to screw the cap back on.

"It broke," Siobhan mutters, pushing past me to pay.

Munching on a chocolate bar, I wait for her in the car, thinking it would've been quicker to cycle and risk the rain. She returns and drives away at breakneck speed, bemoaning her embarrassment as I choke with laughter.

Five minutes later, she's horrified to realise her credit card's still in the shop with the attractive assistant (I tease that this was deliberate).

Everyone at work talks about last night's sex toys but no one admits to ordering one. I revel in my last day of freedom before my new boss arrives on Monday, doing as little as I can get away with. At 5.30pm I walk home (deciding it's safer than Siobhan's offer of a lift).

We spend what seems like an age getting ready to go out and Guy (looking handsome in a dinner jacket) collects us at 7pm, just like he said he would. Siobhan's dress complies with the Officers' Mess code of 'on the shoulder and past the knee', except that it's see-through grey chiffon. However, in the dim evening light, Guy hasn't yet noticed.

Both of us are on our best behaviour and feel rather grown up enjoying pre-dinner drinks in the Mess bar. It's a bit like a

London gentlemen's club, full of wood panelling, chesterfield sofas and cigarette smoke. People wander around in uniform and formal dress – some 'lasses' are wearing tartan sashes across their dresses to uphold the 'old Scotland' theme.

Guy is charming, behaving like a real gentleman, and I begin to wonder why (surely there must be a flaw in this man somewhere?). We find out he was born in England and grew up in Scotland from the age of four. He supports England at rugby but always answers "British" to anyone querying his nationality – that is until Burns Night, when he's an honorary Scot.

"Then why aren't you wearing a kilt?" Siobhan asks, commenting on how sexy men look in Highland dress.

"Never wanted one," he says directly to her nipples, suddenly noticing them.

A gong rings for dinner and I scan the seating plan to see where we are. Guy tells me the person sitting on my left will 'escort' me in and he will do likewise. Captain Ralph Henson finds me first and links my arm.

"Well hello there, gorgeous lady," he says in a deep Texan drawl.

I feel like Doris Day in *Calamity Jane*, wishing we still strapped dance cards to our wrists (born in the wrong era, big time – oh well, at least I can float around in this unfamiliar world of good manners and posh partying).

Guy escorts Trudy (Ralph's wife) in front of us to her seat and Ralph pulls my chair out for me. Siobhan walks past us with arms hooked to a man either side of her. I hear her informing the bloke on her left arm of her body piercing.

"It's for me to know and you to ask," she flirts.

"Do I need a metal detector?" he asks.

"No, you just need to say please," she replies, laughing.

We all say grace before sitting down and I start chatting to Ralph.

"Napkin, darling," Guy whispers to me.

"You want one?" I offer him mine.

"No, use it," he adds, and continues talking to his neighbour.

Keeping elbows off the table, I unfold my napkin and place

it across my knee, introducing myself to Trudy. Ralph and Trudy are a USAF (United States Air Force) exchange family enjoying three years of "how to fly properly", as Guy calls it, and they tell me they're preparing to go home soon because Ralph's 'tour' is almost over. I don't even notice my glass being refilled by the ever-vigilant waiters as Ralph reels off flying stories.

"Today was my very last flight and we flew 'three ship' – three aircraft in formation – low-level through a Welsh valley, so low in fact that as we went past a row of houses on the hillside, we managed to wave at a woman washing dishes."

Guy leans over and mimics what the radio conversation was like as they flew past. "'Alpha here, come in Bravo. Did you see her face?' 'Absolutely, Alpha – I'm right behind you. She waved back at us and is standing open mouthed at Charlie going past now.'"

Confused by the jargon but sure it should all make perfect sense, it feels like I'm learning a new language: A, B, C = Alpha, Bravo, Charlie (quite different from last night's dirtier version in my front room).

Oak-panelled walls and candlelight create a ghostly atmosphere and subdued mood. Light from the tall, silver candelabras is reflected in each shiny object on the two polished walnut tables running parallel down the room (my stomach rumbles noisily).

A chef carries in the haggis and 'parades' it to the top table, accompanied (skirled in) by a Scottish piper playing the time-honoured music. I lean backwards and forwards trying to help the stiff-necked waiter serve my meal but give up, noticing Guy moves left for wine and right for food. Siobhan and I stuff ourselves on 'neeps' and 'tatties', savouring every mouthful. Imagine getting food like this night after night instead of a pizza or pasty.

I think of our humble house and compare it to Guy's, deciding it's no wonder he's a bit formal and stands on ceremony if this is where he lives. Once we all finish eating, a nod from the top table sends the waiting staff into action and they clear our places with expert speed and precision.

"You okay?" I ask Siobhan in the Ladies Powder Room.

"Okay? I'm bloody fantastic – I feel like a 'deb' at a coming-out ball. Think I've pulled Rupert from '234 course' and possibly two waiters."

"That's a bit slapperish for someone with an A grade in A-level English Literature," I tease – and instantly shut up as a stern-looking middle-aged woman walks out of a cubicle to wash her hands.

Poetry comes alive on Burns Night (albeit belatedly), so after 'a tassie o'coffee wi' shortbread' and a 'wee dram o' whisky', we listen to Robbie Burns quoted flawlessly by real enthusiasts.

One fellow gives a short 'Toast to the Lassies' and his female colleague responds in appropriate form with a humorous 'Ode to the Laddies'.

No Burns Night is complete without the Tam O'Shanter. Siobhan told me yesterday it's a verse loosely based on a bloke called Douglas Graham of Shanter (1739–1811), whose wife was a superstitious old shrew. Prone to drunkenness on market day, the 'wags' of Ayr clipped Douglas's horse's tail – a fact he explained away to his credulous wife with a story of witchcraft warning Carrick farmers not to stay late in Ayr markets.

All the lights dim and a short rotund Squadron Leader with a broad Scottish accent stands up, cloaked in darkness except for his face (illuminated by the small flickering flame). He first outlines the tale in modern English, with an ordinary Air Force Officer as 'Tam' on his way home from the Squadron late at night. This imaginary Officer notices a light has been left on in the Medical Centre and peeps through the window to see all sorts of immoral scenes that take his breath away.

Having set the scene, he continues to narrate the real tale in traditional Scots verse, speeding up or slowing down to accentuate the fear. As he speaks, I feel something moving on my lap and look down to see a hand holding a crisp linen napkin across my knees.

"Psst, pass it on," someone whispers.

Without asking, I take the offered corner and pass it to my neighbour, noticing that it's one in a long line of napkins tied together forming a silent tug of war. Then, as I strain to hear the last few verses of the poem, I see someone wearing a kilt underneath the table, followed closely by a girl...Rupert and Siobhan – they're having a race! Must be a dare, I think, joining in with the deafening applause for the remarkable performance of Burns. But judging by their expressions, the top table are not amused (Guy says high spirits are never tolerated at formal functions, but inevitably they happen). Our storyteller deserves an Oscar for his rendition and I only hope he can forgive "the shameful behaviour of those two Sassenachs", as he puts it.

After dinner we change rooms to see a ten-piece Scottish folk band ready for vigorous bouts of Highland country dancing. Hems reel and tresses spin to the Gay Gordons and countless other jigs.

Rupert and Siobhan are deep in conversation when, after a particularly long Dashing White Sergeant, Guy and I rudely interrupt their tête-à-tête.

Rupert brings us up to date with their discussion. "Siobhan wants to know if any of the boys would be interested in her dominatrix service, so I've told her to put a few cards up in the post room," he says.

I look amazed at Siobhan for a second, then frown, demanding an explanation.

"Well, I got thinking after Tallulah left and decided it would be a great way to make money...We just chain a few of these nice boys up, wear leather, shout obscenities at them and they clean our toilet for us," she suggests.

"Get your coat, Siobhan, we're going home," I say, suddenly sober.

A kind MP (military policeman) volunteers to drive a few of us home. As we drop various couples off, I stare at the married quarters in surprise – I had no idea the Officers' families lived here (thought it was a council estate). Feeling a bit naive at believing they had large, upmarket homes, I watch an armoured vehicle drive past us and, for a split second, imagine we're in Belfast. I decide there and then that I could never live in one of these awful dwellings.

Ten minutes later, Guy and I fall off the bus at my house and Siobhan follows behind with Rupert wrapped tightly around her.

"Siobhan, what's he doing here?"

"Couldn't resist him. He's so beautifully hairy – my rug with a dick."

*

Saturday morning should include the afternoon but Guy wakes me up early by jumping out of bed to see what the weather's like.

"Come on…Kate, get your clothes on – we're going flying."

Incredibly enough, I act as though I go flying every weekend and rummage through my wardrobe, throwing different outfits on the floor. Normal people watch a film or go walking in the park, but it's absurdly exciting and I pack my favourite childhood relic, Park-a-Garage, to join in the fun. His mate, Trees, looks at me solemnly from being left behind. But hey – life's tough on teddy bears.

After driving for an hour (and explaining to Guy that nothing weird happened to me during my formative years), we arrive at Cranwell flying club, a small wooden hut on the edge of a weather-beaten, windswept runway. Noticing that the trees around us are doubled over in the wind, I begin to have my doubts that we'll get airborne at all. We sit around for an hour when suddenly the wind changes. Guy pulls on a pair of white kid gloves and announces suggestively, "Come fly with me."

I climb aboard a tiny twin-seated propeller-driven aircraft and try to concentrate as Guy shouts "Chocks away!" to absolutely nobody.

Hurtling down the runway, I hold my breath as he pulls back on the stick and I'm pushed hard into the seat, looking directly up at the clouds. Levelling off in a pocket of turbulence, I regain my bearings by focusing on the horizon.

The skyline is awesome, and as the ground melts away I watch the Lincolnshire countryside slide underneath me, a collage of fields and towns. Cranwell base seems so small it looks like Toy Town, and I notice that the roofs of the enormous fuel dumps are covered in turf in order to be camouflaged from airborne enemies.

Guy speaks on the radio to other aircraft around us and flicks switches on the dashboard. He's very serious and professional – only when we're safely established in the air does he start pointing out landmarks for me. I feel totally safe, enjoying the sense of freedom, and start to understand his love for soaring through space. We circle churches and castles, swooping sideways for a closer look before pulling back up.

"Fancy a shot?" asks Guy, and then he says, "You have control," before folding his arms.

I snatch the control column and try to keep it absolutely still, not daring to move one inch in case we die. One minute later, I'm going decidedly green when Guy relieves me of my terror, saying seriously, "I have control," and squeezes my hand reassuringly.

The tiny runway looms larger and I'm amazed at how he's managed to find it again in this vast expanse of country.

"Easy – IFR," he says. Which means absolutely nothing to me, so I look confused until he explains seriously, "'I follow roads, rivers and railways.'" (But somehow, I can't take him seriously.)

"Thank you for flying Willesley Airways, ladies and gentlemen. Please make sure you take all your belongings with you as you leave the aircraft," he jokes, and I reach for my handbag from behind the seat. What glorious fun it is to drive around England without roads or boundaries (however, I think I might be about to lose my breakfast in the loo).

Guy pulls up outside my house and, engine still running, announces, "I'm going to Germany on Tuesday for a month."

Stunned, I sit quietly for a moment, aware of how different my life will be without him when he's only been in it for a few weeks.

"Sorry, Kate, but that's the Air Force for you," he adds, noticing a look on my face like that of a newly orphaned child.

I manage to persuade him that I don't mind him going away at all and quite like having my independence (but inside my stomach is churning).

*

Rupert's been here all weekend and Siobhan drives him home to Linton-on-Ouse in time to prepare for his check ride tomorrow. I hitch a lift with them to see Guy before he goes away, and inside the Officers' Mess I take vague directions from Rupert towards Guy's room.

"Go along this corridor, turn left and it's the first on your right," he manages to say with his tongue down Siobhan's throat.

I wander away feeling lost but follow my instructions to the door and knock. There's no reply, but I can hear movement inside and strange shouting (like strangled wailing).

The noise starts to sound frantic, with loud banging – so I burst in, thinking he's having a heart attack. Instead, I find him bouncing up and down on his bed wearing nothing but a jockstrap and dirty rugby shirt. He's playing air guitar with a squash racquet and has a metal waste-paper basket jammed on his head with headphone leads trailing out to the stereo.

"Guy!" I yell, laughing hysterically as he gets down on his knees in front of me, strumming wildly.

"Yes, darling," he says from behind me. "Meet Pricey, a slave to music."

In all the winding corridors, I've confused my left from my right and Guy's room is the one opposite. We shut the door as Pricey roars, "The ace of spades…The ACE of SPADES!"

Guy opens the door of No. 74 and I step inside, relieved to know my boyfriend's not the heavy-metal freak. I sit on his desk, laughing about the scene I just witnessed, until he ushers me into an uncomfortable orange nylon-covered armchair to watch him pack. Books, electrical leads, CDs and other such stuff litter the floor and I tell him it's all so unfair – how can he leave when we're only just getting to know each other?

"Will you come back to York?" I ask tearfully, hoping to tug at his heartstrings and keep him in Yorkshire.

"Doubt it. I've requested somewhere else," he replies casually, continuing to pack boxes, completely focused on the job.

Suitcases stuffed with possessions litter the room and it's all too much for me to bear. I throw myself at his ankles, clawing my way up until I'm wrapped tightly around his muscular thigh. "But I don't want you to go," I sob.

"I know, darling," he laughs softly, stroking my hair and dragging me across the room still clinging to his left leg.

"Kate, please let go. I have to leave. Kate, get off, you're hurting…"

We drive home in silence. Outside my grotty house the hairs on my skin rise as he kisses me goodbye. "Why can't you be a bin man?" I whisper into his neck. "At least then I'd see you every Tuesday."

I spend the rest of the evening utterly abandoned and somewhat bloated from a chocolate-induced chemical rush. (Everyone at work is so impressed by his job but I just want Guy, and I wonder how much social standing he'd have if he did get cut from flying training and was forced to be a road sweeper?)

*

"Morn–"

"Fuck off."

New day, new boss, lots to look forward to, but I can't help feeling bereaved.

Beth Carrington is a confident, capable woman with lots of ideas for client campaigns and her own systems to introduce. I'm terrified of her and do everything she says. But I can't help wondering how Piers is getting on and miss his one-way telepathy where he would expect me to know exactly what he wanted doing five minutes before he told me. And somehow I don't think clients will arrive just as she leaves the office, like they did with Piers (because he'd forgotten where the meeting was).

Danny stands in reception and phones through to my desk asking if Siobhan and I want to go for dinner at his house tonight. After a nanosecond's pause I agree, telling him ungratefully, "We go anywhere for free food."

Beth and I continue to tiptoe around each other, learning how to get along, until I suggest she takes me out for lunch. She's definitely in the 'high-maintenance wife' bracket and I pity the man who foots her salon bill. Everything about her is glamorous; even her hair glows, and I notice she doesn't have one single split end.

Over lunch we get on like good friends, gossiping and laughing together, though I suspect she's a career-driven workaholic.

Standing up to leave the quiet café, she startles me by placing cash on the table, saying loudly, "Quickly, Kate. We have to leave immediately – someone's recognised me." We dash outside, leaving customers staring after us, and I realise Beth's got a sense of humour

"She's sophisticated and daunting, but I like her." I answer Danny's intrusive questions about Beth later that evening over a glass of red wine. "She gives me compliments for work done, which is totally alien to me, and rather nice." I tell him about her antics in the café, pretending to be famous.

Waiting for Siobhan to join us, I help him prepare dinner and observe out of the corner of my eye that Danny keeps staring at me.

"How's Guy?" he asks, leaning across me to wash some tomatoes.

"Oh, so Siobhan's told you? He's everything I've ever wanted and more," I start to tell him.

"Kate, you know I care a lot about you, don't you?" Danny says calmly, his warm breath alarmingly close to my face.

"I, er…yeah," I reply

"Well, according to Shiv, he sounds like a typical Rupert."

I wonder if I should tell Danny (who's head is in a cupboard rummaging around for dried basil) about Siobhan and her new beau, but since he's just named him derogatorily, I decide to keep quiet.

"Yoo-hoo, it's me! I hope you haven't started drinking without me?" Siobhan throws her bag onto the sofa and pours herself a glass of wine.

Over dinner she tells us of her decision to dump 'Roo' before anything blossoms and I ask why.

"He wants me to wear his NBC kit during sex."

"His what?" I ask, my imagination running wild.

"Nuclear protection kit. I didn't mind the first time, although it was a bit sweaty."

Danny and I cry with laughter thinking of her all hot and sticky trying to please her man.

"But last time he said to me, 'Get yourself going, I'll be back in a minute,' so I laid on his bed for ages in that ridiculous suit and stupid gas mask wondering where the hell he was. Turns out he'd only gone down to the bar for a quick pint leaving me waiting. Well, excuse me…he's history."

We wipe away our tears but Siobhan can't see the funny side, which makes me worry even more about her bizarre sex life.

*

She's quite bossy, my boss, and I deliberately ignore her demands, knowing deadlines don't amuse her like they did Piers. Why are women so pernickety? I act like a complete cow and refuse to rush more than I have to. Although, she's quite taken with Annabel and wants her to work with us on a few small projects.

"You can tell she's got class," Beth observes. "I knew that from the moment she said she'd grown up with an Aga…Is she 'old money'?"

"More like no money – she's completely broke," I quip, knowing Annabel's spending habits.

Walking in the park at lunchtime, I long to smack any couples I see holding hands. How dare they be so insensitive when my sweetheart is miles away bravely serving Queen and country.

Wasting time in reception, I wish Annabel luck as she leaves to visit a client's building site wearing high heels and listen, intrigued, to Angel's novel technique of answering the telephone: "'Ello Angel speaking, gud mornin' the Pannnash Groooop," she sings down her headphone to every caller before putting them on hold and spitting, "Wait there, fadge face," or, "No, you can't leave a message you silly bitch." As eight lines or more often ring at once, I'm amazed she doesn't slip up and accidentally take someone off hold.

Chewing gum, she directs my gaze to her tummy and shows me a freshly punctured belly button. Dangling in its dainty recess is a cheap silver hoop. I sigh, thinking of the enormous bullock's nosering that would be needed to harness my abdominal flesh, and look past her at the fax machine whirring into life. It's from Guy in Germany! He's arrived and says he misses me. I read it again and again before noticing that the bottom line says 'Come over for the weekend'.

"You lucky mare," Angel exclaims noisily. "I wish someone would sweep me off for a dirty weekend."

"It's not a dirty weekend, it's quality time," I mock, excitedly.

Beth offers to organise my flight and clicks away on her computer, booking it in minutes on the Internet. (I feel enormously guilty for being so lazy this morning and work flat out all afternoon to make it up to her.)

By eight o'clock I'm packed and ready to go, suitcase sat waiting by the front door for Friday.

"Bit keen, aren't we? It's only Tuesday," Siobhan teases. "Why don't you play hard-to-get like me, darling – men love it."

"That why you're not getting any, then?" I reply, and watch her scowl back at me.

*

When you're little and you outgrow a favourite toy it becomes a fond memory. I believe that children are toys owned by their parents who refuse to outgrow or let go of them, even though the toys are far too big to play with anymore. This is the case with my parents – they turn up unannounced, sit quietly or make idle conversation, keeping their coats on for the duration of the visit, and, after being slightly superior, go home again.

Today, they are taking me out for lunch and I meet them in reception, telling them there's no need to whisper as it's not a hospital, but they carry on regardless.

Outside, dad holds my hand as we cross the road and mum tries to zip up my coat. I feel a desperate need to scream but instead suppress a one hundred-decibel yell like my childhood heroine in the 'Raven' fairytale whose silence broke a spell to turn her brothers from birds back into boys. Although, she couldn't keep her gob shut and screamed minutes before the deadline, so one brother ended up with a wing instead of an arm (silly cow).

We eat in a trendy bistro and I want to kiss mum and dad for not knowing what a skinny choca-mocha is (this is my world and they've become my toys for an hour).

Back in the street, I link arms with them, feeling grown up and ten years old at the same time. Mum asks if everything's all right and I'm tempted to say, "Well actually, I'm having a bit of trouble achieving full orgasm unless I go on top and you never told me how naff blow jobs are." But, instead, I smile and hug them goodbye, telling them not to worry – I'm fine.

Everyone from work is standing around outside in the car park and I ask Summer what's going on.

"There's been a fire drill. We're just waiting to get back inside. I wish they'd hurry up, though, 'cos I'm freezing," she says, lighting up a cigarette.

As usual, the girls are bitching about Eleanor, whose return from a conference prompts Maggie to ask Beth if she's met her yet.

"I try to have as little as possible to do with her," Beth replies dryly.

"But what do you think of her?" asks Lauren.

"Don't know, really. She looks a bit haggard, like she had a tough paper round as a kid. You know – block of flats and the Sunday papers."

Angel looks angelic but shouts at everyone like a fishwife,

ordering them to line up for a roll call. Beth asks if she has to wait here or can she mingle amongst the crowd like at a cocktail party?

I feel thousands of miles away from Guy.

Walking home up through The Shambles and down Stonegate, I pause to window-shop on the way. Just before walking into Museum Gardens, I turn to see the huge but intricately carved edifice of York Minster in full twilight. I think of how awe-inspiring it must have been centuries ago and drink in the moment, aware of my youth and freedom, blissfully happy. York has my soul and I don't think I could ever leave it behind, we belong together – my home is me.

*

Before going to work, I leave a message on Guy's answering machine in Germany.

"Hello there, darling. I'm so excited about seeing you tomorrow. My flight gets into Schipol at seven in the evening, so see you there. I hope you enjoy the 'meet and greet' party tonight; in fact, you'll probably get this message late, so if you're drunk, blow me a kiss and put yourself into the recovery position. Bye bye."

In the office, Annabel wants to know why our agency is mainly staffed by women, and Beth answers, "Because we're cheap and loyal, darling...cheap and loyal." Camp Carl takes offence at this remark and refuses to share his cookies, hurt we've ignored his gender.

"But Carl, dear, you don't have an argument," Maggie points out. "You spend most of your time being more female than any of us."

Accepting defeat, Carl nevertheless licks his index finger and touches every cookie in his lunch box; he then offers them round, smiling like a prig.

Siobhan's on the phone organising a date with Nick the policeman for tomorrow night (I know she'll be glad to have the house to herself for a weekend). The afternoon drags painfully by as I get rid of the filing piled up in my in-tray.

At home, I empty the suitcase that's been standing by the front door all week and repack it with completely different clothes. Then my beauty routine takes over and I start to de-fuzz my Neanderthal body into 'sexy babe'. Toes are polished, nails are painted, tash, eyebrows, legs and bikini line all get a good waxing, and I feel slightly better, if a bit raw. Why is it that waxing always leaves you with a shiny filtrum (top lip) and a bikini line that looks like plucked poultry?

*

How did I get through today? I wonder, getting out of a taxi at Leeds Bradford Airport. I'm a bag of nerves, have butterflies in my stomach and am giddy with excitement just at the thought of seeing Guy again. Is this what people call love? This thought brings on a sudden urge to poo and I seek out the Ladies, deciding to go now rather than stink out Guy's toilet when I get there. I can't possibly 'go' on the aeroplane. And it wouldn't be very romantic to greet the man of my dreams, who's desperate to kiss me, by saying, "Can you wait a minute babe? I'm bursting for a dump – back in a sec…"

After ten minutes of straining and two embarrassingly loud farts in the departure lounge lavatory, I admit defeat and wait until it's safe to emerge from my cubicle. Applying perfume and lipstick makes me feel confident again but I'm paranoid a few females are turning to watch me take my seat on the plane knowing I'm the phantom trumper.

The flight is so quick that the next thing I know, my suitcase is in the arrival lounge at Schipol. I queue up to retrieve it, not noticing that the two-way glass screen exposes everyone to their waiting friends and families on the other side. Thinking it's just a mirror, I adjust my bra, retrieve lost knicker elastic from up my bum crack and lick stray lipstick off my front teeth.

"Kate, over here!" Guy is jumping up and down, waving to me from the back of the crowd. As we grab each other tightly,

I wrap my arms around his solid chest, noting there's not an inch of flab on him.

"Are you as giddy as I am?" I ask, eyes sparkling.

"I got a bit excited when I saw your suitcase on the carousel and then two minutes later I saw you queue up for it. I wanted to be sick – with nerves," he adds, quickly.

"Hope that's a compliment," I laugh, punching him in the ribs.

Driving across Holland to Germany, we stop off at a burger bar for a bite to eat and I'm speechless at the till attendant who speaks Dutch to the people in front of us, English to Guy and German to the couple behind us. How ignorant does that make me feel – I can't even say thank you in Dutch to him and here he is working in a burger bar, fluent in three languages.

On the base, Guy shows me around his suite of rooms, telling me I'm the best girlfriend ever as I hand over a pack of real ale brought all the way from Yorkshire. The Officers' Mess has five combination locks, and on his arrival Guy changed the numbers of the various entrances to 1914, 1918, 1939, 1945 and 1966. Luckily, visiting German dignitaries only ever use one door and are therefore completely unaware of the joke.

We make polite conversation waiting for the kettle to boil before Guy says, "Sod the tea, get your clothes off," and locks the bedroom door.

I make a quick excuse about wanting to freshen up and nip to his loo, opening a small window before nervously farting rusty water. Coughing loudly, I'm terrified he can hear me, as the white tiles have excellent acoustics. Subsequently, I can't help contemplating the limited delights of *sex à la soixsante-neuf* to come.

"Nice flange," he says, gawping charmlessly at my newly aerodynamic bits. "And I always say that there's nothing like a well-trimmed bush," he mumbles cheekily into my freshly plucked inner thighs.

My efforts are obviously appreciated and we start to work our way through Guy's own imaginative *Karma Sutra*. I secretly worry that my excess flesh is too exposed, trying to lie flat where my boobs are at their most attractive and least pendulous. But being in love makes one far too obliging and I agree to his manoeuvring anyway.

Exhausted, we lie in a heap as sunlight streams through the slightly open curtains. I slowly drag myself away from him to make a nice rewarding cup of Earl Grey.

Showered and changed into fresh clothes, we drive back over the border to Holland for dinner. At a restaurant, Guy requests a table for two in fluent German and, after a brief conversation with a waiter, turns to face me, explaining we have to go elsewhere because they're full. Halfway to the car park, the manager runs outside and apologies to us. "One moment, sir, I didn't realise you were English. Please come back inside and we'll find you a place."

Guy says okay and tells me not to worry, explaining that it is an ex-occupied country after all, but that this sort of sentiment is quite rare now.

Driving back to the base, we pass a tiny church with three statues outside and small craters all over the grey stone building. Guy says the statues are to commemorate three Dutch nuns shot by the Nazis during the Second World War for hiding British pilots. The craters are the actual marks left by the bullets that killed them.

I look across at Guy, thinking, but for the grace of time, it could've been you.

*

Dragging ourselves out of bed, we meet up with a few of Guy's colleagues at a charity football match and I feign interest in the talents of his two favourite players. Guy makes excuses to leave when it starts to drizzle and we go indoors for a game of squash. I'm not bad at this sport but still make Guy play with one arm behind his back in order to have a slim chance of scoring.

Tired and jubilant, Guy informs me I'm a very magnanimous winner and that he found playing left handed, as well as having one arm behind his back, quite good practice.

Relaxing in the sauna, I think my nostrils are being stripped of hair as the steam burns its way through my nasal cavity. But Guy throws more water on the hot coals regardless. Somehow we manage to have hot slippery sex as I sit across his lap, the excitement heightened by the fact that someone could come in at any moment!

Inseparable from excess, we shower together in his en suite bathroom and I haven't given a single thought to life back home, too blissfully oblivious to bother phoning Siobhan or worry about returning.

Snuggled up in his bed, eating crisps and drinking red wine, Guy lists the films he has on video and I refuse to watch any boring gun-fighting or car-chasing spacemen.

"Haven't you got any girlie ones?" I ask.

Guy suddenly becomes eager to find a film I might like and holds up a choice of *Naughty Nancy's Paris Nights* or *Seducing Selina*.

"I meant Hollywood romance," I sigh, laughing at Guy's Labrador face pleading for Nancy.

We finally agree on a science-fiction movie, or at least he thinks we have, and I become suitably impressed with his surround-sound system. Making coffee, I venture the suggestion that he could start keeping fresh milk inside the portable fridge instead of outside on the window ledge.

"But then there'd be no room for my beer," he argues (I give up).

Halfway through the night, I wake up gasping for a drink and nudge a sleeping Guy awake, asking him to go and get me something to quench my thirst. He wanders down the corridor and returns ten minutes later muttering, "Couldn't find any water, so I made you some toast."

Speechless, there's nothing else for it but to go back to sleep.

*

The minute we wake up, I'm overcome by the thought of going home and leaving Guy. However, I try to smile at his awful attempts to cheer me up.

"Sherpa Tensing says to Sir Edmund Hillary, 'But I thought you'd brought the flag?'"

I start to cry and Guy stands bolt upright, about to launch into another terrible joke.

"Stop it, Guy. I don't want to go. Why do you have to be so far away?"

"I know, darling," he says softly. "But it's the job and I'm afraid I love it."

Driving to the airport, clinging to every precious memory of my weekend with him, I think about when we'll be together again. Three whole weeks to go – it seems like a lifetime to wait but Guy is so calm compared to my woeful blubbering (never realised being in love could hurt this much).

Hugging, kissing, wiping tears away from my face and blowing my nose like a trombone does little for my looks, but I don't care. Tearing away from him is a raw pain and my life seems cruelly shattered as we walk towards the metal security barrier. The fat, emotionless guard has seen it all before and stands too close to me for my liking as he frisks me with an electronic baton. I look over the top of my glasses to avoid having to focus on his oily face.

Looking round for one last glimpse of Guy, I stop dead to see him holding up a large piece of crumpled paper with the words 'I LOVE YOU' written clearly on it in large black letters – he must have done this back at the base before we left. Oh how romantic!

Now in the full throes of wailing, the check-in assistant helps me fumble through my bag to find my boarding card and everyone stares at me.

I'm still crying when they hand me my lunch tray after take-off, and the businessman sitting next to me hands over his miniature bottle of wine, saying, "Here, have this. I think you need it more than me."

I drink both mine and his straight down, saying, "Th... th...thank yo...you," in between large gulps of air.

Falling asleep, I quietly say my prayers, begging God to send Guy back to me, or at least to the UK. I promise faithfully never to moan about anything ever again if he delivers.

*

Carrying on life as normal, I can't help feeling like Cinderella, who's had a taste of Prince Charming and is now serving a community sentence before being allowed back into the palace.

Nothing matters anymore as I drift from one project to the next pining for my lover, pathetically arranging Beth's meetings.

Siobhan throws a huge bar of chocolate on my desk, saying, "Snap out of it, girl. You haven't once asked how my weekend went. So eat this and act interested."

Dutifully, I break off chunks and dip them in my coffee, thinking if I'm going to get fat I might as well do it properly. Siobhan tells me PC Plod proved to be perfect, giving her hope that this could be 'the one', when towards the end of the night she put her hand on his leg to "get things going".

"Well, what happened?" I mumble, mouth full of melting chocolate.

"What happened was I got a complete fright, that's what happened – he'd only got a pair of suspenders on underneath his jeans!" she whispers, and I stare at her in disbelief.

"Kate, close your mouth. It's rude to show your food," she chastises me, as if talking to a child. "Anyway, I told him it was too weird and we couldn't continue the date. So Nick and I are over…before we began, but I think he's going to be Nicola soon if he can get enough money for the operation. I didn't stay around long enough to hear his excuses."

Laughing together, I notice that I haven't thought about Guy for almost five minutes and realise that life does go on, so I might as well make the best of it.

Christian walks past my desk and hands me a train ticket, but when I look closely I see it's a party invitation for Friday night – typical of him and his weird designs.

A few of us go grocery shopping after work and decide to seek refuge in a teashop afterwards. Piles of supermarket carrier bags sit on top of each other by our feet as we order rounds of sandwiches and tea.

The impatient waitress asks, "Do you have milk?" in

response to which Annabel starts rummaging through her bags and produces a carton of semi-skimmed.

"Yes, here you are," she says sweetly. (The waitress just stares at her stupidity.)

Walking home, I smile at a busker feebly juggling two tennis balls. He has a note by his feet saying 'At least I'm trying', so I throw a few pound coins into his hat.

Nodding his thanks at me, he says, "Excuse me, love. Do you want my dog?"

"No thank you," I answer, looking at the scruffy mongrel sat next to him (why am I always the nutter magnet?).

"I've been trying to give him away for ages but no one wants him," he continues. "I hate him and he hate's me."

"Look," I say, "I've never understood pets. The dog licks it's arse and then licks you – where's the fun in that?" and I start to walk away quickly, vowing I will never try to reason with a loony again.

*

Charles calls everyone into the conference room for a staff meeting and we sit around chatting until he arrives.

"Got to make a few redundancies," he says, going straight to the point. "Not nice, but necessary in this changing climate. I do appreciate you all, even though you don't think so, and some of you I even like…a bit. Anyway, I wanted you to find out from me rather than on the grapevine. We'll be announcing them this afternoon in accordance with the policy. Now get back to work."

We file back upstairs discussing the situation, speculating on which one of us will be going first. Maggie refuses to reveal her insider knowledge, saying we only have two hours to wait. Speculation is rife and Siobhan's paranoid she's first for the chop. I don't really mind because I can get another personal assistant job anywhere. However, I do like working at Panache more than anywhere else I've ever worked.

A few of us go and sit in the park at lunchtime to eat our sandwiches, and as we watch children laughing on the swings,

I notice a slice of life other than my own, single, nine-to-five existence – Motherhood.

"I'd like to be someone's mother one day," I tell the girls, dreaming ahead like I have decades to decide.

"Let me tell you, honey, children are far more stressful, emotionally and mentally, than back there," says Summer, pointing towards the office.

"Yes, but I just mean that today's events don't really matter in the big scheme of things, do they?" I sigh.

"Ooh, our Kate's in love all right," Lauren adds.

"Well just make sure you give the little darlings everything that money can buy, including your freedom…I'm talking private school," Beth says dryly.

The conversation moves on to what we'd name our hypothetical offspring and Siobhan thinks that Elvis is a nice name.

"Only if you want him to get beaten up in school, it is – this is Yorkshire, for goodness' sake!"

I finish eating and decide, "I'm going to provide my children with everything I never had but always wanted."

Beth quips, "In that case, give them anorexia and bulimia, darling," putting her cigarette out and getting up to go back. "Come on, let's go face the music."

Camp Carl's crying in reception as we walk in (so we guess correctly that he's a casualty) and Eleanor is loading up her car with cardboard boxes. My heart leaps as I look across at Maggie who smiles back knowingly.

"Thank you, God," I mouth to the sky, knowing my gran was always right in saying you reap what you sow in this world.

Jimbo mutters "Goodbye my little lollipop" at Eleanor through the window. Lauren, incensed by his soppy sentiment, throws a pen which hits his left ear, but she lets him off when he explains that she's "Frozen solid with a stick up her arse."

Carl and Eleanor are the only ones going, but Charles warns us there could be more redundancies coming in the future.

Siobhan and I celebrate our great escape with fish and chips for tea.

*

Work is a breeze for everyone apart from Carl and Eleanor. Carl comes in to clear his desk and asks if a few of us want to go out on an impromptu leaving party tonight. Of course, we all agree and make arrangements to meet in town at 8pm.

Drumming up interest in the leaving presents, Summer dashes out at lunchtime to buy Carl a CD Walkman and I find, unsurprisingly, that Eleanor's collection fund holds little more than four pounds. With such a small amount I'm lost for ideas (other than a pre-paid dry-cleaning ticket) and decide that justice has prevailed. However, I can't bring myself to do it and settle for a pretty box of herbal tea bags.

I spend the rest of the afternoon peeling oranges for Beth who thinks she's got a vitamin C deficiency.

Our gang takes over Carl's favourite Chinese restaurant on Gillygate and, because it's still mid-week, we have no problem getting served early. Lager'd and fed, we wander into a nightclub delighted to find that Wednesday is seventies night and boogie away on the dance floor.

I suddenly spot three of Guy's colleagues chatting up blondes at the bar and pop over to say hello. Listening to them play shag, marry or cliff (out of three girls, which would you shag, marry or throw over a cliff), I'm bewildered by the large number of stunning women who willingly flock around them, clearly impressed by their macho vocation.

"She's a veteran," one of them whispers to me about a goddess walking past him.

I look confused until he goes on to say, "Bin through the whole course – she can smell the pilots from the navigators. We call her the Mess Monster."

Aghast at his blatant narcissism, I protest, "That's awful! Don't condemn the poor girl – *you've* had most of York."

He agrees with me on that one, but still argues, "Yeah, but I'm not looking for a meal ticket out of here, am I."

I gawp at his unbelievable ego. However, I can't help thinking that for every self-assured git like him there are wiser women who know exactly what training stage these boys are at and can pick out the best of them from across a bar.

"Well, she's not so stupid then, really, is she," I declare. "You, however, are an oxygen thief, talking nothing but cod," I mutter to his departing figure, and turning to the infatuated girl, I decide to give him a taste of his own medicine, telling her, "He's not gone and told you he's a pilot, has he love? Said the same thing to me, but I recognised him from the post office." (She swears, annoyed at her mistake, and flounces away.)

Since it's a school night we leave the club early and head home. Sipping a cup tea before bed, I press play on the answering machine to hear Guy say, "Hi gorgeous, got some good news and some bad news…The good news is, I'm on my way home because someone's dropped out and I start a new course on Monday. The bad news…the bad news is, home will be HMS Culdrose in Cornwall – as of this Sunday."

I don't know whether to laugh or cry, deciding its some sort of joke God's playing on me.

"Look," I say to the ceiling, "I know I said just bring him home and I'll never moan again, but I didn't mean to the other end of the country – do I have to be that specific?"

*

Work is boring today and everyone seems to be suffering from mid-week lethargy. Either that or Summer's lavender atomiser is sending us all to sleep. Danny calls into the office and asks if I'd like to meet him at lunchtime for a drink, which makes me perk up a bit.

At noon, I step outside into bright sunshine to see Guy leaning against the wrought-iron railings, looking tall, rugged and handsome in his black jeans and brown suede jacket. I can't believe it – I know he said he was on his way home but this is too good to be true. Running towards him, I jump up and throw my arms around his shoulders, wrapping my legs around his waist in a massive hug, yelping my delight. Guy staggers around trying to hold me before putting me down, groaning loudly.

"Thought I'd surprise you," he laughs, ruffling my hair.

"You certainly did that. Come on, lets get some lunch," I say, holding his hand tightly.

Guy explains he's home (wherever that is) for a precious few days to sort out paperwork and move kit from his old base (York) down to Cornwall at the weekend. Home is a strange word for him since he has such a nomadic life, moving from base to base at short notice. He oozes confidence with an arrogance that I find dangerously attractive; it's almost as if he's not that bothered about me, or at least he's more in love with his job than anything else, but I still want a piece of him – more so, each time we're together. Why can't I go with him? Why can't we be together? Why can't he get a posting back in Yorkshire?

Answering my tantrum, he says, "Because I've got to keep flying, Kate. I need to notch up the hours. And this sabbatical with the Navy gives me a chance to get loads of flying in."

Unsure of the system but already aware he'd go mad doing a ground job, I search for something to say but sulk instead.

"Look, Kate, if I don't go I'll get chopped and then you wouldn't want to go out with me would you?"

I nod my head vigorously (yes, I would still want him, because it's him, not his job, that I'm interested in).

Trying to focus in the dim light of a large, trendy, underground pub, I pick out Danny sat behind a reconditioned beer barrel. He stands up as we arrive and introduces himself to Guy.

Danny gets the drinks in and Guy tells us he's going to find a cash point as all he has is Deutschmarks. He leaps up the steps two at a time and disappears into the crowds of people walking past.

I turn to Danny and ask, "Where's Siobhan, then?"

"I didn't invite her, and I didn't realise you were bringing him." He inclines his head towards Guy's jacket draped across a chair.

"Oh."

Guy returns and plants a huge kiss on my lips before winking at Danny. Danny finishes his pint of beer and gets up to leave, making an excuse about buying a birthday present for someone. Once he's out of sight, Guy leans towards me knowingly. "He fancies you," he says, and picks up the menu card.

"Don't be silly. He's just being a big brother to Siobhan and me," I chastise, and explain I could never fancy my best mate's brother. "I've known him since school," I laugh.

THREE

Summer comes rushing into our office shouting, "Kate, your ring's gone!"

Of course, all the girls know about my ring, since I've pointed it out hundreds of times like a child in a sweet shop. Bubbling over with excitement, three of us rush into town at lunchtime to find out who's bought it.

The unmoved shop assistant frowns at Summer and Siobhan, saying to me, "I'm afraid we can't divulge details of our clients. It's strictly against policy."

"But it's me, I asked you to remember, remember?" I beg.

"Sorry, madam."

Well, that's it then: someone else has my ring and anyone could've bought it; I mean, how many men (and women for that matter) live in York? It could be anyone's perfect ring.

Secretly, I wait for Guy to produce the ring and smile sweetly at him all evening, occasionally raising both eyebrows in suggestion. Guy is visibly disturbed by my odd behaviour and proposes we go out for a drink.

Siobhan appears, just as we're about to leave, and says, "Christian lives in The Groves, right – Diamond Street, isn't it?"

Wow, how prophetic is that? I think, remembering it's Christian's party, and we head towards the action.

"Good to meet you, man," says Christian, unable to make eye contact, instead offering his clenched fist to Guy who pauses and then shakes it in the normal manner.

Music blares out from the lounge and we squash into a narrow kitchen full of Christian's strange-looking friends. Introducing Guy to a few colleagues he hasn't yet met, I get the feeling he wants to leave and worry what could possibly be wrong.

Guy shouts directly into my ear over the deafening music, "I can't stay here, sorry, but I have to go," and walks back through the lounge and out into the street.

Hurrying after him, hoping people don't think he's being rude, I leave Siobhan staring after us, looking puzzled.

"What's going on?" I ask.

"Kate, couldn't you smell it in there?" Guy states.

"Smell what?"

"Dope…That place reeks of the stuff."

My face is blank as I'm completely naive regarding the aroma of drugs.

Siobhan steps outside and asks if everything's all right, and Guy tells us, "You two go back inside and have a good time, but I can't be associated with any type of illegal substance. It would cost me my career – I'd lose my flying licence, for God's sake."

"Totally understand," I tell him, and I wave goodbye to Siobhan, not bothered about the party. We walk slowly back into town along the medieval streets before sitting for a while on a bench, enjoying the atmosphere of people rushing over Ouse Bridge from one pub to the next. Stopping at a late-night shop, Guy buys a bottle of champagne and we stroll home to 'Bolly in bed'. (If he proposes in bed I'll never forgive him – how unromantic.)

*

Dehydrated from the champagne last night, I assume Siobhan's not home and listen to the answering machine messages.

"It's me," Siobhan slurs. "Christian wants me to stay over but I'm coming home 'cos I don't fancy him anymore. Hang on, he's handing me a joint saying it may change my mind." The rest of her message is incomprehensible as she succumbs to a bout of giggles, and the line goes dead.

Hearing the toilet flush, I watch a very green-faced Siobhan walk out of the bathroom.

"Coffee?" I offer.

"No thanks, I'm off to bed…just got in," she explains, and groans all the way up to her room. "It seemed like a good idea at the time," I hear her moan before the door closes softly behind her.

Guy wants to go for a walk in the country so we wrap up warm and drive to the moors. I hope he's going to pop the question, but then again I thought he was going to do that last night with the champagne and he didn't (suppose we still hardly know each other).

Long, windy walks always stir up an appetite, and after yomping through too many puddles, we stop in a little teashop, sit beside a log fire and stuff cream cakes into each other's mouths. On leaving the teashop, Guy sees a street entertainer playing a violin and throws all his small change into his case.

"Thanks, mate," says the busker gratefully, unaware that the pound coin I've just tipped in adds up to twice as much as Guy's German offering.

"Come on then, let's go back to the car," I sigh, pulling on Guy's sleeve.

"Hang on a minute," he says. "I want to listen to my money's worth of recital first." And he stands there watching the violinist play to him for over a minute.

Every fairy tale has to end and mine is an unhappy one as I spend another evening helping Guy load up his car with boxes to take down south. Whoever said parting is such sweet sorrow was emotionally bereft because I think it's painful and exhausting. Clinging to Guy, I promise to be brave and wait for him to rescue me from looming spinsterhood. One last hug reveals he does not have a ring-shaped box on his person so, despondently, I wave him off, wondering what he's done with it, and go visit my old friend the chocolate biscuit.

*

Guy leaves a phone message at lunchtime to let me know he's arrived safely in Culdrose and is already a minor celebrity as the Navy's only Air Force pilot.

"Very happy for you, I'm sure," I shout at the machine, jealous of his absence. "France is closer to York than Cornwall," I whinge to Siobhan, and I start to mope around, exasperated with boredom.

Siobhan ignores me, and starts telling me of Danny's new business venture. Vigorously arranging her skirt around the ironing board, she says, "I mean, director of an outward bound company – he's going to make some girl a great husband isn't he…Kate, you listening?"

"Mmm? Oh, absolutely," I answer vaguely.

I decide to go visit my friends Susie and Tim, thinking that I really do like being a free spirit and making instant decisions for myself. So, armed with decent tea bags, I phone Tim to check if they're in.

Sobbing into my Darjeeling, Susie sits on the floor (because I refuse to let them sit together like a happy couple) and I proceed to inform them of how wonderful Guy is. After two hours, Tim's had enough and offers to drive me home.

*

Get to lie in bed all morning because I'm on holiday – luxury! Siobhan bangs the front door loudly to make sure I wake up as she leaves but I ignore her petty envy and turn over to see a photograph of Guy smiling at me. I smile longingly back for a second and then throw it at the wall across the room, angry at our long-distance relationship and the yearning it breeds.

Packing a bag for the week ahead, I catch a train to Catterick and sit in Isobel's large, warm kitchen drinking coffee, discussing how bizarre it is that we've both got a bloke in the armed forces.

Complaining about Guy being away, I soon shut up, realising that Hugh's gone for a month. But she doesn't mind and lets me bang on. (Hugh's battalion is frequently away on exercise or active service, for anything up to a year, and it amazes me how marriages can last such huge separations.)

Patrick, her three-year-old son, stands at the window shouting, "Mummy look...man!" mainly because he hardly ever sees one.

Both Isobel and I run over to him asking, "Where, Patrick darling? Where?" elated at the discovery of men in the vicinity, until we see the postman wander slowly past next door, and I return to finding Patrick's missing jigsaw piece.

Nip to the loo and suddenly the door opens with an arm thrust in the gap. A little voice, presumably attached to the arm but I can't tell, says, "Got bogie," and startled but unperturbed, I wipe the snot off the protruding finger, which disappears as quickly as it had appeared. (Next time I will lock the door.)

Isobel flicks through a magazine looking at pictures of thin film stars, sighing, "Oh, I really want a bum like that again," and strains to view her post-Patrick bottom.

"What do you mean, 'again'?" I tease.

An hour later, the crisp, morning air fills my lungs as we walk by the river with her bearded collie, Lady. Isobel yells loudly at Patrick to stop before he gets to the waterfall, convinced he's going to fall straight in.

"I do shout at him a lot," she confides to me, grabbing Patrick by his hood. "But I don't care, 'cos it makes life easier – he's well behaved in public, but I suspect he'll end up in a lifetime of therapy...I only hope he earns enough money to pay for it himself."

"Don't worry, sis, he'll do okay *in spite* of his parents," I reassure.

I buy ice creams for all of us, and we walk home deciding what to do with ourselves for the rest of the week. Isobel suggests I get on a train back to York but get off in Cornwall. What a brilliant idea! I grab my mobile and try Guy's room. He's not there, so I decide to leave an urgent message for him. "Don't you feel sick?" I mouth to Isobel, pointing to her finished strawberry lolly.

"In my dreams," Isobel replies mockingly.

Guy calls back early afternoon, thrilled I'm on holiday, and agrees to me coming, but is unsure of the rules for guests. I smile excitedly as he tells me I'm more than welcome to help him revise and get to grips with the new base.

Twenty minutes later, I'm booked on the next Intercity and scream at the thought of seeing Guy in just seven hours' time.

"Will you be okay?" I ask Isobel, leaving her home-alone. "Shall I ask mum to come and keep you company until Hugh gets back?"

"Don't be silly. You know she won't drive if it's cold, late or raining."

Associating train stations, airports and travel with Guy, I quash the giddy bubble of emotion rising inside me. Anticipation and delight form a heady narcotic and I begin to accept that this mad-dash approach will be the norm in our whirlwind liaison – snatching three days together here or two days there. Toasting Isobel's bright idea with a gin, I relax into my seat and watch villages blur past me, mulling over the restrictive regulations in Guy's life. Fancy saying he doesn't know the visiting procedure? Being me means that I can have whoever I like in my house whenever I want, but being Guy it's entry visa this and formal procedure that.

Connecting trains at Birmingham cause a delay for travellers and I arrive at Truro just before midnight. Guy meets me on the station platform and I fling my arms around his neck in a déjà vu embrace. He picks me up, holding tightly, and spins me around, just like in the old Hollywood movies.

Wheezing, Guy asks, "That about right?" regarding his romantic welcome.

"That was wonderful, thank you," I reply, pleased he remembered my fantasy.

Culdrose is a massive, land-based naval station, but apparently I'm supposed to believe it's really a ship at sea, as are all Navy bases.

"Floating on a million tonnes of granite called Cornwall," Guy observes dryly, driving up to the entry gate.

We wait for ages trying to gain access to his new home but the guards don't want to let anyone 'aboard' after midnight – especially a woman! It doesn't help matters that Guy teases me in front of the official, saying, "Sorry love, what's your name again?"

I'm not going all the way back up north, so we argue with this jobsworth for ten minutes before completing identity papers in triplicate and finally being allowed in.

His room is very similar to the one in Germany, only smaller, and there's no Ladies in sight, meaning Guy must stand guard in the corridor opposite the Gents until I've 'been'. And the shower block's communal, so forget that, I think, inspecting the rows of cubicles hiding old-fashioned, chipped, white enamel baths – it's like a public washhouse.

I read the fire-drill notice pinned to the wall and am amazed to see they expect Guy to abseil down from the roof when the alarm goes off, instead of walking out through the main entrance or using a fire escape.

"Just like you would on a ship," he points out. "No booze or television, either," he continues, but adds slyly a second later, "However, I'm Air Force, not Navy, so stuff that."

Worn out from the journey, I ignore his surreptitious attempts to get my head underneath the duvet, thinking, if he wants a blow job, he can bloody well ask.

*

Guy takes me on a tour of the base and we leave the Wardroom (Mess) to drive down the Galley (a long, wide road looking nothing like a kitchen) and park up outside his very own hanger. Guy is bursting with enthusiasm showing me his aeroplane and I make lots of appreciative noises regarding the tiny cockpit, asking what this switch here operates and that button there does.

Lazing around all day taking time to unpack massive boxes, Guy sets up his television and music system with methodical precision. I watch, thinking he must be able to do it with his eyes shut by now considering the amount of times he has moved base.

Sitting on his bed, we face a plastic cockpit and I try to help him run through the standard checklist but find I am more of a hindrance; eventually, his revision notes are imprinted on *my* mind. Early evening, we walk half a mile up the road towards the base entrance gates hoping to catch the next bus into Helston when two guards block our exit, saying, "Sorry, sir, no one off ship after 1900 hours."

"Eh?" Guy queries.

One of the solemn watchmen informs us, "'Fraid the Liberty Boat goes at 1830 hours, sir."

Beginning to understand the situation, Guy enlightens me saying, "The Liberty Boat takes sailors ashore. In this case, it's a bus and we've missed it, so we're stuck on deck."

Our captors nod slowly in unison.

Guy looks at me strangely, then orders, "Take your clothes off, Kate."

"Wha…? Feck off, mate. I don't think so."

"Just do it." Guy starts stripping off and throwing his shoes across the road. "We're going to have to swim for it," he smiles.

Amazed I'm indulging in such madness in the freezing-cold weather, I throw my bag, coat, warm woolly jumper and, reluctantly, jeans towards the bus stop opposite us. Guy starts to make exaggerated arm movements, pretending he's swimming, and I copy every move, lifting my knees up waist high while crossing the road. Once safely at the other side, we dress hurriedly to peels of laughter and I thank heaven I remembered to wear matching bra and pants.

The two watchmen give us a round of applause. Thankfully, a double-decker bus appears in sight within seconds of our escapade and I disappear aboard, grateful to leave HMS Cudlrose behind.

*

Waking up to realise my head is yet again being furtively shoved under the bed covers, I begin to get annoyed with this man's expectations of me. (At least let me open my eyes before presenting an enormous erection in front of my nose, thank you.) Guy attempts to convince me that it's perfectly normal…Every male does this manoeuvre first thing on a morning, so get on with the job in hand.

I lift the covers and get hit full in the face by a methane

explosion from Guy's nether regions (he just smiles and tells me that costs extra).

Saved by the phone!

Annoyed, Guy reaches across to lift the ringing receiver and I listen to the start of a heated discussion. He throws the phone down and tells me someone has reportedly heard a television on B deck so would he object to a search.

"Absurd way to treat an Officer," he grumbles, throwing the set into his wardrobe along with bottles of whisky. "Sit there and don't say a word." (I stare back in agreement, not daring to speak at all.)

Minutes later, a knock at the door shows they're well aware it's him and I sit out of sight, listening to the discussion.

"I joined the Royal Air Force and live by their rules, thank you," Guy argues.

The Officer replies, "Okay, we accept you've only just arrived and are staying for a short time but please try to live as we do. By the way, sir, your visitor's papers have expired. I trust she's gone home?"

Sitting in the room, I think, oh shit, we didn't get them stamped again, and hear Guy answer, "Yes, of course – she left last night."

"Then you won't mind if we look inside your room."

With stealth-like movements, I swiftly seat myself on a box next to his television in a large walk-in wardrobe and try not to make a sound.

The men take a token look around and then leave, utterly convinced Guy's lying but just doing their job.

After they've gone, we breathe a huge sigh of relief and crack up laughing over the whole perverse situation. Flicking through books, he insists I ignore him for a few hours while he speed-reads coursework and crams up on revision.

Guy is worried about how to smuggle me off base without being found out. Suddenly, he declares that he's fed up with this stupid ship so we're going to stay in a hotel for our last few nights.

He checks the coast is clear before signalling and I run towards his waiting car, where we spend two exasperating

71

minutes in heated argument. Reluctantly, I agree to get in the boot so we can drive undetected through the checkpoint barrier and beat the system. Promising faithfully to stop and let me out the minute we're out of sight, Guy helps me climb in.

Tears pour down my face as I curl up in the small space and I lie there wondering what kind of man would ask a woman to do such a thing? Thirty seconds later, I completely hate him and want nothing more to do with him – how could he be so arrogant and why on earth did I agree?

After about five minutes, sunlight burns my eyes as Guy pulls me out and I stagger to my feet before slapping him hard across the face, saying, "You utter bastard!"

"Fair play," muses Guy, rubbing his cheek.

We spend the rest of our journey in silence, arriving eventually at an old country lodge overlooking the sloping Cornish landscape.

Taking me passionately in his arms, Guy vows to make up for my claustrophobic ordeal, begging me not to leave, saying I'm everything to him even though he still hardly knows me.

*

Silk sheets are so much more comfortable than Naval regulation cotton, I think to myself, aware that we spend most of our time together in bed. Oh, what bliss to be away from the military in any shape or form. Guilt is written all over Guy's face as he tries to satisfy my every desire in order to be forgiven.

"Well, you can start here," I say, as I push his head beneath the sheets.

After three blissful minutes of shouting "Higher – no lower!" I suddenly remember my abhorrence of oral sex (oh well, it's too late now).

Extremely turned on, Guy emerges shiny-faced from down-under, smiling a slippery grin before attempting to plant a kiss on my lips.

"Your turn," I say, heaving his heavy weight off me, avoiding the slippery snog.

"But I'm yours to command," Guy protests in pathetic argument.

Oh well, here goes, I think, wondering why no one ever warns you when you're growing up that one day some bloke will expect you to suck (not blow, even though it's called a blow job) deeply on the thing he has a wee out of.

Looking around to see what interesting implements I can find in order to enjoy the task ahead, I spy the remnants of our room-service breakfast. Pouring yoghurt liberally over him, I get down to business, slowly licking all the way along his smooth erection.

With yoghurt on my nose, chin, cheeks and in most of my hair, I carry on, avidly trying to avoid making loud slurping noises (unfortunately, one or two slip out as I swallow what I hope is yoghurt).

Glancing now and again to see if he's enjoying the show, I'm aware that he's beginning to subside and try even harder to keep up his interest.

Guy lays sprawled across the pillows with hands placed behind his head and watches me, saying, "Never mind, darling. It's not your fault."

Hunched on all fours, I gaze up at him forlornly.

"Ten out of ten for effort," he giggles, before adding, "But next time, don't pick something that was recently in the fridge."

He tries to comfort my apologies by saying, "It doesn't matter. There is just no such thing as a bad blow job – ask any bloke."

Dancing to the radio after a shower, the DJ informs me it's Valentine's Day and I wonder if I should ask *him* the big question. (Is this year a leap year?)

After what seems like hours of watching him revise, we drive to Lands End and The Lizard (both perfectly good places to propose, even on a cold, wet day like this), but once we've got the 'experience tick' in our book of life, I climb dejectedly back into the car. Still single, I resign myself to the fact that I may have to sit this one out like a castle siege – but it could take years to penetrate his solid wall of self-preservation.

How can I make him realise that I'm the best thing he's ever had or will ever know?

He should marry me as soon as possible and be desperate to have babies before I take my best years away and look elsewhere. The annoying thing is, I can't walk away as something inside – call it gut instinct – tells me he's the one.

Ugh! Men are such idiots.

In ten years' time I'll be thirty-six! And consequently I don't have long left to fit in everything I want to do. (Mum thinks I'm foolish and should enjoy life, saying I have ages to go before worrying about settling down, but it's not true – the years are simply rolling away far too fast. I want to be doing the private school run to and from our converted barn by then.)

Guy thinks I'm footloose and fancy free, living life for the moment. But deep down I'm playing the game, hoping he's aware that I'm not nineteen and infatuated. I'm twenty-six and eager. Staring out to sea, I calculate my options:

1. Be a career woman.
2. Forget marriage and just have a string of lovers.
3. Ignore the ache from within to have a baby.

Option 1 means I'll never be truly fulfilled as office work bores me rigid. Option 2 means I'll end up bitter and twisted, angry at the world for denying me a chance of togetherness. And option 3 is just too painful to contemplate.

I glance at him and smile tenderly, screaming telepathically at him to rid me of this long-distance heartache and for us to start living like a normal couple. If I say how I feel, he's bound to think I'm a crazy, sad bint of a woman and run very fast in the opposite direction (because men are repulsed by the thought of divulging their emotional future). Why is it so wrong to be open about what you want in life? Oh, why did I have to fall for Guy? He offers me no commitment whatsoever and has made it perfectly clear I'm a luxury in his life, but I can't help being obsessed with him.

Guy sighs aloud, saying, "I was just thinking."

"Yes…?" I venture, looking at the raw splendour of Mother Nature spread out in front of us.

"I was just thinking…which connection do I need to link my digital camera to the computer?"

"Right."

Back at the hotel we dress for dinner – it is Valentine's Day after all – and stroll arm in arm into the village for a romantic meal. Our restaurant, tastefully decorated in shades of pastel pink, is full of happy couples busy drinking champagne and being affectionate (or at least I think they are).

Accepting a cellophane-wrapped rose from the wandering table tout and then quickly returning it to him after Guy finds out the price, I order a gin and tonic to calm down. Must stop looking for more than he is willing to give, I tell myself.

Halfway through dinner, Guy leans over the table to speak to me and excitedly I lean forwards to hear him whisper, "Kate, look at all these women in here expecting marriage proposals."

Fist clenched, I repress the urge to hit him, amazed he could be so heartless, until he says apologetically, "Sorry, darling. I meant to say those three little words a girl loves to hear," so I melt away into my chair waiting for him to say "I love you".

"Sale now on," he laughs, until I poke him in the eye, and he mockingly adds, "Give me a break. You can't *wait* to marry me and be whisked away from secretarial school."

I try to fend off his ego with sarcasm but Guy's suddenly turned into a chauvinistic pig right before my eyes.

"I'm suddenly liking you less and less," I advise him warily.

"But I'm such a good catch. Most girls get accidentally pregnant to trap a pilot. Believe me, it's happened to a few of my mates."

Standing up to leave, I declare, "The egotistical pilot bit I can cope with, but you're too much of a pillock to be worthy of most girls – especially me!"

Trying to get out of the restaurant in a hurry, I push past a hopeful beau on bended knee and inform his expectant sweetheart, "Go for it, love. I wish you all the luck in the world, because when we girls order a prince, they deliver a cave man," and run out into pouring rain, tears running down my face.

Guy rushes after me but I scream at him to leave me alone. The cold wind whips hair into my face, taking my breath away as I run up the hill to Greenacres Lodge Hotel. Thankfully, I'm not being followed (he probably thinks I'll calm down), which gives me time to pack my bags and dial a taxi. Bet he won't expect me to leave, but I'm tired of not being a priority or even his equal in this relationship. Well, he can love himself forever – at least he's totally focused on that.

Thank heaven for small mercies: I manage to catch the last train north. All the way home I cry and can't sleep a wink, thinking bastard, bastard, bastard. Why are men such hurtful, vain bastards? What hurts most is that some of the things he said are true. Yes, I do want to be with him, of course I do, but I want him to love me too, not scorn any adoration I offer. I have so much love to give and he just threw it all back in my face leaving me valueless.

(Good catch my arse.)

*

I spend most of the day crying, eating toast, drinking tea and telling Siobhan about my week of heartache. Oh, why is life so awkward? The 'I like you, you like me – let's get it together' scenario never happens, because instead, a stupid game of malicious commitment begins until one or the other is confused enough to fall in love and get hurt. I can't hurry Guy (he's in no rush to do anything involving me) but this fast and furious long-distance relationship lulled me into believing he actually cared. Now I feel abandoned.

I answer the door looking as crap as I feel – it's Danny standing in the cold. He immediately notices my tear-stained face and gives me a big bear-hug, upsetting me even more by being nice. I sob into his arms, rubbing my snotty nose on his sleeve.

Offering me a handkerchief, he says, "This must have something to do with Guy. Honestly, Kate, I can't understand what you see in him."

"He's really nice and funny – when he's not being awful," I argue pathetically.

Danny rolls his eyes and declares, "Why is it that women always fall for bastards? I wish I was a bastard," then snatches my last piece of toast.

*

Back to work, back to the rat race. Am I to do this for the rest of my life? Will the monotony never end? Too emotionally drained to explain my tangled love life, I put on a brave face and get on with the job. The only problem with trying to hide your feelings is that you can't do it in front of twelve women. Sooner or later, they're going to notice the quiet sobs and despondent attitude. Charles, however, holds a conversation right next to me totally unaware of the tears streaming down my face.

Beth gets up and closes the office door before coming to sit on my desk.

"I always wanted a French plait and a tennis-playing boyfriend," she starts, not expecting an answer. "But instead I disappointed my mother by marrying poor. And, if I'm honest with myself, then yes, I suppose I did marry beneath my aspirations, but I was in love you see. Not for long, though – I learnt from that mistake, I can tell you. And at least I had all my children with the same man. It's easier – less paperwork at the divorce."

Taking a tissue from her, I cry, "Beth, I love him, but he's so insensitive."

"Darling, I know, they all are – that's because he's never had to grow up. Look at him – he's just a big kid playing with big boys' toys. Tell me, how old are you, Kate?"

"Twenty-six," I mutter through a handful of soggy tissues.

Beth looks pained before expressing, "Ooh, ouch. Not much time to waste then, have we dear? Over halfway to the menopause already. I'm definitely encouraging my daughter to marry young, have children and get them over with before the inevitable divorce. Then she can get on with her life."

I stare at Beth, wishing I could find life as trite but strangely feeling a little better, and I can't help thinking I must be taking the Guy scenario too seriously. I'll try forgetting him for a while.

Working quietly away all afternoon, I look up surprised as Jimbo walks across the office towards me and places a portable radio on my desk. Placing his finger on his lips informing me to keep silent, I watch him switch it on and listen to Radio 2 announce the latest travel news.

"What's this all about?" I whisper.

"Shut up and listen, you mad bunny-boiler," he replies.

The DJ bleats on about today's Golden Choice coming from Cornwall and I gasp to hear him introduce Guy.

"Hello there, caller. Our researcher tells me you're not having a good time of it lately – is that correct?"

Guy's all-too-familiar charm fills the office. "Yes, I've been a complete prat."

"I know the feeling. Can we play a tune for you?"

I daren't breathe, unsure of what's going on as I notice the whole room begin to fill up with Panache employees; even Charles stands by my door.

Guy speaks and we all listen intently. "Could you play 'Stars' by Simply Red for the girl I lost recently?"

"Oh dear, my heart is breaking, Guy. Listen, man, is there anything you want to say – will she be listening?"

"I hope so. I rang her office, Panache in York, and asked them to put a radio on her desk. So Kate, if you can hear me, I'm sorry for being such a git. Please forgive me. I was so wrapped up in myself I thought you were like all the rest – impressed by the uniform." He pauses for a second before adding, "Kate, you're the best thing to ever happen to me and I can't bear the thought of losing you. If you still want me, say you'll marry me and make me the happiest man on earth."

The radio station goes bananas with cheering in the background and I hear our host shouting, "Wow, fantastic! Well, you heard him, Kate – or at least we think you did if they got it organised. Phone back and give us your answer, after this..."

Mick Hucknall conveys Guy's feelings in the clearest lyrics

and I have tears pouring down my face. (It's all so naff I could fart, but poignancy stops me behaving foolishly, as I appreciate something very real is happening.)

Jimbo picks up the phone receiver, looks into my eyes and asks, "Well – shall I dial and let you tell them?"

I haven't the courage to speak and nod as he dials the number before informing the receptionist who's calling. Covering the mouthpiece with his hand, I hear the song ending and he tells me I'm being put through – straight to the DJ, live on air…

"Hello there, Britain. This is the UK's biggest radio station and I believe we have Kate live on line two who heard everything Guy said. Okay, broken heart – what's it to be?"

"Tell…tell him," I stutter through tears, "tell him…yes, I'll marry him."

The whole office breaks into deafening applause and I cry straight into the phone, laughing with delight before hanging up. Charles plants a big kiss on my head, saying, "Good girl for getting us on air," and walks back into his office.

Still reeling from shock, I look across at Siobhan sitting at her desk smiling, tears smudged over her cheeks, and we both start to shake with laughter. With a voice barely audible from the trauma of witnessing my engagement, she squeaks, "Kate, what the fuck have you just done?"

Everyone flaps around congratulating and gossiping for a few minutes before Maggie shoos them all back to work and I phone mum.

"Mum, it's me – I'm getting married," I say, filling her in on the drama.

Passing the phone to dad when she can't speak anymore for crying, I hear dad boom, "Hello, Princess. Congratulations, but we sort of knew already. Guy came to see us before he went to Cornwall and asked if I'd object."

"He did what?" I stutter.

"Yup, love. Told him I didn't mind at all. 'Fact, I was quite pleased to hand over the endless problem of feeding your belly and bank, especially when he pulled out a bottle of single malt. But I am bothered about selling the Jag in order to pay for a 'do'…Ouch, your mother's just thumped me. Here, 'ave her back…"

Mum takes the receiver off him and tells me how proud she is. I wonder why, because I've not saved a life, passed an exam or changed a tyre. I've just agreed to follow a stranger around the world for the rest of my life.

"Bit quick, though, isn't it dear?" mum worries, until I remind her she met and married dad within three months. Maggie leans around the door to tell me Guy's waiting on the other line, so I hastily say goodbye before nervously taking his call.

"Kate? You okay? Sorry, darling, didn't know how else to get you to listen – you ran away so quickly. I wanted to propose in the restaurant but you took offence at my teasing before I could say anything."

"Well, you were being a first-class shit," I mumble.

"Yes, it was a mess – thought I'd blown it and you'd never speak to me again," he admits nervously.

Tentatively, I ask, "What happens now?"

"We live happily ever after – according to the fairy tale."

"Where?" I ask, not trusting myself to speak more than one word at a time.

"In Wiltshire," he replies.

"When?" I should be saying something more constructive but can't think of anything instantly and realise I have become a monosyllabic fiancée.

"OCU starts…sorry, the operation conversion unit starts on Thursday the twenty-fourth of April at RAF Lyneham. I've booked leave before then – come with me, Kate."

Looking at my wall calendar, I quickly calculate the weeks, saying, "If you want me with you when your leave commences, then that gives us just over six weeks. I can't organise a wedding in six weeks!"

"Bet you thirty quid you can," he replies.

*

How things change in such a short time, I think to myself brushing my teeth, and I advise Park-a-Garage it just goes to show you can never rely on life being predictable. His threadbare face stares silently back. I've wanted this so much but I can't believe it's actually going to happen…I'm going to be married – to a man. Me, married!

But this isn't how I'd dreamt it would be in my teenage years. I thought a girl had months to prepare for her big day and here I am with only six weeks. And my bridal fantasy of cellulite-free skin and a perfectly flat stomach has evaporated. The image of perfection is just that – an image.

Wow, can I actually be someone's Mrs?

Deliriously giddy at the thought of being Guy's wife, it suddenly dawns on me that I am about to start a completely new and extraordinary life. I'm not just getting married; I'm moving nearly two hundred miles away, leaving behind York, home, friends, family and my job, and going to live with the Royal Air Force.

Can I do it – will I be able to manage without my beloved Yorkshire and familiar, friendly folk? I shrug and wink goodbye at my fat old teddy, muttering, "Oh well, I suppose all the best-made decisions are hard ones."

Following office procedure, I hand in my resignation to Maggie with an unusual request. Since I have such little time to organise a wedding, I ask for a week's holiday starting immediately, just so that I can go and book the necessities – hotel, church, cars, etc. Maggie agrees as I've given plenty of notice and knows I'll be back to tie up outstanding projects. I plan to leave Panache at the end of May, giving me plenty of time to hand over my duties to Pippa, Beth and Annabel.

"Off you go, then," she says, and as I walk out of her office, she calls, "Oh, and Kate – don't worry about the hen night, we'll sort that…"

I look over my shoulder slightly apprehensively. I'd completely forgotten I would have a hen night. But what the hell; they can do what they want – I have enough on my plate. Now, where's the vicar…

Walking over Lendal Bridge, I stop on the brow to watch the

bright, sparkling water flowing underneath me. Breathing in sharp fresh air and laughing at a clear blue sky, I resist the urge to throw my handbag over the parapet just so I can see it go 'plop' into the River Ouse below. A gorgeous racing-green TVR sports car pulls up at the traffic lights behind me and I notice Danny waving at me from inside. Holding up the traffic, I jump into the passenger seat and insist he puts the top down even though it's bitterly cold outside. Waving goodbye to the queues of commuters, we jump a red light and leave them waiting impatiently behind.

"What are you doing 'on the outside'?" he shouts across at me.

"Shopping for vicars," I say, turning up the heater.

We cruise through town twice (at my insistence), knowing there's no limit to the number of times a girl can be seen in a flashy sports car. Dropping me off outside York Minster, Danny congratulates me on my engagement.

"He's not good enough for you," he says as I heave myself out from the seat.

"Oh yeah? And you are, I suppose," I flirt. But before walking away, I ask him to lend me a tenner. Danny looks confused for a second but opens his wallet and pulls out a crisp ten-pound note as instructed.

"Thanks," I say, and walk into the nearest newsagents to purchase an armful of bridal magazines.

Laden with wedding literature, I saunter into St Michael-le-Belfrey and sit at the back, savouring the atmosphere. In normal circumstances, this building would be considered huge, but because it's right next to York Minster, it's a picturesque, dwarfed little church. I read of their most famous christening held on 16th April 1570 – a Master Guy Fawkes – and marvel at the fact that I, a mere serf, am hoping to be married in the company of such a legendary scoundrel.

"Can I help you?" A friendly African vicar approaches me and interrupts my daydreaming about walking up the perfectly sized aisle.

"I want to get married here," I reply, shaking his hand.

"Well, you'll need more than those," he says, pointing to my magazines.

"Oh, I have a fiancé – just need to book the day," I tell him.

We go into the vestry and I'm surprised to be asked questions regarding my faith, realising he thinks I'm wanting a church wedding purely for aesthetic value.

"Look, Vic," I start to argue.

"Call me John," he interrupts.

"Okay, John. I can get married in the back of a car if I want to, the law is so lax. But as it happens, I want to be married here, with God's blessing, in my parish. You charge a small fortune for the privilege so its no wonder couples prefer to jump off a cliff and say their vows in mid-air."

Our Kenyan friend smiles and flicks through his diary. "What date do you have in mind?" he asks.

Rejecting a week on Friday as perhaps slightly too soon, I'm delighted to find they have a slot free on Saturday 4th April at 2.15pm.

*

Guy phones to tell me he'll be up at the weekend to help organise the wedding and suggests we go to choose a ring together.

"What? You mean you've not got it?" I ask amazed.

"No, of course not. I thought you'd like to choose one."

Disappointed but not surprised that he obviously didn't hear my instructions about the ring when we met, I tell him I'd be delighted and start drawing it from memory on scrap paper.

"Guy, Siobhan hasn't stopped crying since the day you proposed to me," I worry aloud.

"She's jealous, happy and sad to be losing her best mate so suddenly," he advises. "And she'll have to get somewhere else to live."

I find Siobhan in the kitchen crying over her breakfast and give her a big hug, reassuring her I'll keep in touch.

"I'm not crying over you, you silly cow," she snaps. "Look at my hair – I look like Douglas Hurd on speed."

I pay particular attention to the bright-red spots of dye appearing on our tablecloth and realise her hair is running straight into the cereal bowl.

"What did you use?" I laugh, grabbing a towel.

"Henna, warm mud and red wine," she sobs.

There's no time for leisure in this frantic week of logistics but I deserve a break and arrange to meet my old friend Tristan for lunch back at the house. Siobhan throws a sickie, unable to face work with such a macabre hairdo, and I promise faithfully to return with cream cakes.

Shopping for wedding dresses all morning is tiring work and I couldn't manage without Hattie's honest opinion.

"Too frilly," mum informs me, or, "Too tarty." (We've looked at about fifty dresses already.)

Getting totally wrapped up in hats, tiaras and shoes before noticing the time has flown, we head home, grabbing doughnuts 'to go' on the way.

"Shiv? You in?" I shout, walking into the lounge.

Hearing banging upstairs, I instruct mum to put the kettle on and meet my old friend Tristan frantically fastening his trousers on the stairs. Siobhan lurks behind him wearing the awful PVC French maid's outfit.

"Tea's almost ready," mum shouts, and I raise my eyes at Siobhan who smiles and yells, "Hi there, Hattie," before coming downstairs unabashed.

We drink tea and eat doughnuts in silence apart from Siobhan asking Hattie about wedding-dress designs. Tristan suddenly remembers he has an important meeting somewhere else and apologises for wanting to rush off – but rushes off anyway.

As soon as he's gone, I challenge Siobhan. "What are you doing? You can't just grab my old friends who have popped round for coffee and shag them!"

"Can if I want to. But now you mention it, I wish I hadn't. He kept stopping and saying 'Is it good for you Shiv?' every ten seconds."

Mum spills her tea and I realise its all a bit much for her and her safe existence to take in. Siobhan stomps off to get changed into something less provocative and I change the atmosphere by checking-off the invitation list.

"Don't send your invites out until you've decided on the list," mum advises.

"You're priceless sometimes, mum."

*

Guy refuses to have the reception at RAF Linton-on-Ouse because he doesn't want to get married at work. Fair enough, but it would make life so much easier for me and be one less thing to organise.

I meet Beth and her just-as-glamorous youngest child, four-year-old Genevieve, outside York's most prestigious hotel. "Thanks for coming," I say, arriving late and trying to catch my breath.

"No problem, sweetie. Working part-time means having time for fun, and this..." she says, sweeping her hand around the large foyer, "is definitely fun."

We wait for a member of staff to come and greet us, but after a few minutes no one has bothered to even acknowledge our presence. Genevieve begins to get a little agitated and asks, "Mummy, why are we here?"

"Because we're rich, darling," answers Beth loudly.

Almost instantly, the manager appears, smarmily offering to attend to our every whim. But I decide he's a few seconds too late and decline his offer, rather enjoying getting swept up in Beth's confidence.

Driving along and applying lipstick at the same time is something I've never been able to do but Beth can do it easily (and talk to her daughter in the back seat).

"Max Mara, darling. What did mummy say?" she asks, pouting into the rear-view mirror.

Genevieve just mumbles "Max...max" and carries on crayoning in her books.

Pulling into the car park, Beth clarifies, "Always buy Italian, sweetie, and you won't go wrong," then she turns to me and smiles, adding, "Got to train them young..."

We search a few more uninspiring hotels, and as we walk through the bedrooms of yet another, Genevieve manages to sum up our opinion in three short words: "Smells of dog."

Feeling dejected at the never-ending task of planning this wedding, we wander into a revamped stately home and Beth looks scornfully at the day-trippers taking tea in the lounge.

"They look like the type of people who go into banks during the day. You know – comfy coat brigade. Anyway, hurry up. I have to collect Hugo from school soon."

Calling at our fourth shop to please Beth (who refuses to be dragged round hotels without light relief), I point at my watch through the window to show her we're late for the next appointment.

"Stupid woman," she says stepping outside. "Genevieve picked up a flimsy headband and she had the audacity to warn me it was ten pounds."

"What did you do?" I giggle.

"I bought it of course – I said to her, 'And…?' Put it in the bag, dear."

Outside our final venue, I notice it's very close to the church, has plenty of room for parking and looks authentically ancient. It's not much more than an old medieval hall, but inside I begin to get a good feeling about the place and speak to the owners who are, for once, genuinely interested. Promising to return with Guy at the weekend, we leave on a positive note and hit the nearest coffee bar for much-needed ice-cream sundaes.

"How did you meet your husband?" I ask Beth over a large serving of calories. "The current one, I mean."

"My girlfriend and I were playing tennis at the club and I saw a lovely deep-purple sports car parking up. 'I'm going home in that,' I told her. I did, and here I am."

Knowing I should be on a diet (but not wanting to appear rude), I put a splodge of cream on the end of my nose, making Genevieve giggle.

"Not joining us, Beth?" I ask through a mouthful of banana and ice cream.

"Darling, when you get to my age it's just not worth putting it in," she purrs. "Now, come on Evie, darling. We've just enough time to nip to ASDA and look at the poor people before getting Hugo."

Smiling at her definition of grocery shopping, I kiss her goodbye (on both cheeks) and feel very chic for five minutes. After she's gone (in a wave of bags and pink pashminas), I look at the half-eaten banana split and feel bloated.

*

Must get my act together and tidy the house before Guy arrives tonight, but no matter how hard I try, I just can't seem to drag myself off the sofa. Instead, I laze around, flicking through morning television and sipping fresh orange juice.

My hair is greasy, and judging by the static sparking off my legs, I need a shave. But to hell with it all for a few more minutes; I'm sure I can allow myself the luxury of stewing in my smelly pyjamas while I read another magazine (I call it 'Zen time'). Turning the glossy pages over, I miss my mouth and drop a jam-smothered muffin on my dressing gown. It's full of articles promoting women with unattainable figures and, being a true ad-man's dream, I'm convinced I need every thing I see to make me the person I've always wanted to be. I add them all to the bottom of our wedding list.

Two hours later, I'm woken up by the sound of my own snoring and slowly start to sort out the groaning pile of ironing in the corner. By early afternoon, I've vacuumed, dusted and put two loads of washing in the machine, but still haven't showered or started on the mess in the kitchen.

The radio is blasting out at level nine as I sing out of tune at the top of my voice and then stop suddenly, struck by the awful thought that one day Steve Wright will die. What will future generations do without him? He was with me right through my teenage tantrums and now peppers my day with his reassuring drivel, somehow extracting a smile and nod of agreement from me every forty minutes.

Defeated by the thought of last night's dishes, I decide to run a bath and pinch some of Siobhan's new aromatherapy oil. Just as I'm about to step into the scalding water, I hear a knock on the front door and quickly throw on my dressing gown.

Sliding back the latch and chains, I shout through the

letterbox at whoever's outside to wait until I find a key and stumble around the kitchen without my glasses, lifting yesterday's newspaper out of the way.

Eventually, I open the door expecting a parcel, but instead it's Guy standing there, smiling. "Clear run on the motorway, so I'm here early," he says. "Hope you don't mind."

Horrified, I kick myself for ironing instead of cleaning my teeth but do my best to appear pleased to see him. "I am not apologising for this – you're early," I say, exposing a kitchen full of yesterday's pots and pans, adding, "Give me five minutes to take a bath."

"Forget that and come here, gorgeous," he says, reaching out to hug me. "God I've missed you, Kate. Do you know how much I love you? Man, you look so good. You are *gonna get it girl*," he teases, chasing me up the stairs.

(Amazing, I look like shit.)

Screaming with fear at him seeing my knickers on the bathroom floor, I think this must be animal magnetism at work and run into the bedroom. Guy's naked before he reaches the landing and I decide that all the expensive advice in glossy magazines must be total crap when primeval pheromones work this well. Abandoning my jam-encrusted dressing gown in the frenzy to feel his bare body against mine, I decide that foreplay can wait for another day.

After a bout of particularly frenzied and athletic sex, I lie cuddled in his arms.

"I think you've just bruised my coccyx."

"That's a new one on me," he smiles, and then points out calmly, "Did you realise your curtains are open?"

Appalled at the thought of the old couple opposite watching our wild lovefest, I leave Guy and lay in the now tepid bath. He goes downstairs in my dressing gown to search for two clean mugs and ends up doing all the dishes.

As I'm stepping out of the bath, he hands me a cup of steaming hot tea and teases, "Next time, wax those legs, you filthy slut!"

*

Guy kisses me awake, whispering, "Good morning, my darling. And how is my beautiful finance today?"

"I'm not your finance, I'm your fiancée," I reply.

"Same thing," he mutters, looking at my list of things to buy, and we agree to go shopping for rings.

Getting dressed, Guy asks, "Why don't you always look this smart?"

"Because I'd spend my whole life ironing, that's why," I remark, putting on a crisp, cotton shirt for the first and last time this year.

He queries my suggested wedding list. "Are we really asking our relatives to buy us a Prada handbag? Wouldn't a kettle be more useful?"

We spend the morning looking at jewellery, and I allow Guy a twenty-minute reprieve in a large electrical store before heading towards another shop crammed full of more things that glitter. Choosing an engagement ring almost identical to my beloved 107, we decide to get our wedding rings at the same time. I want to have the date and a few poetic words engraved inside each gold band but, at £2 a letter, Guy refuses. He finally agrees on the word 'Forever' (£14) and then negotiates a cash deal on all three rings.

Over lunch in my favourite coffee shop on High Petergate, I moan about the sheer workload involved with organising our big day.

"Just tell me where and what time you want me, and I'll be there," he promises, ignoring my plea for help.

"But you have to take some of the donkey work," I insist, handing over the list of things to do, and Guy reluctantly offers to arrange the cars.

Confirming our booking at the Merchant Taylor's Hall removes one job triumphantly from the itinerary. As we walk over the magnificent tapestry of colours chalked onto the flagstones outside York Minster, I marvel at one amazingly accurate reproduction of Monet's water lilies awaiting the next downpour to wash it away.

Spending more time than necessary with the vicar (just to

prove to him Guy is real), I ask if it's okay for the blokes to wear uniform.

"As long as I can wear mine," he smiles.

Looking at his dog collar, I ask, "Don't you always?"

"Well, I don't mean my Masai warrior one," he replies, laughing.

We leave the church and aim straight for the nearest bar. Relaxing with a pint of real ale, I can't help thinking how ironic the lyrics are playing over our heads – 'You're just too good to be true' seems totally apt and I'm aware that Guy is exactly that (but fancy the challenge anyway).

*

Packing boxes and bin bags into dad's car, I turn to Siobhan for a hug and can't help gazing over her shoulder into the hallway for one last look at that disgusting wallpaper. For something so garish, it's going to play a huge part in my happy memories bank.

I stand on the pavement and sob, "Where has this month gone? Everything's happening so fast."

"Hurry up, sis," Tom instructs from inside the car (as if it's his), which only makes us take even longer.

"Keep yer nose clean and wrap up warm," Siobhan instructs me, grannified, and presses ten pence into my hand, whispering, "There you go, luvie. Don't tell your mother."

"Shiv, stop it," I wail, laughing.

Being quiet for a second, I hold on tight to her unconditional friendship.

"Thanks," I say, knowing such a short word can convey a million emotions.

"Just go, you old slapper – I'll see you tomorrow at the hen night," she mutters, tears flooding her eyes.

"Excuse me a minute, girls…are you leaving us?" says Mr Thorpe from across the road, shuffling towards us. (I die with embarrassment at the thought of him seeing me and Guy through the window, shagging like beasts.) "Only wanted to wish you all the best. It's been a pleasure having two young ladies in the street," he tells us with a toothless wink.

"Thank you, Mr Thorpe," I say. "But Siobhan's not moving, so you can still enjoy watching her." And before he can reply, Mrs Thorpe appears in the doorway demanding that Norman return inside. He wanders back, ignoring the traffic, nodding happily.

At home, I find mum clearing the attic of my things, muttering about how much tidier the place will look without me. But I know she's about to burst into tears at the thought of my impending marriage.

Dumping the contents of dad's car in the hallway, we start sorting through years of priceless junk together and I flick open a flimsy red journal from 1987. Diaries are so good at whipping you back to your most embarrassing events, silly confessions, lost dreams and infatuated loves. Oh look – I wanted to be a fireman...

I hear Aunty Val cooing her hellos outside and go say mine. Congregating in the kitchen, mum starts making a brew – she always uses every cup in the cupboard regardless of how many people there are.

"Hattie, love, there's only five of us," Aunty Val says, looking at eight cups of tea.

"Oh, is there? Never mind, someone will drink them."

Mad as a box of frogs, I think to myself, and ask her where dad is.

"He's gone for a Sierra," she tells me, meaning siesta.

(Aaargh! I've only been here an hour and already I'm going insane.)

Six egg custards sit neatly on the top shelf of the fridge and I'm reminded it's Lent. Mum always gives up chocolate and consoles herself with soggy egg custards – our local baker's makes a fortune from her throughout March. I help myself to one and hear her telling Aunty Val, "Next year, I'm giving up sex" (almost choke on my egg custard).

Aunty Val replies without batting an eyelid. "Ooh, I did that years ago, dear – that and fish."

However, I can't help but love mum for trying to get 'with it' for my homecoming.

"I know you like Italian food, so I've cooked pasta tonight," she says at dinner, presenting me with a plate of cold ham, steaming broccoli and a portion of soggy tagliatelle.

"Not quite there, though, are you mother," I comment (but she's not listening).

*

Maggie holds my hand, showing remarkable restraint as I gouge the flesh from her palms with my French-polished fingernails.

"Can't have a hairy bride," Susie says at my prostrate, lobster-red body.

"Yes you can," I argue. "And why am I here being tortured in public – Maggie, don't leave me!" I moan, grabbing her arm as another strip of hot wax is torn from my plump calf.

"Mum booked a job lot," sis explains without looking up from her magazine, "…cheaper."

"I'm meant to be a princess, not a bargain-bucket bride," I say, getting off the slab to allow Hattie a turn, and watch fascinated as the beautician perms her eyelashes.

Without moving an inch, mum manages to snap, "Young lady, the cost of this wedding could easily cancel out the debt of a small African country but morals being what they aren't means we're having the mother of all parties instead. Now wait there for a pedicure."

Next stop hair, and a practice run leaves Hattie unhappy with her new hairdo, complaining she looks 'set' – like a cruise-ship duchess. I settle for a simple colour and trim. Dad meets us after lunch in the suit-hire shop with Tim, Hugh and Tom. The effeminate assistant announces a special offer – groom's outfit free if we book today, but just as I'm about to tell him Guy's not here (and will be wearing dress uniform anyway), dad pushes Tim forward, saying, "Fabulous, son. There you go, then, fit him out."

I look surreptitiously sideways at Susie who's trying not to smile and start to pass myself off as Tim's fiancée. Only when we're leaving the shop does the assistant glance at Tim's wedding ring, visibly puzzled.

"Second time," Tim clarifies, and walks out.

Dipped, tucked, wrapped, dyed, steamed and waxed all in one day! Totally au fait with the expression 'feeling like a new woman', we start drinking cocktails in the conservatory (against health-spa advice) while waiting for my hen-night limo to arrive.

Friends turn up dressed in authentic naff eighties' outfits, looking like a bad-taste girl band. This even includes mum and Aunty Val. We all climb into the back of the white stretch limo and start a tour of my old teenage haunts. It's far too much fun to be incognito, so I drunkenly command the driver to stop outside every shop/pub/park we pass in case I recognise someone.

Aunty Val nudges mum and tells her, "Fancy us getting to fifty and going in a limo."

After eating too much in a Sardinian restaurant, we waddle it off two hours later on the dance floor of some seedy club in Leeds. Siobhan, as usual, goes missing and I find her in the car park talking to a bouncer (always her Achilles heel). Returning inside to the warm smog of the nightclub, she tells me that nothing happened...mainly because she couldn't find his dick. Eventually, she found it but thought she'd been grabbing her own thumb and went off the idea of alfresco sex.

"Oh all right," she confesses after another grilling. "Felt sorry for him and gave him a blow job, but he went deep throat with no warning and I threw up all over his trousers."

Visibly surprised, I say, "My God, Shiv. What did you do?"

"Oh, I told him it was nothing personal and that I just vomit a lot. Shame he was so small, really, because it really was the perfect penis – velvet skin, long wide girth and no smell." (By now I have my hands over my ears.)

Beth looks fed up and I ask what's wrong.

"I feel so old," she says dejectedly. "I used to laugh at women over thirty years old in nightclubs when I was a party girl and now I'm worse – I'm forty-two!"

Finish the night dancing on a tabletop to ABBA (as is every bride's dream). I'm delighted to escape the crass bin bag and condoms makeover as well as the other awful peer pressures Friday-night hens succumb to these days. However, everyone signs their name on my bum as I lie comatose on the floor of the limo going home.

*

Playing the good virgin bride, I get up and go to church with mum and a few friends, silently noting where yesterday's wedding placed their floral displays. I get out my little gold notebook (stuffed full of stolen ideas from coveted weddings old and new) and quickly flick through the headings to 'Flowers' and scribble down my latest thoughts.

Noticing we're the only ones wearing hats (at Hattie's insistence), I wave hello to a few familiar faces and explain that Guy is unable to be with us until the wedding. The vicar obviously mishears "He's away in Cornwall" as "He's away in conflict" and halfway through the sermon asks the congregation to pray for his safe homecoming.

Trying to leave without making too much conversation, I notice Beth sitting in the row behind us.

"What on earth are you doing here?" I ask, knowing she's a devout agnostic.

"Purely business, darling," she says, pointing across the aisle to a potential client.

*

Last day at the office today. It's a strange feeling.

"Morning," I sing, sprinting up the stairs.

"Good morning, my dear Kate," Charles answers in a fatherly fashion and I trip up with shock. Looking furtively behind me, I'm relieved no one witnessed my fall 'up' the stairs and stride over to my desk as if nothing happened.

"They supposed to be like that?" asks Jimbo, pointing to my legs, and I see a gaping hole revealing two, white, knobbly knees where my tights once were.

Mid-morning, a fax comes through advising me to smile at my boss, assure her I'll finish all projects before five o'clock and file everything away in the bin (it's from her husband).

I'm too demob-happy to do any proper work, and spend ages with my Oscar de la Renta bridal knickers (£40) on my head, crying every time someone comes in to say goodbye.

Cards and streamers strew the room, testing my emotions. I donate manky old mascots to everyone, including my favourite red proof-reading pen (never misses a comma) and a set of bathroom scales which I keep beside the window to frighten me into slimming now and again. Pulling down the wallchart of target weigh-ins for the office, I see that Lauren lost 3lb last week (and that Christian signed himself up to gain 2 stone).

The MD calls everyone into his office to say a few farewell words. I sob like a baby – he's never been this nice to me before. My thank-you speech is punctuated with noisy nose-blowing as I inform them of my intention to 'friend cull'.

"Can't possibly keep in touch with you all," I banter.

Everyone gets completely wrecked in the pub – and I am acutely aware that time cannot stand still to keep me safe in this posse of friends, nor do I want it to. I have begun a new chapter in the book of life; this is it, the end of an era. Soon I start my new life as wife of Guy.

FOUR

Run downstairs two at a time to discuss urgent wedding trivia with mum, who's succumbed again to her compulsive sandwich-making disorder. Dad wanders in smelling free food, and little bro's searching the fridge looking for extras.

"John, have you decided which poem to read tomorrow?" mum asks dad.

"Aye," replies dad.

"Oh good. Is it the *first* one?"

"Aye," he says, walking off with a sandwich.

Friends and neighbours call by to give me their best wishes and I dutifully accept a face full of lipstick from well-meaning villagers. Mum keeps pouring tea until every cup in the cupboard is used up, and I hear Siobhan's car pull up on the drive.

"Where have you been? Come on in, dad's about to open some bubbly."

Siobhan and I will spend the eve of my wedding sleeping on the spare-room floor to make space in my old bedroom for seven bridesmaid's dresses, 'the' gown and a pageboy outfit (not to mention shoes, hats, morning suits and other wedding tackle).

Hours later, after sharing stories with family and friends, too much champagne, and wiping away happy tears, we stagger to our makeshift beds, giggling like schoolgirls. Mum kisses us both goodnight and so does dad, followed by Tom (wonder if anyone else in the street wants a snog, as sleep is now impossible).

We talk for ages about the fun times we've had and the

enormous changes to come. I look over at Siobhan nodding off and whisper, "Night night, then."

"Good night, Miss Ashcroft – for the last time," she says, giving me a hug.

*

Five hours later, mum pokes her head around the bedroom door. "Are you two awake?" she asks quietly. I raise my head and force an eye open; Siobhan snores soundly on.

"Mmm," I reply.

"Oh good. I'll put the kettle on and make a cup of tea. I can't sleep a wink," she giggles excitedly.

Leaving Siobhan, I crawl out of our makeshift bed and into the early morning light. Mum's stood in the kitchen humming a tune while warming the teapot. She always sings to herself or anyone else who happens to be in the same room – ever since I was a child I can remember her making up songs and dancing around the house with us. Her favourite ditty went: "WoooOOhh, all of a sudden a blummin' great puddin' came flyin' through the air, it missed me muther and hit me bruther and knocked him off the chair woooOOhh."

"Your big day, sweetheart," she says, handing me a china mug of Assam and a helium balloon with 'New Home' written on it (bizarre combination, but that's mum).

Siobhan wanders in and remarks how strange it is to see a bride with an appetite as I tuck into a large bacon sandwich.

"It takes a lot to put us Yorkshire girls off our food," I laugh, and then remember my childhood vision of being six foot, blonde and a size ten on my wedding day. Instead, I'm five foot eleven, autumn brown (or whatever it says on the packet) and a svelte size – yes, well…

I drink my first glass of champagne at 7am in the bath and we spend the rest of the morning discussing high-level beauty with Jane the beautician and Sheryl the hairdresser. Zoë and Susie turn up, ready for action.

Dad asks, "Has yer muther bin done yet luv?" not daring to enter.

"Dad, anyone passing through this conservatory goes

through a process of transformation: nails, face, hair and outfit. It's a wedding production line – of course she's been done."

A huge pink hat walks past him and dad gasps, "Hattie? Is that you?"

"Keys, hankies, Smarties for the kids and confetti," mum says, checking the contents of her handbag.

Waiting in line to be pruned into shape, Zoë watches mum with interest. "I would like to be mother of the bride," she muses.

"Yeah, me too," says bridesmaid number four.

"But I suppose it does help if you have daughters," Zoë adds.

"Or a gay son," I chip in. Everyone looks at me. "Well, at least he'd be wearing white – even if it was only for a short ceremony in San Francisco."

Mum comes in with a pile of ham sandwiches, convinced I'll faint during the service if I don't eat again. Zoë and I give each other knowing looks over yet *more sandwiches* coming out of Hattie's kitchen, and Susie impresses us all with her ability to eat and not leave lipstick marks on the bread or her teeth.

Hattie instructs, "Shout up if any of you want a cup of tea."

We all shout "'Up!'" but mum's oblivious.

Siobhan smiles seductively at a passing video camera. Alf introduces himself as Don the video man's assistant and wants to film me putting on my dress (or "frock", as dad calls it). I tell him to get stuffed.

Radio 1 refuses to play ABBA for me and dedicates a mindless chart-topper instead. I ask Alf if he can put Björk's 'It's Oh So Quiet' and Louis Armstrong's 'We Have All The Time In The World' on the video, because…once we're married, the Air Force can't separate us again.

"Thanks, Tom," I say to my brother for trying to get us on the radio (I think he's just keeping out of the way).

People come and go, wanting to see the bride, and wish us all good luck for the day. "Shame about the weather," they say. (Apparently, it's raining, but I haven't noticed, mainly because I'm having far too much fun.)

Big sister Isobel, in the role of chief bridesmaid, turns up with her edible two-year-old son, Patrick, and wickedly satirical husband, Hugh.

"Hello, Cheefey," I say, kissing her.

She looks at me and says, "Hi, sis. When is it your turn for the hairdresser?"

"I went first, thank you!" I say indignantly.

Mum approaches, looking as though she's on a mission. "Something old?" she queries.

"My stockings," I reply (and receive a frown).

"Something new," she says, pointing to my dress. "And Val's handkerchief is your 'borrowed', so give it back to her after the service."

"And something blue is my garter," I say, putting an immediate stop to her fussing with a hug, and I suddenly realise that this is it, the end of my childhood. "Get going, mother, before I start to cry," I choke.

"Good luck, love," she says. "You're leaving us for the last time." (Actually, I left home years ago but keep coming back because the rent's free.)

One by one, cars pull off our drive as couples depart in order to find the best-view pews in church, leaving just me and dad behind.

Standing alone in my old bedroom looking around at years of moderately disciplined freedom spent with such eccentric, loyal and loving people, I smile at some painful memories of teenage arguments. My eyes fill with hot tears, as everywhere I look screams home, happiness and parents. The familiar room is now small and empty, as if telling me to leave. "Goodbye, Kate Ashcroft," I say to the mirror.

Alf films me walking precariously down the stairs in all my glory to dad waiting in the lounge.

"Will I do then, dad?" I ask him.

Dad's eyes glisten with pride. "I've only ever seen two people look as beautiful as you do today, princess. Your mother and our Isobel."

"Ready?" asks the chauffeur.

"Ready," we reply together.

Twenty minutes later, the Rolls Royce pulls up outside St Michael-le-Belfrey and, as crowds of tourists and shoppers stop to watch our arrival, I begin to feel a few nerves in my full stomach. Four of Guy's friends stand outside in the rain looking handsome in full dress uniform, holding up swords to form a guard of honour. The five bridesmaids and two pageboys wait warm and dry inside the doorway.

"If you want to change your mind we can just have the big party," dad whispers, winking at me.

"Thanks, dad, but no…let's get this show on the road."

Guy watches me walk down the aisle towards him, and I hold on to dad for dear life (my knees are about somewhere but I can't quite feel them). Clarke plays 'Trumpet Voluntary' much to Guy's dismay – he wanted Iron Maiden's 'Bring Your Daughter…To The Slaughter'.

"Hi, gorgeous," he says when I finally arrive, every inch my Prince Charming.

"You owe me thirty pounds," I whisper, reminding him of his bet.

Our happy vicar starts the first hymn, 'I Vow To Thee My Country', with such joyous gusto that everyone catches his infectious mood.

Japanese tourists stand on benches at the back to get a clearer shot with their cameras and Guy's Scottish pal Calum knocks over Bibles and hats in an attempt to leave his seat quietly, politely persuading them to "hang fire".

A solemn sermon preached with humour moves some to tears as the vicar says, "We are each of us a product of our parents – they are responsible for our past, as the poet Larkin tells us, but from this moment on, Guy and Kate belong to each other…"

Speakers relay the service outside for damp shoppers determined to ignore the rain and join in our day. A flautist plays in the minstrels' gallery above the congregation while we sign the register, and then, all too soon, Handel's 'Arrival Of The Queen Of Sheba' announces that Mr and Mrs Guy Willesley will emerge shortly.

We walk out into a well-timed burst of sunshine and

euphoric pandemonium.

"There's nothing like a wedding to lift the spirits," says one aunt to another.

"Not bad for one of yours," gran tells dad about the service (she's Catholic).

"It was one of yours before it was one of ours," dad retorts kindly.

Smiles hold for flashing cameras until jaws ache, while the men in kilts ask directions to the nearest pub (noticing the Air Force boys have already disappeared to find it first). We eventually set off towards the promised big party in the medieval Merchant Taylor's Hall just around the corner.

Conversation drowns out the soft notes of our harpist as yet more photos and a few welcome glasses of champagne precede a sumptuous feast of lemon chicken. I originally wanted chicken chasseur but Guy insisted he wouldn't eat "school dinners" on his wedding day.

"You went to a posh school," I argued. "We got fish fingers at ours."

Since we're eating in such an elaborate medieval setting, I asked for meringue swans for pudding because that's what gentry ate hundreds of years ago. And also, I wanted to watch everyone struggling with the long necks and see heads flying off into people's laps.

Time for the speeches. Dad tells of my "off the wall" childhood and of his offer to give me anything I wished for at six years old. Unfortunately, he couldn't deliver a rainbow on wheels at the time but decided to fulfil my wish twenty years later, and suddenly he presents me with a handmade wooden version. He speaks of his delight that not only have I met someone else constantly on cloud nine, but he's flying it, too. Ending his address with a poem about how each and every guest has made our day special, just as the letters on a page make up a philosopher's scroll, I receive a huge bear-hug from his six-foot-four frame and say (with tears running down my cheeks), "I love you, daddy."

"Oh, and one more thing…" He stands up again, calling for

quiet in the room. "Guy came to see me last night and agreed to end his now 'extra-marital' relationship, which has been going on without our Katie's knowledge."

I look suitably perplexed (Guy looks confused).

"So, would the guilty person still holding a key to their rendezvous residence please return it to him and we'll say no more about the matter." Dad sits down, and after ten seconds of silence, a girl gets up, walks towards Guy and hands him a key, saying sorry it had to finish. Then another does the same and then another, until most of the women in the room give him their keys.

Dad calls again for quiet over the cheering. "I will ask one more time – would the real culprit please come forward."

Huge rounds of applause erupt as Calum strides across the room in full Scottish regalia holding a key and plants a big kiss on Guy's cheek.

"Follow that, sonny," dad teases as Guy stands up to make his speech.

Guy thanks my father for his kind words and informs everyone that someone remaining nameless (Tom) has started a sweepstake on the length of the groom's speech and that the kitty currently stands at fifty-eight pounds. A few encouraging words of "Hurry up!" or "Take your time!" interrupt him, and he plays along by telling the tale of how he asked dad for my hand in marriage.

"I bribed him with a very expensive and rare bottle of whisky," he says. "Once he agreed to our match, I replaced the cork and put it away for safe keeping. This means that John actually gave his daughter away for a short measure." Cheers of approval echo around the hall.

I notice mum's still wearing her hat three hours into the wedding breakfast and begin a battle of wills to get her to remove it (but she's quite happy hiding from view).

Guy remarks on the exquisite craftsmanship of our wedding cake, made by my grandfather, a retired master baker. Granddad does all our family cakes and gran even had the decorations blessed by her local priest.

Finishing his speech, Guy thanks his mum, Gloria, for her

love and devotion in keeping the family together after his father died. He says, "I think dad would have approved of the wife I've chosen. I know he would have liked the family that comes with her, but I also know he was extremely proud of the wife he had." Feet stamp, tears stream and spoons clatter on bone china in appreciation of this touching address.

"Shame Danny couldn't come," I comment to Siobhan.

"Yeah, he's mountain-climbing in the Cairngorms for a week – couldn't get out of it, apparently," she answers.

By now, everyone's steaming drunk because dad insists that wine glasses shouldn't be empty – ever. Guy's brother, Scott, takes to the floor with confidence and gives a witty best man's speech, delivering jokes while fending off drunken banter, ending by saying how proud he is of Guy.

As etiquette demands, mothers, bridesmaids and children receive presents and I laugh to see the balloons used for guiding lost children back to their chairs. They have 'Two Today!' on them instead of 'Congratulations' or 'Wedding'. (Thanks, mum – done it again!)

From start to finish, I don't think I've seen a dry female eye in the house; electricity buzzes around the room and people look expectantly for more entertainment. A quiet chant of "Ka-tie, Ka-tie, Ka-tie" gradually gets louder and louder.

"All right then," I say, standing up.

"Hooray!"

Totally unprepared, I grasp for suitable thoughts to use in front of eighty inebriated people, and start with, "I've spent the morning being introduced to the cooker, microwave, washer and dishwasher, and, as you can see, I'm dressed in the colour of all new domestic appliances." More cheers. "My only hope is that Guy can keep me in the manner I want to become accustomed to, and I'm afraid I have nothing else to say apart from thank you for coming, keep in touch and the bar is now open." And with that I sit down.

Returning from the loo, Siobhan stands in front of my throne and exclaims, "Oh feck, fecking feck, Kate! A blast from my past has just walked in."

"Ooh, goodie…where?" I try to look through, over and around her ample cleavage and silk torso before I notice she and Lauren's boyfriend are staring at each other in disbelief. He walks towards us and makes polite conversation until Lauren wanders off. As soon as she's out of sight, Siobhan stutters, "Fuck me stupid…Adam!"

"Already did, five years ago," Adam says to a fuming Siobhan. "And please keep it quiet in front of Lauren."

"Does she know what a two-timing shit you are?"

"Shut up, Shiv. You've got a worse reputation than me."

"Yes, and don't you forget it."

Adam forces a smile at Lauren and quickly leaves Siobhan gurning after him.

Fifty more guests arrive for the evening reception and I stand on a chair to announce the band's arrival. The Lard Arses are hugely famous in Yorkshire. Trying to balance on the chair is awkward and I stand on the hem of my dress, trip over and fall backwards into a huge, open fireplace. Guy's totally unaware of my plight and carries on talking earnestly to my grandparents.

Seeing two feet sticking out above the fender surrounded by a mass of white net skirts complete with orthopaedic slippers (it's a long day and I wanted to be comfy – no one knew until I fell over), someone grabs hold of my waist and pulls me out. The band can't play a single note for laughing and Zoë rushes over to me asking, "Are you okay?"

I whimper hysterically.

"You're not okay, are you," she says. "You've that same look on your face as you did when we were kids doing hand stands to the back of the chip shop, and they opened the door thinking a delivery boy had knocked. You fell straight in, landed on the potato sack and hurt your back, remember? You tried to laugh it off, afraid of looking stupid."

"You know me too well," I say, wincing.

As another banquet of hot, mouth-watering savouries and puddings arrives, I watch around forty people slamming tequilas in a Mexican wave.

Annabel offers me a plate piled high with food, saying, "Go on, eat up. You can now – you're married…"

A group of Panache girls are gossiping in the corner and I muscle in on their conversation, sad to know our posse is no more. A few of them admire the rear view of Guy's torso, and Pippa, tipsy on her usual two vodkas, says, "I can quite understand why you've been swept along in a whirlwind romance, Kate. I mean, I'd happily shag that."

"Me too," admits Camp Carl to a chorus of disgusted screams. Maggie asks Carl how he discovered he was gay.

"I was twenty-two and kept wanting to spend time with my girlfriend's brother instead of my girlfriend," he replies, loving every second of the spotlight. We all try to imagine him straight, but he's the most conspicuous homosexual we know.

Beth joins the food queue and tuts loudly as Christian pushes in front of her. "Do you have any brothers or sisters?" she asks him.

"No," mumbles Christian, filling his plate.

"Thought not," she replies curtly.

The polished floor of our majestic hall is packed solid with bodies dancing to the Monkeys' 'I'm a Believer', except that the band are singing "'Cos she's a retriever".

The boss's wife joins our gang and glares at Charles standing at the bar. I comment on her outfit – it's not the one she was going to wear (I know that because I was in Charles's office the day she bought it).

"Don't ask," Sophia tells us when I ask her why she's not wearing it, and we all nag her relentlessly to reveal why.

"He got blind drunk last night, came home late, fell asleep, and then at three o'clock in the morning stumbled about trying to find the bathroom and pissed all over the spare-room bed! Yes – all over my beautiful new suit. Good job the children were on a sleepover…"

Amazed and delighted to hear such dirt on our managing director, we look over at him chatting to the vicar like a true professional.

Angel walks past enthusing, "This fudge cake's delicious," and scoffs a whole bowl-full.

Beth, poised and cool, exhales smoke into my eyes and remarks quietly, "Of course it is – everything's delicious to a bulimic," before exclaiming innocently to our gawping faces, "What? As if you didn't know – I guessed hours after joining the company."

At 11.30pm, the party's at full mayhem when a short, bespectacled chauffeur summons the bride and groom away and we bid our guests goodbye. Laughing at Becky throwing up into the ornamental bay trees outside, my new husband shouts, "Hurry up and get a move on, Mrs Willesley – it's time for bed," as I hug everyone twice.

The Rolls pulls away, leaving a space in the crowd where it stood just seconds earlier, and I know exactly what it feels like to be famous for a night, seeing those smiling faces frantically waving and blowing kisses – except that each face here belongs to someone we know.

We drive through the dimly lit streets of York, waving at anyone walking past or sitting in restaurant windows, and arrive at our small, exclusive Edwardian hotel (just a stone's throw away from the massive, corporate, plastic block that I booked everyone else into). Muffling screams as buttons pop, skirts rustle and shoes fly, our lovemaking knows no bounds – until three minutes later we fall peacefully asleep.

*

After scrambled eggs, smoked salmon and more sex, we wander down the hill to the hotel next door and surprise everyone by joining them for morning coffee. Still sporting my tiara, I can't believe so many hangovers can fit into one room. We relive yesterday's magnificence over and over again, happily insulting recently hitched friends by saying it was the best wedding we've been to in a long time.

Becky, Megan, Zoë and Siobhan are discussing men in uniform over black coffees. "Okay, what happened after I left?" I ask, helping myself to their breakfasts.

"I got off with the only single Scottish bloke and Megan

bagged the divorced Air Force one," Becky tells me. I raise my eyebrows, wanting more details.

Zoë moans. "I woke up so incredibly thirsty at four o'clock this morning, I almost drank my deodorant."

Ignoring Zoë, Becky continues her story. "I couldn't wait to seduce Calum in his kilt, but in the three seconds it took me to kick off my heels, he was completely naked – I was gutted. And halfway through our throes of passion on the bedroom floor, Pippa shouts, 'For fuck's sake, hurry up!' I nearly died of shock – where'd she come from? She could've told us we were in her room!"

Pippa walks slowly over to us and I notice a pair of pants poking out from the hem of her trouser leg as she sits down. "Oops, yesterday's," she mutters, stuffing them into her handbag.

Kissing my pals goodbye and vowing to be a model wife, I admire the excellent job Tom and Tim have done of sabotaging Guy's sports car (ours now), and we drive away, dragging shoes, cans and toilet rolls behind us.

Four hours (and one ten-mile detour to pick up my forgotten passport) later, we arrive at RAF Lyneham in Wiltshire to garage the car before going off on honeymoon – mainly because Guy doesn't want to leave it standing on the Officers' Mess car park when sixty pence a day rents us a draughty garage.

With exaggerated grunts, he heaves me over the threshold and drops me loudly on the kitchen floor. It's just so silly to be married – that's for grown ups, I think, acting far too juvenile for my years, and I look around at the empty house.

Guy disappears upstairs shouting questions to me about the water. Is it on or not? I vaguely hear him and turn the tap on. Feeling like a visitor sitting on the Formica kitchen table staring out of the window, I try to accept this place as my new home and flick through a pile of leaflets inviting the 'occupier' to various clubs and coffee mornings.

Kitchen – white and bare (reminds me of a student hall of residence). The cupboards have been painted so many times they don't shut properly. Pulling open a drawer in the dining room makes the one on the other side in the kitchen disappear (they're joined together). Anyone sitting at the kitchen table will get a fright, watching drawers move on their own. And what bloody awful curtains – a nasty green floral pattern in every room.

Rabbit droppings scattered all over the grey lounge carpet turn out on closer inspection to be dead woodlice. Ugh!

I am Mrs Kate Willesley, wife of Guy – ha! Wonder when the bubble will burst and I can return to the real world of a singleton, working nine-to-five at Panache?

"Get a grip, woman. New name, new life, new home," I say to myself. "You live here now." (What have I let myself in for?)

Standard-issue RAF furniture throughout the house makes the place look quite alien. Without our things around us it doesn't feel like a home, not yet anyway. Outside, a spacious garden offers not quite enough room to cover the largest anthill in Wiltshire.

"Time to go, wife…the taxi's waiting," smiles Guy, walking into the kitchen. He keeps calling me "the missus" or "wifey".

From the safety of the taxi, I watch curtains twitching up and down the street as neighbours peep out to see us. All the houses on the estate look the same, some bigger than others: dark-red brick, sturdily built and desperate for larger windows.

My thoughts turn excitedly to the three-week honeymoon in Singapore and Lombok in Indonesia (Guy organised everything as a surprise).

*

Sorry, diary – no time to write. Too busy being blissfully happy enjoying sun, sand, sea, shopping and sex.

Trying to get used to my new surname and the life-changing identity that comes with it.

*

Return to the wettest summer England has known for over a century, and as the taxi breezes past queues of early morning rush-hour traffic on the M4, I vow never to work on that side of Swindon.

Jet lagged, we unpack into the Officers' Mess to grab a few hours' sleep in Guy's old room. But before hitting the pillow, Guy books a transit van so we can drive up to Yorkshire later. The bed's so narrow we both lay on our sides, and turning over is a carefully synchronised operation.

The alarm wakes us up late into the afternoon, and we rise from our fitful slumber feeling decidedly unrefreshed. We make it just in time to collect the van and set off north to pick up our wedding presents and my belongings. I feel like a driver's mate in the extremely responsible role of navigator, and promptly fall asleep. After my nap, Guy tells me about moving up and down the country from base to base – he started off with a saloon car big enough to put all his worldly possessions in (but now he's got me, he needs a one-tonne truck complete with hydraulic lift). Travelling light is almost impossible after a few years of 'service', although most of his kit consists of flying regalia and electronic toys, including a computer, modem, printer, speakers and more. Guy teases me that the only useful working implement I'm contributing to this marriage is a sandwich toaster.

"It's almost my turn to ride shotgun," Guy says, yawning. "Fancy a dog burger?"

We pull into a fast-food restaurant and grab two coffees before changing seats and I take over driving.

Susie and Tim are waiting for us when we turn up late into the evening. With mum and dad away on holiday, my brother Tom cooks all the food they have left in the fridge while Susie fills me in on missed gossip (apparently, Megan's still dating the divorced Air Force bloke). After we've eaten, Susie and I look through photographs of the hen night while the boys help Guy load up the truck with my stuff (and quite a bit of mum and dad's).

At midnight, we get back on the road, heading home to what I've named the 'new world' – RAF Lyneham in Wiltshire.

"Can we stop for coffee?" I ask, trying to stay awake.

"You want chocolate more like."

"Now there's a thought…"

What amazes me about housing on a military base is the blatant segregation of rank. Each estate, or 'Patch' as it's known, is split into areas for Airmen, Sergeants and Officers, with houses getting bigger as rank increases (very politically incorrect, but hey – it's a different world in the Air Force, and one I'm trying to get used to).

"Should've worked harder at school," Guy shouts as we drive past one Patch.

"Don't be so mean," I say.

Unmarried service personnel live 'behind the wire' on camp in separate accommodation blocks known as the Officers' Mess, the Sergeants' Mess, etc. Personnel can live off camp but the only way to do this is to buy property. However, frequent transfers to other stations and the difference in regional house prices means this is really difficult.

Guy's just a lowly Co-pilot, so he's required to live in married quarters until CR – combat ready (available to fly non-training missions). We really want to own a home but choose not to rock the boat, as the boss prefers all his boys 'in training' to live on the base. (It's like starting a new school and I have to learn the system.)

Moving in together feels a bit weird as we're not accustomed to each other and didn't get a chance to live together first. The Air Force is quaintly old-fashioned, preferring couples to be married before allocating a marital quarter. Some cohabiting couples do jump through administrative hoops in order to get a service house but I'm pleased I got to wear a big white dress and taste the cake most likely to put women off sex, first. Also, girlfriends aren't taken into account when 'he' gets posted abroad. A wife tags along but sacrifices her career – forcing her to end, tailor or manipulate employment (or choose a long-distance relationship and stay behind).

This time, we grab a luxurious few hours of fully clothed sleep in our bland new home on the Air Force's excuse for a bed.

Morning arrives in minutes, and since we have to return the

van this afternoon, we start to unload our furniture. One of the neighbours offers us cold drinks as we work, exclaiming, "Gerry…No kids and a pinball machine. God help us!" (But we can't get it through the front door, so Guy's dream of a games room is relegated to the garage.)

Unpacking small mountains of boxes, our separate personalities spill out into the magnolia rooms. It's slightly more homely but we still need vital pieces of furniture – I've refused an Air Force sofa (good job judging by the choice of curtains) so we'll manage with mum's futons until a shopping trip (or ten) can replace them.

The van definitely earns its hire money as we go back and forth to the base, moving Guy out of the Mess once and for all. (I'm intrigued to see exactly the same wooden bookcases and curtains that they had in Germany.)

Guy walks through reception, saying quietly, "If you've seen one Officers' Mess in the Air Force then you've just about seen 'em all."

I think it's rather grand on entrance: full of manners and an atmosphere of respect. Old Station Commanders' portraits hang on the walls along with a few paintings of our monarch in her youth. Miniature replicas of aircraft and pictures of sky-fought battles remind you that you're honoured to walk these corridors.

I decide Lyneham's Mess has seen better days and would benefit from simply opening a window. And I agree with Guy about the regal aura – it's faded, leaving only the main entrance, communal rooms, bar, ladies room (not a loo) and dining room in pristine condition. Step behind the scenes and you see long, unpainted and uncarpeted accommodation blocks more in keeping with a prison.

Sitting on Guy's desk, I watch him pack. I already hate doing this as it means parting company, but this time it's different because we're married…Yippee! – married (loved and fancied enough to be rescued from looming mid-thirty spinsterdom). I'm as giddy as a little kid at Christmas and admire my shiny new wedding ring, trying not to interfere. Out come beer mats, bar towels, old faithful university jumpers and long-lost odd socks.

One for the bin, I keep thinking. How on earth could someone so professional keep so much crap?

Heaving boxes the size of coffins down two flights of stairs and into the van outside is tiring work, but we finish eventually, say goodbye to his bachelor pad and drive off into the sunset. Well, just around the corner actually, to Daffy Avenue.

*

In this strange place everyone salutes each other. Guy refers to people on the phone as 'sir' and then someone will nod and call him 'sir'. I can only observe this alien etiquette feeling curiously isolated.

Guy's friend, Flight Lieutenant Rory Spinner, very kindly 'marched in' for us during our honeymoon. 'March in' is the initial inspection survey carried out by the Ingoing Tenant (that's us) and the Defence Housing Executive (that's them), during which the former party accept responsibility for the quarter and agree to return it in the same condition at the 'march out' (an exit inspection of the highest standard). Bernadette Fitzpatrick from next door tells me horror stories about the Families Officer walking around wearing white gloves looking for dirt, but thankfully most of her tales are from bygone days. However, we're still warned that if inheriting a house with lots of nails hammered into the walls, then we should point them out immediately or pay a fine on departure (our lounge wall looks like an unfinished dot-to-dot picture).

The number of items available for rent from the Air Force is staggering: they list the obvious fixtures and fittings like a bed, dining-room table and sofa, but even small things such as kettles, frying pans, doormats and yard brushes are included. Everything you could possibly need is on offer.

One of the more annoying things is that we're not allowed to plumb in a shower (but it's obvious someone has done so before, judging by the awful plastering job climbing up our bathroom wall). No quarters at Lyneham (nor most military bases) are equipped with anything so luxurious – just an old enamel bath and ill-fitting windows. If we do plumb one in, it'll have to come out again when we leave, otherwise our house would be more desirable than the next.

Waiting for Guy to come home for lunch, I watch daytime television, drinking coffee, until I remember Siobhan and the others working at the office and guilt floods over me. Turning the TV off, I read the notes for guidance on handing back a married quarter – it makes me laugh out loud. Only I realise that they're not joking and that when we leave, march-out orders will cover the most surreal things like making sure the outside rubbish bin is emptied and scrubbed spotlessly clean.

We can expect a fine if the following is not done prior to leaving: lawn mowed; garden left weed free; cobwebs removed from behind radiators; carpets shampooed; curtains washed; windows and woodwork cleaned; oven completely stripped, soaked, rebuilt and polished; lampshades dusted; loo bleached; walls repainted if coloured paint has been used; bath left limescale free; roof space emptied; loose covers removed from the sofa ready for examination; and bed springs dusted – to name but a few.

My hero cycles up to the back door wearing his flying suit and I giggle at the very important job of organising his meal. I normally eat lunch in a bistro with Siobhan but here I am like someone out of the Battle of Britain, kissing my husband hello and taking his hat as he walks through the door (wondering why it's got solid-gold scrambled egg on the peak).

"Get rid of the oven," I order.

"Why?" he mumbles through mouthfuls (of cereal).

"Because when we leave here, I'm not cleaning, stripping and soaking the bloody thing in acid to return it to its original condition."

Guy reads the march-out rules and agrees, suggesting we find a second-hand version in which to burn our culinary delights.

And I can't let him go back to the Squadron without having sex first (it's the uniform…).

*

Still feel as if I'm on holiday or just visiting Guy for a week. Not yet used to being down south, not going into work or seeing my old friends. I wonder what's happening back at the office – how can they cope without me?

We have nice neighbours: Gerry and Bernadette on one side and George and Samantha on the other (both have kids). George and Samantha saw two cars parked in our drive quite often when we were away on honeymoon, and Guy's friend, Pricey (Bradley Pryce), fits their description, as does Jude, his girlfriend. (On questioning, they owned up and said they were trying to fill the house with balloons and sweets for our return but couldn't get in.)

Maggie arrives for the weekend fuming at my crap directions, so I ply her with vodka. Having only wedding presents and Air Force furniture, we eat dinner off bone china plates and use silver cutlery. Samantha loans us a few ordinary plates and mugs until we get a chance to buy something a bit more robust (but I quite like using bone china…).

Guy started his course yesterday and has arrived home late every night this week getting ready for it. We still have heaps of unopened presents because I want to wait for him to open them with me, and we're just about to rip into them when Maggie suddenly becomes the fun police – she makes a note of every gift and giver for thank-you letters

We received rather a lot of crystal wine glasses from friends (for some reason people think we drink a lot) and my love of the china plates causes Maggie to nickname me 'Hyacinth'. I secretly love this title and aspire to be as pompous as possible, saying at every opportunity, "I have two 'services', you know…"

*

I love playing 'house' and make Maggie take photographs of us so that it looks like we've been married for years. Guy wields a hammer assembling the all-essential 'drum' barbecue, bought on a trip abroad (any self-respecting Air Force person won't be seen dead without one), and I pose as if I know exactly what to do with a sponge tin. Guy complains that he'll have to teach his flying suit to fly again, since I've washed it with fabric conditioner and made him smell nice.

I feel like I've lost my identity and don't really know what my role is. It's as though Kate Ashcroft's life came to an end and I've taken over the life of Kate Willesley. But I hold onto the 'Mrs' tag, enjoying the romance of having a husband to take care of me.

*

Maggie leaves late morning and I beg her not to lose touch with me. I'm tempted to jump into the passenger seat and go back up north with her, but instead run inside to answer the phone. Guy's old friend, Will, introduces himself and invites us to Sunday lunch. Eager to make new friends (and eat home cooking), I agree, and an hour later we drive over to RAF Brize Norton.

Eve and I instantly like each other and discuss the oddities of living with the Air Force. She brings me a booklet they received when Will joined his Squadron.

We read through *A Guide for Dependants*, devised to help spouses find information quickly, but it is blatantly patronising. We're encouraged to write down how to work the central heating, where the water, gas and electricity are switched off, and when the car tax is due – just how stupid do they think we are?

Halfway through the booklet, I desperately need the loo and disappear off for five minutes. Being naturally nosy, I admire her colour scheme and look around the room at interesting ornaments. On finishing my 'business', I'm intrigued at the moist toilet tissues kept in a plastic box on top of the cistern and, always wanting to try something new, help myself to a sheet.

Back in the lounge, Eve points out (worryingly) that the information booklet asks spouses to locate their husband's last will and testament and reassures non-drivers that bus timetables are displayed in the station shop.

"Great, thanks a lot. How about listing the more important things in life, like the phone number of the Indian takeaway?" I ask.

I listen in amazement as she tells me of one chap on Will's Squadron who takes his flying boots off in the cockpit and puts his slippers on during a flight.

"Never!" I gasp.

"Yes," she continues. "It's true. And another smokes a pipe during debrief."

Fidgeting about, I try to get comfy, but my bum is on fire and I excuse myself from concerned expressions, saying, "Weak bladder," and dive back into the toilet. Sitting directly on cold porcelain to relieve the sensation, I look at the box behind me…Oh my God, I've just rubbed my arse with a disinfectant wipe!

Guy knocks on the door, asking if everything's all right, and I sob my plight to him. He returns with help, gasping with laughter, and Will suggests I use the haemorrhoid cream in the wall cabinet. I emerge, red faced, after a few minutes of anal repair. Embarrassment is a great leveller (I can never appear glamorous in front of these nice people again).

Saying a hurried goodbye, I hide in the car, but Will taps on the window as we reverse out of their driveway. "At least 'Zingfresh' claim their disposable sheets kill 99.9 per cent of bacteria," he wheezes, and then weeps with uncontrollable laughter.

Guy feels sorry for me and stops at the nearest shop to buy a huge bar of chocolate.

*

Receive a postcard of York Minster from Siobhan. There's nothing on it except the words 'Go on, chuck yer bag in', and Guy can't understand why I burst into tears at the sudden blast from my oh-so-recent past. I explain we used to dare each other every day to throw our bags into the River Ouse off Lendal Bridge (but he's nonplussed).

Mum and dad arrive in the afternoon and I'm horrified to find dad, under instruction from mum, taking photographs of me hanging out the washing (they've come for a week and I'm probably going to kill them).

She says to dad, "Oh love, our little girl's grown up," and wipes away a tear.

"Stop it, mother!" I protest. "I left home almost ten years ago and have been doing my own washing ever since, thank you very much."

"Yes, but you're married now," she replies, as if that's the beginning of everything.

Later on, Beth phones for a chat and I tell her of Hattie's antics.

"But getting married to the 'right' man instantly fulfils a mother's wish and stops her worrying about you waiting for the first round of divorcees," she says. "My mother phoned one afternoon when the local vicar and I were discussing Genevieve's christening. She was overjoyed to find out I couldn't stop to talk – too busy entertaining the clergy."

(Laughing has a strangely cathartic effect on my oppressed mood.)

"Well, she absolutely loves vicars," Beth carries on. "She was convinced I'd end up a spinster and here I am fulfilling her dreams of marriage and motherhood. You see, darling, the trouble with parents is…they know their children intuitively but only until they leave home. Then, when we grow into adults, our parents assume they still know us inside out. Everyone liked your vicar immensely because he realised this and said we were a product of our parents, although I don't agree – I think we're a product of hormones depending on the number of factory-farmed chickens we've eaten. But what I'm trying to say is that parents will always think they know us better than we do, when in fact they don't know us at all."

(Comforting advice, but I still find myself play-acting to please them and run around like the good little wife they want me to be.)

*

They've been here just one day and I've decided to confiscate their camera – we are not zoo exhibits. Mum gets dad to take photos of Guy, saying, "Ooh, hurry up, John, he's got his clobber on…" (meaning flying suit).

Guy's horrified and can't understand the attraction. To him it's work, nothing special, but to them he's a hero. When will they grow up and realise – we have.

Guy is Orderly Officer today, nicknamed 'Orderly Dog' because it's such a hound of a job. He's on duty for twenty-four hours, during which he's responsible for co-ordinating all out-of-hours emergency procedures on the base. (It's usually given to single people living in the Mess, but Guy's taking a turn as a favour to one of the chaps.)

"Sorry I'm late, darling," he says. "We were expecting royal movements and I had to hang around for the 'pocket rocket' – the royal flight – to land." (This makes me giggle and I think of HRH sitting on the loo.)

Whenever a member of the royal family travels through RAF Lyneham, the Orderly Officer has to stand by the entrance gate and salute the royal car as it drives away.

Guy is normally very supportive of our monarchy but seethes after standing in the pouring rain (in full uniform), waiting to salute the noble passenger, only to see a stately head turned away without even a flicker of acknowledgement.

"You poor thing, standing there cold and wet, paying your respects," I comfort.

"Believe me, that kind of ignorance happens all the time," he replies.

Looking dashing in 'blues' (full uniform, not a flying suit), he tells me to delay serving dinner until he's back from waving at Jack, another custom I've never heard of.

"At sundown, I have to salute the Union flag – Jack – as it's lowered, and then return again at dawn in this bloody tight uniform while it's hoisted back up."

He dashes out of the house, saying, "Bloody hell, I'm late. See you in five minutes, darling," and sprints across the Patch just in time for the bugle-sounding.

Over dinner, he explains that sometimes the boys are required to appear in the Officers' Mess bar wearing uniform just to make it look busy while a VIP (often royal) passes the time waiting for connecting flights.

What a pain in the arse for their families, I think.

At 10pm, the whole Patch experiences a power cut and Guy's duty bleeper starts going off as people try to contact him. Mum is very impressed and thinks he's the most important person on the base.

We wander outside to find both sets of neighbours gazing at the stars and use our torch to signal silly Morse-code messages around the other houses. Everyone gathers outside, chatting and holding cups of coffee, and it becomes 'signal city' for a few minutes. The blokes put on deep voices, saying, "Who goes there? Friend or foe?"

"It's only me – TLSP," answers one chap walking past as his golden retriever cocks a leg on the neighbour's car. Wondering if TLSP is code, Guy whispers to me that it's his nickname: 'Tall, Lanky, Streak of Piss'. I decide not to enlighten mum and dad.

*

Walking to the corner shop at lunchtime, I meet a couple of women who talk to me in three-letter abbreviations (TLAs!).

"Oh yes, Guy's on CPT today, isn't he?" one says, and introduces me to her friend as Flight Lieutenant Willesley's wife.

I correct her by saying, "Hello there, I'm Kate," and smile, thinking what the hell is CPT? Can't Play Tennis? When she asks me if Guy fancies going SF, I think of him Sugar Frosted.

Are these people out to impress me with Air Force jargon? Hope not, because I haven't got a clue what they're saying, but they continue anyway…

"My husband's spent all day writing ACRs," her mate twitters (Addictive Cake Recipes?) and she offers her hand, saying, "By the way, I'm OC Op's wife."

I shake it firmly, asking, "So, do you have a name?" I'm amazed at her eagerness to surrender her identity.

I don't want to waste precious time with them and voice my

opinion with my feet, making a lame excuse while walking away. I'm sure they wouldn't like the feeling of isolation if I started talking in a language only Guy and I could follow.

I realise all professions use terminology, but unless you're in it then you're being ostracised and it's downright rude. I call them RCWs, Rank-Concious Wives – or maybe that should be Complete Officers' Wives?

I made another acquaintance on the way home and managed to alienate myself from her instantly by asking if she was from Essex.

"How was I to know she's French Canadian – with a name like Porscha?" I moan to Guy.

"No shit, Sherlock," Guy says, implying her accent told all.

Guy's being tense and snappy due to the stress of coursework, so I lace his mashed potatoes with Bach Rescue Remedy (to comfort and reassure…).

We snuggle up in bed together and his idea of foreplay is trying to tune my left breast into Radio 1 (when I suggest a new technique, he directs my right arm towards the window for better reception).

*

At ten o'clock this morning we're off to get an identity card, which gives me access to the base day or night so Guy doesn't need to sign me through the 'Control of Entry' building (and I can drive straight to the Mess for him after debrief drinking).

What a farce. Passes are issued from an office on the other side of the base (no problem there), so we go together and find the relevant person who issues the forms, filling them out in triplicate.

Wait an hour for the card to be signed, processed and verified. By this time, Guy's sorting out my photograph, which can only be taken back at the Control of Entry building between the hours of 9.30am to 10am and 2.30pm to 3pm.

"What? This would never happen in commerce," I sigh to Guy, who's in a rush to get back to work.

I finally get my identity card at 3.30pm (no wonder some people don't bother).

Bernadette rings up and invites me to tea on the Squadron and, thinking it's a general get-together, I go along to meet a few more people. Over too many biscuits, she tells me about the Officers' Wives Committee and asks if I'll support a charity fashion show they're organising.

"We need tall women to be models," she coaxes.

"I'm almost six feet tall and a size substantially more than a ten," I say, but vanity gets the better of me and I agree.

Daphne, the ex-model choreographer, assembles us in order of height. She has amazing organisational skills and takes no prisoners, barking out step routines at us. Time is of the essence, we're told, as we have five different routes around the same room to learn in three weeks. Sets need designing, music compiling, and everyone with a bit of spare time available is roped in.

Daphne pairs everyone off with someone of similar height. My partner, Caroline, has porcelain skin, long jet-black hair and a perfect figure (bitch). We quickly introduce ourselves and have fits of giggles trying to pose properly, me going blue sucking in my stomach and forcing my hips out (I have attitude if nothing else).

Collapse into a heap for the rest of the afternoon before getting ready to attend Guy's end-of-course black-tie dinner. We meet in reception and drink champagne cocktails. Nervous at meeting everyone, I relax as soon as I recognise Pricey and Jude and chat away like I've known them for years. The nice woman opposite tries to make polite conversation by asking Jude (a strict vegetarian) if she eats chicken or fish. One chap eats alone and I enquire after his wife.

"She's not here, couldn't come – too busy looking after our fourth new arrival," he explains.

"Oh, congratulations are in order, then."

"Not really," he replies, filling up his wine glass. "Every time I shag my wife she has another baby."

Jude tells the nice woman that she did accidentally eat tomato sausages once, and seeing no acknowledgement starts explaining the difference between tomato in sausages and sausages made from tomatoes (she's in for a long night). Pricey introduces me to a lovely couple from Yorkshire called Richard and Gwen Arndale who live just around the corner from us on Pintail. This is a part of the Patch famous in the 1970s for wife-swapping parties. Everyone talks about these but no one really knows what happened (apart from the fact that no one minded until the fun police came along and posted the guilty to the four corners of the world).

I can't bear it any longer and ask Pricey, "Why the waste-paper bin?" (I'm still unable to forget the squash-racquet rendition of Motorhead in the Officers' Mess at Linton-on-Ouse).

Pricey turns white with shock at my being privy to an enactment of obvious fantasy but then smiles broadly, saying, "You saw...I thought someone had come in – thank God it wasn't Jude. Er, well it helps wedge the headphones on – you know...better sound."

I can't get any more sense out of him on the subject – he's too embarrassed (and pissed) – so I give up.

Richard and Gwen are brilliant fun. Gwen tells me she was one of the few who pulled me out of the fireplace on my wedding day. She looks like Goldie Hawn and says that when she isn't teaching Spanish, she gets to grips with the rough life of the Auxiliary Air Force. Turns out she's been in longer than Richard and has even worked with Honorary Air Commodore Stella Rimmington (the MI6 boss). Richard says she's so keen to do things right, she salutes parked cars.

By now, dad-of-four is incredibly pissed and confides to me over port and Stilton that they didn't think kids were possible since their first baby was an IVF conception.

"How amazing to think that after all that trying, you're blessed with so many children," I say politely.

"That's not amazing," he slurs. "What's amazing is having to wank into a jar in four minutes flat with no porn. They only had a copy of *Caravan Weekly*."

I get the giggles as he applauds himself for doing it, but he admits his wife had a much harder time, injecting hormones and suffering emotionally draining tests.

"It's hard enough going through IVF when you're employed in a normal day job but I was away on detachment so it was extremely difficult."

"You're very proud of her, aren't you," I detect.

He smiles faintly and falls slowly into my lap. I manage to prop him up and hope no one notices he's sound asleep.

After the meal, we listen to a few witty speeches from various course representatives before the Wing Commander offers a toast to the wives, thanking them for their constant support. Guy goes through the motions of raising his glass but he can't understand why he should be thanking them.

"Surely the wives are spongers, onto a good thing," he says.

I'm not sure if he's joking. Suddenly, I feel very alone and realise I don't know this man at all – in the last few weeks, I've experienced a massive change of lifestyle and a baptism of fire into Guy's pompous world and he can't see it, thinking I should be grateful to ride the crest of his testosterone wave.

Oh shit, what have I done?

FIVE

"Darling, I have no socks," Guy says.

"And whose problem is that?" I ask.

"Oh, come on – you know me and the washing machine don't get on…"

"You and the washing machine have never met. So, I've left the instruction booklet out and I'm going to see Gwen."

Passing relatives keep pitching up for the weekend – today it's the turn of my brother Tom (taking time out from Bristol University) hoping to get his washing done.

"You'll be lucky," quips Guy to him, at my departing figure.

Gwen invites us to her birthday party tonight and I spend the afternoon helping decorate her lounge in preparation. Their walls are covered in artefacts from Richard's travels, and Gwen moans, "He can never walk through the souk in Muscat without buying loads of crap. He loves bartering, you see."

Grab a couple of hours' sleep before tonight, thinking, so far, all I've done is party – must start looking for a job and prove Guy wrong. His words last night have put me in independent overdrive and I'm determined not to let myself lean on him ever again. (I'm no sponger.)

House parties are always the best kind but I can never understand why everyone congregates in the kitchen.

At midnight, Richard serenades Gwen for her birthday on his electric guitar (apparently, he does this every year), strumming the most awful rendition of 'Happy Birthday'. The whole thing is painfully clichéd – he's playing an electric guitar holding a can of beer in one hand and a cigarette butt in the other. Gwen smiles at him as if he's Romeo reciting a love poem. Love really is blind!

I feel like I've met everyone in Lyneham as people come and go throughout the evening. The hardest part is trying to remember names, especially nicknames. Some of them are unbelievably cruel – one chap's called 'Buff', which stands for 'Big Ugly Fat Fucker'. Another is called 'Sledge' (he's pulled by dogs), and another, 'Tick-over' (next up from idle). The list is endless: 'Zulu' ('cos he's always late, an hour behind British Summer Time), and 'Gimlet' (small boring tool). 'Sierra India' belongs to one unfortunate chap, being a subtle way of saying 'Stupid Idiot' (the phonetic alphabet for 'S' and 'I' is 'Sierra' and 'India').

It's even worse for the girls. One female crew member is called 'Emu' (big bird, can't fly), another is known as 'The Johnson Twins' (a lovely girl with more than ample breasts), and another as 'Seagull' (have to throw stones at her to make her fly). A female Navigator is nicknamed 'Tac One' (it's a piece of navigation equipment on the aircraft that's unreliable in range and bearing).

My favourite of all belongs to a Navigator who's the most easy-going person I've ever met. Nice quiet chap – just wants a smooth life and no hassle – his nickname is 'Cyclone', because the dictionary describes it as 'a slow-moving depression'.

Standing by Guy's side, I listen to his conversation with some bloke from the Squadron.

"Yeah, mate, we came back through Germany yesterday, and while pulling a pallet of beer through customs, some jumped-up air stewardess holds her hand out ordering me to stop. The silly bitch tells me that I can't possibly go any further as the hold is full. 'Not on my aircraft, it isn't,' I reply, cruising past – she was fuming."

I laugh and the chap talking is suddenly aware of my presence.

"Oh hello, Mrs Guy. What do you do for a living?" he asks, and condescendingly adds, "Let me guess – you must be a hairdresser because you have nice hair."

"I work in a cake shop," I tell him and leave them talking. A few minutes later, Guy follows me into the kitchen and quietly asks why I'd told him that.

"He couldn't give a toss what I did – could've been a brain surgeon for all he cared. I'm just your wife, end of story."

Tom acts as DJ, smiling as he looks through Richard's CD collection.

"Look at this, sis. He's got all the stuff dad listens to," he whispers.

"Great collection, eh Tom?" Richard boasts, wandering over. "Put Bazza on, mate."

Barry Manilow croons away, and Richard knows every word. This is followed by Frank Sinatra, and Gwen knows every word. I can't bear any more and go outside to find my husband in the driveway, sitting on an inflatable pink sofa smoking cigars – three at once, all in one hand (he doesn't smoke).

Stunned, I ask if he's enjoying them, but he's so pissed he replies, "I'd rather shove a stick of dynamite up my arse and enter a fire-eating competition," and continues regardless. I sit on his knee and, as the sofa slowly tips over from my added weight, accept a drag on two large Havanas.

*

Guy has finished the training course and gets 'posted' (I suppress silly thoughts of him squashed into a huge envelope) to 47 Squadron.

There are four Squadrons, 24, 30, 70 and 47, and two types, tactical or route. Both 70 and 47 are tactical. He'll join other Co-pilots straight from the OCU (Operational Conversion Unit) course – the transitional link from student to operator.

I don't understand his excitement, so he tells me, "A lot of the workload is fast and furious. The main freight is weapons, explosives – or 'bang', as we call it – and para-troopers, who for some strange reason leave halfway through the journey, usually off of the ramp at the back. This kind of flying is more fun than route flying because I get to go low-level."

"Oh," I say.

"Yippee! I'm not a route queen, I'm not a route queen," he continues, jumping up and down.

"Eh?"

"24 and 30 are known as 'route queens', 'cos they fly high up in straight lines. They're north side of the airfield."

"Oh," I say again. "Which way is north?"

Undeterred, he shows me the Squadron badge on his flying suit shoulder. I ask why it's stuck on with Velcro.

"Easy to pull off if captured," he replies casually.

I suddenly become intensely aware of his less-than-normal job: this is no ordinary life. Even though he's nonchalant, I start panicking about him being killed.

"Stop worrying," he smiles. "Theatre, war, is part of my job, but that's what we sign up for – and I love flying."

The phone rings and Bernadette tells me that at the next fashion show rehearsals, Caroline and I will no longer be a couple: we're a threesome. Tanya has just moved onto the Patch and wants to help out. She's well over six feet tall and a size eight.

"Eight!" I scream.

Bernadette sighs.

"I can't go on. Oh no, do I have to?" I plead. "I don't want to be the big tall fat one at the back."

"Oh, you'll be all right," Bernadette reassures me, not very convincingly.

*

Meet Tanya at rehearsals and, much to my disappointment, she's really nice. We all have a laugh practising each outfit's 'routine' to music in my back garden – the more wine we drink, the better we think we are. If they start taking things too seriously, I mess about and get into trouble from Caroline (who keeps throwing up in my downstairs loo).

Picking up an open file on the coffee table, I notice a picture of Guy's Squadron badge (the one he wears on his flying suit). It shows a Nile crane on a blue and white background.

"What's that all about, then?" I ask, interested in everything and sounding like a three-year-old.

"The Squadron formed in 1916," he answers. "I was given the history file to read this morning. The background is supposed to be the river Nile…Between the wars, 47 were based in Khartoum, East Africa, and to gain the confidence of the local natives, their chieftains gathered to see the River Nile set alight. Our chaps managed this by pouring petrol into the river and then bombing it. One chief was so amazed he said, 'The name of the Nile shall be an omen of your power,' and the Squadron motto, 'Nil Nomen Roboris Omen', came from his phrase."

I think about this for a while and say, "Guy…isn't it incredible how the African chief spoke fluent Latin?"

Guy mumbles, "Honestly, Kate, you invite mockery."

"Although, it's better than your last badge," I say. "You know, the bearded clam? I never understood that."

Guy just smiles.

"And the one of the mushrooms sat on the toilet."

"That's 'cos we were kept in the dark and constantly fed shit," he replies.

The telephone rings, interrupting us. He takes details of a trip going at three o'clock – he's off 'en route' (away) for a fortnight, leaving me to begin a long friendship with the woodlice.

*

Silly design, woodlice. They dash across the carpet, and as soon as I speak to them, they stop dead in their tracks.

I shout, "But I can still see you! Go on…run for it."

Most of them fall over and don't get upright again, waving their little legs in the air, so I just vacuum them away.

My wedding dress hangs next to our bed like a shrine, mainly because I haven't organised boxing it up, and also because I can't bear the thought of boxing it up. So I put it on and wear it around the house. (Pop next door to show Samantha, who thinks I'm barking mad. Wonder why? I think it's such a shame to wear it only once.)

Register myself with the Med (Medical) Centre, just in case I need a GP. A tall, thin man wearing green camouflage clothes introduces himself as my new doctor.

"Right then, Mrs Willesley. I've got some notes through from your old surgery. Everything okay?" he asks. "Nothing unusual to report?"

(A man dressed as a tree is asking *me* if everything's all right.)

"I'm talking to framed photographs and crying at sad stories on *News at Ten*," I reply.

"Husband down route?" he barks.

"Er, yes."

"Fine, that's just fine – don't worry, you'll soon get used to it."

And that's it – patient induction medical completed. Lonely and new to this extraordinary place, I walk home wondering if I'm going to cope.

Receive a note through my door from the OWC (Officers' Wives Committee) saying House of Fraser is inviting us to meet their 'personal dresser' tonight to choose suitable outfits. Apparently, the fashion show covers casual, evening, contemporary and beach lines, so we need to look the part.

We spend ages deciding on outfits, crammed into a small changing room. Being an ideal size, Caroline is easy to cater for and Tanya looks good in a T-shirt. I, however, look like 'the mother of the bride' (more tears).

"Well, I got myself into this so I suppose I'll have to go on," I sob to Bernadette back at home.

"Kate, people are really suffering in the world," she says with no hint of humour.

I shut up.

*

I decide to weed the borders before sunset when Samantha leans over our fence and invites me to their barbecue. As I've been living on porridge and coffee (it's easier), I gratefully accept and abandon my untouched gardening tools.

Find out George is an engineer in charge of 'B line' (as if I know what B line is – beginning to realise I need to do my homework to keep up).

We sit eating and chatting until the sun goes down. George throws logs into the barbecue drum to keep us warm. Another couple join us and invite me to carry on drinking with them after George and Samantha hint at bedtime.

So off I go, three-parts cut, with two of the nicest strangers, Garry and Diane Harding. I'm amazed by the hospitality of Air Force people. Some of my friends back home have never even met their neighbours after years of living next to them and here I am making new friends in next door's garden. I've even got a small telephone directory with the name and rank of everyone on the Patch (it came with the welcome booklet).

Garry's an engineer in charge of 'A line' (getting the hang of it now). Two gin and tonics later and we go on a guided tour of their quarter. Bored by the standard magnolia walls, Diane has totally obliterated the place with bright colours.

"Can you do that?" I gasp.

"Absolutely not, darling," she says, laughing at my naivety. "We have to repaint the whole house back to its original putrid colour before march out."

Looking around, she asks, "Do you like my bathroom?"

I think no, because there's no enamel bath with claw feet, but say, "Oh yes, it's lovely."

The rest of the evening subsides into a drunken haze.

*

Wake to see a little face one inch from mine asking, "Mummy says do you want tea or coffee?"

"Eh, wha?" I reply, head throbbing. "Where am I?" Tunnel vision blurs the room.

"I'm Phoebe, I'm four," says the face.

I stagger downstairs with a pounding hangover. Diane says, "Sorry, no milk, and we've only got Stilton for breakfast."

I look over at Phoebe tucking into a chunk of pungent blue cheese and accept black coffee instead. Mad people, I think. Must keep in touch with them.

Desperately in need of a shower and clean teeth, I walk home across the Patch, realising I don't know where I am – or where my house is for that matter.

Help!

All the houses look the same. I stare at door numbers, knowing my own (two fat ladies, eighty-eight), and wander around for a while trying not to look lost. Then, eureka! I spot Guy's car, and therefore the house in front of it must be mine.

Safe at last (wonder if anyone saw me?).

*

I've been here two months, I think to myself, reminiscing about my old life, when...

Siobhan! Siobhan!

"Thought you'd never invite me, so here I am." Siobhan walks in through the back door and dumps her case at my feet. "Where's Romeo?"

"He's away. Come in...have a drink," I say, hugging her before placing two glasses of wine on the table.

"Thanks. For one awful moment I thought you meant tea."

Amazed and delighted to see her, we drink wine and discuss work as though I'd never left. She tells me Mr Thorpe still watches our house from across the road, so now and again she goes into my old room and flashes her tits at him (I wonder if Lyneham is ready to meet this wild child...).

"Had a couple of disasters on the male front," she giggles, and goes on to explain how she fell asleep 'on the job', knocked herself out and broke a tooth. "My own stupid fault," she adds. "The idiot asked for tomato sauce at dinner – I should've left there and then, that way this wouldn't have happened..." (I inspect her tooth, cracked from colliding with his bedpost.)

We spend the rest of the day catching up on gossip and events since I last saw her, and gorge on the triple-layered chocolate cake she's brought me from The Shambles (I'm a slave to puddings).

Late into the evening, we're still drinking and laughing at

anything remotely funny (as people do when they're profoundly drunk) and I ask, "How's the family?"

"Still alive, otherwise I'd be RICH," she ponders aloud. "Grandpa's Alzheimer's is getting worse, which is fine, 'cos he's the only person who doesn't know he's got it. And mammy only has two names in the drawer this week."

(Anyone who pisses off Siobhan's mum gets their name written on a piece of paper and put in the knife drawer.)

"Danny's done nothing but mope around since you left," Siobhan continues. "Told me he was going to marry you one day but lover boy got in first."

I stare at those words, dumbfounded as they float around my kitchen like transparent alarm bells, and I poke her snoring face into consciousness. She's slumped over the table, empty glass in hand, adamantly refusing to move. Eventually, I persuade her that the regulation Air Force bed in our spare room is slightly more comfortable than cold Formica.

*

Wake Siobhan up with a full English breakfast and instantly interrogate her on the Danny situation.

"Oh fuck. Sorry, did I tell you? Must've been pissed. Danny will kill me – promise you won't say anything," she moans.

Typical! Not one man in sight for years and then two come at once…

Siobhan reveals that Danny always fancied me (that figures, looking back) but didn't think he could compete with Guy since his last girlfriend (Marina) ran off with a pilot from Doncaster.

"Think she met him in Winnalots, the local night club."

I'm flattered but at the same time a bit bewildered about him fancying me, although I'm not surprised that we never got together – I've known him too long. Growing up with Siobhan made him invisible as my best mate's brother.

(But it's an intriguing idea, and for a few seconds I imagine what life would be like married to Danny…then look at a picture of Guy and know I probably would've done the same as Marina.)

Changing the subject, I suggest we go check out the men in uniform for her, by making use of the facilities on offer – we are on the edge of a camp stuffed full with aerobics clubs, squash courts and a huge gym. (Siobhan is surprisingly enthusiastic for someone with a hangover.)

The nice man with the gun at the entrance gate tells us to go through Control of Entry. We do, only for them to stop us in our tracks.

"You're okay to pass through," they tell me, "but not your friend, ma'am."

Turns out Siobhan is not allowed into the camp without Guy (who vaguely knows her) to vouch for her character. I'm authorised to accompany parents and siblings only (I didn't realise everything rests on Guy and his magic wand).

Hang on a minute; I've given up my home, job, friends and family to live here. Yes I wanted to because I love the man I left it all for, but the least they can do is let me and my mate enjoy a game of squash!

No chance, because I'm just a wife – worse than that, I'm just a wife without a husband at home to authorise entry into his world (without him we can't do anything). He joined up and signed the dotted line, not me. I can't even go for a drink in the Mess without him, not that I'd want to, as I don't 'belong' there.

"Strange this life of being married to the military," I wonder out loud to Siobhan. "On the one hand, I'm the epitome of a good supporting wife, attending various dinner parties and signing up for Squadron functions, feeling like a big part of the picture. But once Guy's away I'm an outsider, standing at the camp gates holding my squash racket and not allowed in. I'm beginning to see how tenuous this link to my new life really is."

So we go shopping instead and spend a small fortune, and surprisingly (for someone with no morals), Siobhan refuses to let me buy some new underwear with the leftover wedding-present vouchers.

Collapsing onto the futons with our bargains, Diane phones

to invite us to an impromptu garden party. Half an hour later, Siobhan and I are relaxing in the sunshine on Diane's lawn, drinking Pimm's. As we explain what happened with the hoped-for squash game, Garry listens to our tale, horrified.

"What a welcome for a new wife!" he states, all indignant and manly. "I'll have you both collected at ten o'clock tomorrow morning."

*

True to his word, Garry picks us up at 10am, signs us in, and we both wave vigorously at the same guard from yesterday as we drive past. Garry shows us the workings, inside and out, of an RAF Hercules. He explains the whole procedure from start-up to take-off. This is invaluable to me as I have no idea what my husband does exactly, apart from "I strap the aircraft to my back and go flying", as he puts it.

RAF Lyneham is the biggest transport supply base in the whole of the Royal Air Force and home to the C130 Hercules, more affectionately known as 'Fat Albert', after a male cartoon character with a big nose. "Look Kate, there's Albert", Guy always says when we see a Herc on the news.

"I'm told that's a laser," I mention to Garry in a questioning tone, pointing to the broom handle protruding out of the front of the aircraft.

Garry chokes, saying, "I think Guy's having you on – as much as he would like it to be a laser, I'm afraid it's just a refuelling probe," and explains that in order for the Task Force (military units stationed around the world) to be supplied at longer range, probes are fitted so aircraft can refuel while airborne. Sorties are stretched as far as the Falklands, involving multiple refuelling on flights lasting over twenty-four hours.

"Oh," I reply, genuinely interested but appearing ridiculously dense. "Sorry, I don't understand."

"There's no reason why you should," Garry drawls.

Ignoring him, I question why some Hercs look 'stretched'. Patiently, he tells us some of the Hercules have their freight bays enlarged in order to carry more weight.

"I like the green ones," Siobhan states, deciding the grey aeroplanes look far too boring (Garry just stares at her).

The closest I'd ever been to an Air Force base before we married was driving past one on the motorway, or sometimes catching a glimpse of the action from Guy's window in the Officers' Mess as a girlfriend. I'm a civilian first and wife second, totally uneducated with regard to the immense operations of the Royal Air Force. Even though I now live in the midst of it, it still means nothing to me and I find it all completely confusing.

I've always wanted to ask a particular question and can't stop myself from asking Garry, "Helicopters…Do you really get your head chopped off if you don't bend down?"

"Yup," he replies, sarcastically.

I worry about Guy being far away, trying to understand what he's doing and why. (Of course he explains, but I can never be expected to appreciate the full-on responsibility of his day's work, until now. I love Guy the husband, not Guy the pilot; he could be leaving on a morning and delivering the post for all I care.)

Sitting on a makeshift seat in the 'hold' (cargo bay), I marvel at how basic the fittings are. Looking around at bare metal, I imagine being a 'troop' travelling in these squashed conditions, deafened by engine noise, and not even a window to gaze out of – the anticipation of warfare is all consuming. Cargo netting hangs from the roof and it's nowhere near like being on a holiday jet.

As Garry answers Siobhan's question about how people manage to sleep during flights, I remember George told me that when he travels as a passenger, he often hangs up a hammock from the ceiling in order to snatch a few hours of frequently interrupted sleep.

We're particularly interested in how the crew go for a wee (sad, I know) and are amazed when Garry points to an impossibly small hole mounted in the side of the cargo hold.

"Wee," he says pointing to the hole. "Poo," he adds, pulling down a bucket on a metal frame from above our heads and dragging a rough curtain around us.

I suddenly feel intensely proud of any female aircrew member, not only because of her mental ability and commitment to survive in a male-dominated world, but to pee in that!

Seeing my thoughts of how a woman might straddle this tiny hole, Siobhan enlightens me by whispering, "Kate...I suspect the girls use that bucket."

"Oh yeah, right...Who sits here?" I ask, squeezing into a cockpit seat. I resist the urge to push buttons and flick switches above my head.

"Push that and you eject," Garry remarks sternly, making me feel like a naughty schoolgirl, but I can't help sensing he's teasing (and see him wink at Siobhan, confirming that the Hercs don't have ejector seats).

He talks us through each crew member and their roles. I don't know what each crew member does in the air, so at least now when Guy talks to me, I'll be able to picture what's happening. (I didn't join the RAF – I just married it.)

The Captain...

In the tiny cockpit covered with panels, switches, buttons and levers, the Captain sits on the left and the Co-pilot sits on the right.

The Captain has overall responsibility for the crew and the aircraft. He (or she, as there are a few female pilots) verifies each aspect of the crew's flight planning and checks the aircraft diary if they're going away en route, making sure diplomatic clearances are confirmed. He also calculates the fuel required and the take-off performance. Before take-off, he walks around the aircraft to ensure everything's in order and then takes a briefing about the 'log book' (from the Flight Engineer), which identifies the aircraft's restrictions and gives details of current service status.

Garry tells us of one Captain who was returning to the cockpit after taking a stroll 'down the back' (going for a wee) when he noticed an army acquaintance sitting in his chair. After chatting with him for a while, he interrupts, saying, "Sorry, old boy. I'd love to stay and chat but I must get back up front."

Bored army bloke asks why, to which the Captain replies, "Because I'm flying the plane, me old mucker."

Army bloke turns white, stuttering, "Yes, yes, don't let me stop you."

The Co-pilot…

Siobhan climbs into the right-hand seat and Garry defines this role as if she were a Co-pilot.

"Sadly, Siobhan, you are the butt of most jokes because one day you'll be a Captain and the crew will have to do what you say, so they get a stab at you now while they still can.

"Your responsibilities are to check pre-flight information, draw up a list of alternative airfields to land at if conditions become too dodgy, put all pre-route documents in the route bag, gather weather conditions and identify any specialist communications required for tactical trips. Specialist communications are mostly pages and pages of cryptic text allowing the 'ships', or airborne aeroplanes, to talk to one another without 'outsiders', or terrorists, understanding."

This explains why Guy ran around with his head on fire, writing out alphabet codes and reading aviation books on a trip last week.

The Air Engineer…

In between the Captain's and the 'Co"s seats, set slightly back, is a smaller seat. This is known as the jump seat and is usually home to the Engineer. Garry, being an Engineer himself, knows this role inside out.

"My job as Air Engineer is to be the technical expert on the flight deck. I collect the aircraft's paperwork from the servicing Squadron and check all servicing has been completed, identifying which restrictions will affect the mission. I then meet the Air Loadmaster to 'pre-flight' the aircraft, checking and setting up systems in the cockpit and freight bay. I also visually check the outside of the aircraft for any problems – and kick the tyres. When the rest of the crew arrive, I brief them on the state of the aircraft. During start-up procedures, I talk through start drills and deal with any technical problems.

Throughout the flight, I monitor flying performance as well as managing fuel, electrics, pressurisation, anti-icing and engines. After the flight, I am responsible for liaison with the ground crew and ensure that all servicing and repairs required are fully documented.

"So, as you can see," he finishes by saying, "I am a very important person."

Siobhan asks what they do to pass the long hours during flights.

Garry answers, "Oh, we have the most deep, scientific, moral, bizarre and sexually deviant discussions."

"And there?" I ask, pointing to a small desk behind the pilot's seat.

"That's where the Nav sits. He makes the tea and says, 'Ooh, look…a tree.'"

Siobhan and I look blankly at Garry, not understanding the joke, so he goes on to describe the Navigator's role (or 'Nav', as they're known).

The Navigator…

This chap cross-checks all pre-flight planning details with the Captain and Co-pilot and is responsible for ensuring that maps are fully prepared. His specific attention is given to the fuel plan and calculation of the safety altitude. During start-up and throughout the flight, he reads and actions a checklist, monitors fuel consumption and, of course, navigates. (In the civilian world, navigators don't exist, hence Garry's heinous comment.)

We're shown a 'frame' (empty aircraft) ready for flying by the tactical Squadrons – the seats are in two long rows, one against either side of the aircraft, leaving just enough room in the middle for equipment. During sorties, paratroopers stand at the back of the aircraft on a large ramp, waiting for a red light to indicate it's almost time to jump out.

Thoroughly enjoying our visit, Garry keeps us laughing by telling us about a crew member with a speech impediment. A group of paratroopers were standing on the ramp, carrying 60lb packs on their backs waiting to jump off into the wild blue yonder, when this chap shouts "Wed on" (red on) followed by "Gween on" (green on), and not one jumps out. The pilot queries over the intercom what's going on, and the engineer explains that most of the 'paras' have fallen over laughing and can't get up again.

The Air Loadmaster…

We go 'down the back' to complete our tour and discover that the final member of the crew is the Air Loadmaster (ALM), or 'Loadie', who stays in the back of the aircraft managing the hold. He or she ensures the safe loading and unloading of kit (Garry tells us that 'passengers' are better known as 'self-loading freight'). The Loadie also looks after customs documents, sorts out the in-flight catering, and sees to the general welfare of passengers and crew. Before take-off, he briefs the Captain on the load and passengers, discussing evacuation procedures in case of an emergency.

"Know any stories about Loadies?" we ask.

"Of course," Garry replies. "When we were coming into land over America, the Co-pilot spoke over the intercom, saying, 'Ladies and gentlemen, this is your Co-pilot speaking. We are currently flying at four thousand feet and will soon be coming into land. If anyone cares to come up onto the flight deck, they will be able to see quite a few icebergs. The particularly large one on our left is the actual iceberg which sank the *Titanic*.'

"Then, as soon as he turned the intercom off, he turned round and said, 'Who's looking?' An immensely gullible Loadmaster came up on deck hoping to see that fateful iceberg."

Back in Garry's office, we thank him for his time and patience with us. He accepts praise modestly and hands over our coats from the back of his door, exposing a huge poster exclaiming, 'Dip me in honey and throw me to the lesbians'.

I return home jealous that Guy has always known of his goal in life. At twenty-six, I still don't have a clue about what kind of career I want, but one of the invisible provisos of marriage to a serviceman is that it has to fit in with moving around the country.

Finding out first-hand what Guy does for a living jolts me into reality: this is no nine-to-five job – he goes to war zones! All I get to see is him leaving the house and then a few days later coming home with jeans, a lawnmower or barbecue for friends, and CDs (American bases have huge retail department stores).

But life is precious, and trying to get to sleep that night, I have a nightmare about Guy dying, waking up in a hot sweat and crying real tears. I immediately phone him on the mobile to check he's still alive.

He thinks it's funny, asking about the dream, "What happened?"

"Oh, it was lovely," I sob, describing his send-off. "You had full military honours, I wore Chanel, and Tina Turner sang 'Simply the Best' – everyone turned up…including your ex-girlfriends, you git."

Guy apologises for the indiscretion and asks if he can go back to sleep since they are in Norway and it is two o'clock in the morning.

*

I keep confusing the neighbours by inviting them for dinner and they turn up eight hours late to be faced with a pile of stale ham sandwiches (must remember I'm down south and that 'dinner' is the evening meal).

Read all the families magazines to find out about the various clubs on offer. There are too many to list them all, so I write notes next to a few, stating why I do or don't want to attend:

FOLIS (Friends of Lyneham Infants School) – great, but we don't have any children.
Station Library and Village Library – these I will join.
Meals on Wheels Volunteers – happily unaware of this, and

if I read the booklet closer will feel obliged to volunteer (so ignore instead).

Cheshire Homes – making beds, tea and coffee for RAF retired residents…too busy doing nothing.

Mother and Toddlers Under Fives Club – I need a toddler under five.

Under Threes Club – could I borrow one?

Under Ones Club – same problem.

Lyneham Ladies Triathlon – forget it.

Officers' Wives Club – amalgamation of all Officers' Wives Clubs. Recognise quite a lot of names from each branch so I'll go along. Gives dates of Summer Suppers or any excuse for a get-together (surprised to see a man listed amongst members, but his wife serves in the RAF and he being a spouse is perfectly entitled to join). Will make a mental note not to get roped into the committee…

47 Squadron Wives Club – Guy's Squadron…suppose I should join.

Station Wives Club – too busy in my own hectic social life.

Lyneham Air Training Corps – don't think so.

Lyneham Stage Club – hmm…

Lyneham Bridge Club – can I drink gin?

Lyneham Ceramics Club – don't fancy dusting my creations.

Looking Good Feeling Great Club – already look good and feel great thanks.

Aerobics Club – attending and crawl home weakly.

Lyneham Saddle Club – like horses, can't ride.

Ladies Badminton Club – too idle.

Ladies Bowling League – too young.

Simply Cross Stitch – I'm all fingers and thumbs.

Windsurfing Club – cold wind on my lovely soft skin, no way.

*

Siobhan goes home vowing to return again soon to try out a serviceman or two.

Receive a phone call from the temping agency offering me a job in a domestic appliance factory (starting Monday). I'm to be Personal Assistant to one of the directors.

Yippee! I'll be contributing financially to our marriage and can get away from the Patch (meeting people who Guy doesn't already know).

Think I'm losing my Yorkshire accent – I've started pronouncing words such as 'the' or 'of' in conversation, instead of saying "top o'stairs" or "on t'door" (dad thinks I've "gone posh"). And whenever mum phones, I have to drop my voice an octave and speak loudly so she can understand me.

In Yorkshire, siblings are always referred to as 'our' (e.g. "our Tom") and I notice how peculiar it sounds when I don't hear terms of endearment like that down here. I miss the straight-talking irony of northern folk – Spyder's family call their dog Mother and shout "Sit down, Mother" or "Go on, Mother, fetch" without a hint of laughter.

People here have never heard of bread cakes and I force myself to say bread roll instead. I'm a northern lass and will always remain true to my roots. (However, I have taken to drinking dry sherry before dinner…)

*

I report for work looking immaculate and join a few others on the induction morning. As the day progresses, I notice that most of the management wear jeans and that not many of them have a clue what's going on because they're also fairly new to the job.

The gigantic, open-plan office above the equally large workshop is cluttered to the rafters with boxes of literature, photocopier paper and product parts (yet there's only one photocopier, with a long queue of yawning people). This highly successful business has grown so rapidly it exudes chaos everywhere.

Someone manages to find me a vacant desk until one can be built for me in my designated area. I think the whole situation rather strange but decide to make the best of it anyway.

My boss, a charming, troubleshooting salesman, walks up to me and barks loudly "Kneel" at my face. I drop to my knees and then immediately feel like a berk as he adds, deeply, "Neil…Neil Robinson," and extends his hand to shake mine, completely unperturbed by my dwarf-like predicament. We sit in his office as he dictates a few rules, tells me he's often away from the office, and then goes out, leaving me with not much to do except organise his diary (I'm bored within minutes).

Coming from a background in public relations, I climb and clamber over piles of brochures into the marketing department (which consists of five desks surrounded by a large purple screen) to offer my services. Surprisingly, the section is run predominantly by women (most of them in their early twenties).

One teenage advertising director tells me, "Yes, the managing director does like his team to be fresh from university and uninhibited by industry."

They don't want my help (or have anything for me to do for that matter), yet they seem tremendously busy and stressed out. I'm used to becoming totally absorbed in a client, working on campaigns from start to finish, but here I feel like a spare part wandering around clutching a large diary. Teamwork is non-existent as everyone strives to fulfil their own ambitions.

At home, Guy's absence echoes round the house and I switch on the answering machine to hear Gwen say, "Hi, Kate. Heard you're on your own – want to join us for supper?"

What a kind thought; she's just become worth her weight in gold (that's better than any support system). I won't have to talk to the microwave again – I'm out of TV-dinner land tonight.

Later, I lie awake in bed, fed and happy, listening to the aircraft engines starting up or winding down. It's comforting and reminds me why I'm here (except when a major operation's being launched – then the noise is so deafening it's almost impossible to sleep).

*

Guy's due home tonight so I quickly clean the house (and wash up two days' worth of dishes) before going to work.

Finding out exactly who's who and how the office system works becomes my obsession. I'm concerned to hear about the high rate of staff turnover, not only throughout the company generally, but also by the amount of predecessors I've had. However, I throw myself into the job and try to make an impression by being conscientious.

My nomadic existence ends when a new workstation finally arrives for me right outside my boss's glass-fronted office (which means I can use the director's kitchen and make my beloved Earl Grey instead of drinking disgusting, additive-laced machine crap).

I go through this guy's post, organise meetings, sort out diary bookings, look after visitors and arrange hotel accommodation – easy, but I wish someone would show me how to operate the word-processing package as I've never seen it before. No one tells me about the in-house training courses, because unless you know who to ask, you won't find anything out (and I haven't worked out exactly who to ask yet).

Personnel (human resources) can't remember my name and smile a lot whenever I visit. The people in my own department are always too hectic to explain anything – never mind, temps don't usually get instructions, so I'll just play around with the program and try to work it out for myself.

Receive a call at 8pm asking if I can pick Guy up from the Med Centre (strange, but okay). I drive up to Control of Entry and dim my headlights so as not to blind the guard while showing my identification. I always forget to switch them back on again and happily drive through the gates wondering why the guard's waving frantically at me (I wave back).

Worrying about Guy but glad he's home, I forget to mention to him that I've got a job and listen to him explain about the minor aircraft fire they had.

"Nothing to worry about," he says. "We managed to extinguish it ourselves but didn't want to report anything 'cos my least favourite people – medics – get involved, and that means no debrief drink in the bar."

They eventually landed in a designated, remote part of the airfield to see fire engines come sprinting up the runway, lights flashing and sirens screaming. As feared, Guy and the crew underwent smoke inhalation checks and he missed out on a beer (hence the phone call home).

"I can understand the fire engines' prompt reaction," he says over a Chinese takeaway, "but why have the lights and sirens switched on? Who are they telling to get out of the way? No one else is on the runway."

"Maybe they just had a sense of adventure," I giggle, and go on to tell him about my new job, Siobhan's visit, our tour of the base – and getting lost on the Patch after drinking with Diane.

"Your flight crew sound like a good bunch," I say, unaware they're different on every trip.

Nodding, he describes the guys, saying that they did have a laugh, and that for the Navigator's birthday present they bought him a lap dance in a decidedly suspect bar. I'm a bit unsure of how to react to this information (the fact that he's going into lap-dancing clubs) but force a smile, waiting for the rest of the story.

"Fantastic, thinks birthday boy, until a fat fifty-year-old appears from behind a curtain and starts wiggling about, attempting the dance of the seven veils in his face."

"What did he do?"

"He complained, all right," Guy says. "Said we'd scarred him for life – especially when he found out that we'd paid the equivalent of two pounds fifty."

*

Today, I learn that my boss will be involved in an important interview next week in Germany and make the necessary flight arrangements. Mid-afternoon, the main interview candidate phones to tell me he can't attend as his brother-in-law died last night, and can we possibly rearrange in order for him to be present at the funeral

I fax my boss at home informing him not to bother working on the interview notes as Mr Bickersdyke is no longer attending (because his brother-in-law has kicked the bucket).

Try to fill the audience at tomorrow's fashion show with my

work colleagues so that I will feel less vulnerable amidst those two beauties (regardless of the fact that Caroline and Tanya are now good friends, they're still thin and pretty). I need to survive – all the girls at work buy tickets and I tell Guy to bring some mates.

*

The big day arrives – Lyneham charity fashion show.

I slump in the hairdresser's chair, waiting for them to create a miracle with my tangled locks.

Backstage at the Juliana Goss theatre, chaos rules. Half-clad girls squash into one small room looking for their wardrobes while hired personal dressers are kept busy dashing around straightening clothes.

A young, wispy man (I nickname him 'Serge') applies perfume to upturned wrists – he fascinates me, being incredibly camp. Aware that I'm staring at him, I wonder if he really is French as he proffers his atomiser.

"You want, darlink?" he purrs.

"Gimme all yer got, mate," I say.

White wine always gets me drunk faster than any other drink and I knock back gallons of the stuff. Not like me to be nervous, I think, helping myself to another sandwich from the piles of food bursting over a makeshift buffet table.

"In for a penny, in for a stone," I snort, giggling at my own stupid joke.

"Kate, you're pissed," Tanya whispers.

"Yup, and fat compared to you," I slur.

"That's not fair – give me some." She takes the bottle off me and pours herself a large glass.

I manage to sober up a little bit in make-up as the beauty-counter assistant shovels vast amounts of foundation onto my face and draws in black eyebrows. It feels like I'm wearing a mask but it looks surprisingly good (from a distance).

A photographer directs his lens towards us, cajoling, "Come on girls, don't be shy." Half an hour later, he pleads with me to move out of the way so he can take shots of the others, but now I'm glamour-puss Katie, model *extraordinaire*, and not about to let the other girls take my limelight. Tipsy and on a roll, pouting for king and country, I begin to enjoy myself.

I'm amazed I can fit into any of the clothes, let alone model an outfit (I always buy clothes specially tailored for tall women, otherwise I end up looking like an overgrown schoolgirl). We walk each outfit on and off stage in time to music without a hitch. Every change of clothes brings about a new confidence in me. And my fans, sensing my humour survival tactics, cheer every time I appear.

Muttering the number of steps to myself, I start to have a laugh and walk right up to the bright lights at the front and blow a kiss to Guy. The audience cheers. Next time I wink at the audience…even louder cheers.

Each outfit and routine gets sillier and sillier – humour conquers nerves.

By the end of the night, we've raised over £1,000 for a women's refuge.

*

Arrive at the office early (must be ill…or keen) to be told the boss is working from home again. Minutes later, a few members of the senior 'management' ask me into his vacant office.

"Hi there, Kate. Please take a seat," smiles one woman.

Wondering how she knows my name, I ask, "And you are?"

"I'm the Human Resources Officer, and this is my colleague," she says, nodding towards a tall, thin blonde on her right, who's trying to look expressionless (and doing a good job of it).

Sitting down, I raise my eyebrows in the direction of a short, middle-aged woman.

"Oh, er, I'm a witness," she mumbles.

I feel the colour quickly drain from my skin.

"We want to inform you that this company operates a policy of political correctness and that you cannot write or say 'kicked the bucket'," the first woman reports.

I look at all three incredulously. "Eh? Is this a bollocking?"

"And that's another word you can't say," 'colleague' retorts. "Kate, this meeting is a disciplinary hearing."

I begin to regain my composure and ask, "Okay, which one of you is in charge here?"

"I am," says the tall, slim one wearing slacks and a T-shirt.

I decide by now that I don't want to work for a nit-picking, politically correct organisation that holds disciplinary hearings over such trivial matters and has obviously undergone a sense of humour lobotomy. Why can't people tell it like it is instead of pussy-footing around? Why are they being so pernickety? I do my job well and work hard (it's not as if my boss has even met the bloke in Germany). Imagine how long Charles would last in this place.

I look the girl in charge straight in the eye and say, "You, you're in charge, are you? Well, you could've fooled me. I have trouble identifying management in here because you all dress so scruffy. You look like a cleaner – put a suit on, for goodness' sake."

She just stares at me impassively.

Aware I'm being politically incorrect again, I think, oh well, I'm finished here, time to leave, and speak calmly to all three of them. "I really don't want to stay and work here anymore. All I said was that the man's brother-in-law had kicked the bucket."

Suddenly, the middle-aged woman pleads, "Kate, please don't go. You're like a breath of fresh air to us."

But I continue valiantly. "And while we're together, can you tell me where my boss is? He should be discussing this matter with me privately instead of sending in three smiling assassins. How unprofessional is he that he can't talk to his staff face to face? I don't need to work – I choose to, and I certainly don't want to work for a bunch of amateurs. Good luck with your unsurprisingly high staff turnover."

I leave the office and walk around the floor saying goodbye. Don't think anyone realises I'm actually leaving except for a few of the sales girls who readily accept my stash of chocolate biscuits. Guy's sports car is parked right outside the main entrance and I open the driver's door like I don't have a care in the world, waving goodbye to the receptionist.

Thirty minutes later, I pull into our drive realising I've just walked out on a job after one week, and promptly burst into tears. Bernadette gives me lots of cuddles, and over two big gins she listens to my tale of woe.

What am I going to do? Back to square one again, wondering what to do with myself.

"Have a baby," she advises.

*

Guy's away on a weapons course called 'Chaffing' (I thought that was what causes sore thighs in summer, but no, it's anti-radar missile tactics).

They use 'chaff' (milk bottle tops) to confuse missiles if one 'locks' on to the aircraft. But when speaking to him on the phone, it sounds like they're throwing beer bottle tops at the enemy judging by the amount of partying going on in the background.

Ah well, me and the spiders in the kitchen are getting along just fine – only conversation I ever get, apart from John Humphrys on Radio 4 in the morning.

Ring the agency to see if anyone wants a temp. Swindon has a 90 per cent employment rate and they're keen to fill places quickly – I take a booking for four days' work in Marlborough, starting this afternoon.

Come home from the Marlborough assignment fed up after getting completely lost. I can't park Guy's sports car, there are too many roundabouts in Wiltshire, this loneliness is deafening, and I miss the North, my family and friends. I go to bed with Guy and wake up with Albert (well it sounds like it; those blasted aeroplanes are so noisy).

"What's the point, he's never here?" I say to myself. "I'm going home."

Thoughts of Yorkshire fish and chips spur me on up the motorway and I arrive at mum's four hours later. Nicola and Becky call in to say hello and I gradually relax, gossiping with them for ages, when Zoë appears at the back door with boyfriend Jack.

"Hi, how are you?" I ask Jack, inviting him into the lounge, but Zoë interrupts before he can answer.

"He's morngey – yer morngey, aren't yer," she tells him. Jack ignores her and starts reading the newspaper.

"It's nice to see you, Zoë. What have you been up to since I left?" I ask her.

"Oh, nothing much, except from retaining water," she replies, grabbing handfuls of her flesh.

Megan shows up after dinner wearing an engagement ring and, although everyone's delighted, I quietly hope she can cope with the military vortex waiting to engulf her (as his first wife obviously couldn't).

Mum and I drive over to see Tim and Susie (me clutching a Russian Caravan tea bag – they only have nasty tea), and I promptly burst into tears. Susie says it's like when I used to call in on them missing Guy because he was in Germany, and how I still offend their hospitality by refusing "builder's tea".

Mum asks me if we've done any wallpapering together yet and incredulously I answer, "No, we're not allowed to – mum, it's an Air Force quarter."

She nods wisely and says, "Sign of a good marriage… wallpapering together."

*

Dad brings me breakfast in bed and I look around my old room, which is fast being turned into an office.

"You told me I could always come back and that this room would forever be mine," I moan at his double-crossing.

He sighs, draws back the curtains, blinding me with sunlight, and says, "Of course it is, love, and we're always here for you. We've just swapped those awful Duran Duran posters for a computer, that's all. But seriously, love, don't you remember what the vicar said?" Helping himself to a sausage out of my sandwich, he continues, "The day you married Guy, your mother and I ceased to be the nucleus of your world. Guy is your home now – that's where you belong. You're Mrs Kate Willesley."

The old git's right, I think to myself. I don't need them

anymore; in fact, I don't need anyone – I am my own person…but Guy does need me.

Visiting the folks allows me to be more candid and open than I am with 'wives' back on the Patch, mainly because my family know me inside out, warts and all.

Everything I show on the base is what I want people to see – nice, polite, fun-loving Kate (and I'm sure everyone else does the same too). On the Patch, I can't behave like a spoilt teenager, but here in York I happily tantrum away in front of mum before getting told in no uncertain terms to grow up or go to my room (would if I could…).

Realising running away is the easy part, I pack my bags and set off home to Lyneham (where Guy is, not Yorkshire where Kate Ashcroft was). Almost crash the car watching my engagement and wedding rings sparkle in the sunlight.

Return to the unfamiliar culture of the Patch and our empty quarters. Don't allow myself to feel lonely, but instead think of how fast this year is passing – I've been here six months already. Still not sorted in a career but that will come, and I am coping with the spasmodic separations at short notice. I actually enjoy being apart from him (is that wrong?) – gives me a chance to see old friends and family before feeling giddy at the thought of his homecoming. Hardest part is getting used to someone else sleeping in my bed. I'm so used to having my own, big, lovely clean space. Seeing a large hairy man one inch from my face (steaming with farts) on a morning is quite alarming.

Especially when, before I even move or open my eyes, he teases, "Get off my dick, woman!"

Samantha and George inform me of their 'posting' (I stifle thoughts of them both being stuffed into a bright-red postbox). George is to start a new tour (job) in Lincolnshire. This is another factor I have to get used to – friends are so transient. Their gardens are full of terracotta pots, making it easier to pack up and move on (suppose it gives service families a sense of living normally in the face of impermanence).

151

Phone Isobel, and Patrick answers the telephone, saying, "Mummy's on the toilet," before noisily hanging up. Phone back two minutes later to hear Isobel go ballistic at me for not visiting her, but somehow dad's words were profound and I wanted to get back (even though Guy's away) as soon as possible.

*

My pimp (temping agent) calls, complaining I'm unreliable since I didn't turn up for the second day of work, and I argue that marital stress is more important than telephone canvassing. Turns out they're short on workers and he agrees to let me finish the job.

Guy comes home from his chaffing course unaware of my pilgrimage to York and I envelop him in a blaze of affection. Obviously in a rush to be somewhere else, he goes straight upstairs, changing out of his growbag (flying suit) into his full dress uniform.

"Not again," I say, dreading Orderly Officer shenanigans. "What's going on?"

"Hello, darling. It's the Annual Reception. Hurry up and get changed – we're going to be late," he urges.

"What's that, then?" I shout, rushing after him to freshen up, thinking, he could've warned me. I choose a pair of silk trousers with full-length soft jacket, knowing it looks very smart.

Grimacing, he says, "You can't wear trousers. You have to wear a skirt or dress."

"What? Why on earth not?" I ask, stunned, getting ready to uphold feminism.

"Look, hon, I'm dressed straight out of the 1940s. Just trust me and put a skirt on…please."

I stomp back upstairs, amazed at what I'm being asked to do, and change into a dress, shouting, "Guy, is Britain still an empire? What out of touch, pompous, tradition-hugging establishment have I married?"

As we walk towards the base, Guy says I look gorgeous and asks, "Why don't you ever wear skirts?"

"'Cos I get fat rash," I reply nonchalantly, before realising he hasn't got a clue what I'm on about. "My legs rub together at the top and I'm afraid I'll spontaneously ignite from the friction."

Arrive at the Officers' Mess just in time to see the local mayor emerge from a big black car. The Annual Reception is a formal function held in honour of local dignitaries. After the formalities of a military procession, musical parade and fly-past, everyone retires to the Mess for champagne (it's a way of saying thank you to the community for its support throughout the year). All service personnel and their spouses are required to attend.

An expectation that wives will be present makes me angry because we also return home after a long, hard, working day and don't particularly want to dress up (in a skirt) to meet a bunch of strangers. My job doesn't demand this of Guy (and remember, I am not the one in the Air Force), but the Air Force requires me to be the supportive wife whenever it suits them.

I can't forget the fact of not being allowed in to play squash or have a solitary drink in the Mess when Guy's away, and think it's all a bit hypocritical.

However, everyone looks extremely smart in uniform and I feel terribly British. We congregate on the top field, waiting for a group of young cadets to march the 'Beating of the Retreat'. (Guy explains it's a ceremony that dates back to 1727. Half an hour before sunset, drummers used to go to the ramparts and 'beat the retreat', signalling to soldiers outside to return, preventing the enemy from making a sudden attack.)

"They've been practising all week," I hear someone say.

Looking around, I note that not one single woman is wearing a pair of trousers; all are wearing skirts or summer dresses.

"It's just like *The Stepford Wives*," I whisper to Guy.

Guy is being Mr Air Force and doesn't think my remark funny (he goes into pompous mode at formal functions), so I ask the lady standing next to me if she thinks it's odd.

"Well, you don't expect your husband to get promoted if you wear trousers, do you my dear," she advises.

"Wha?" I can hardly speak…She is obviously barking mad.

In my astonishment, I gaze into the distance, watching a spectacular sunset, and see that someone has painted a large steel container with the 47 Squadron flag. I point it out to the mad woman.

"Oh, wonderful. Is that a jolly jape?" she asks.

Smiling at her comments, I think she's brilliant, the archetypal military wife – late forties, upper-middle class, and would probably label me impudent if I dared to suggest we no longer rule India.

The Station Commander stands on a podium in the midst of two hundred silent uniforms, silhouetted by traditional peaked caps. I watch a crimson sun settle on the horizon as we wait quietly for the fly-past to arrive. Service personnel salute when four Hercules fly overhead in textbook formation. The atmosphere is eerie; no one moves an inch and all eyes focus on the impressive sight disappearing into the darkening sky. Immense pride wells up inside me, until I notice that the Station Commander's trousers are too short and that he's exposing over an inch of sock – how very British.

*

Wander over to collect our car from the Mess, taking in all the sights and sounds around me. Mist lingers between hedgerows and the church spire scrapes at passing clouds. My spirits soar. I love England and often stop to look around me instead of ignoring the landscape, too busy wasting life.

Sunlit houses stand in rows while in the near distance engines drone monotonously, starting up ready for take-off. Walking past one of Lyneham's veterans, a jet-engined Comet that now guards the entrance gate, I can see a long line of Hercules, large and imposing on the tarmac, each one painted either camouflage green or gunmetal grey.

I watch 'movers' busy loading cargo in and out of the aircraft, buses despatching aircrew, and queues of Army troops waiting to get on board. Pallets of aid destined for Third

World countries are incongruously stacked next to weapons and fighting equipment. Dismantled helicopters are slowly wheeled down ramps from inside the hold, all suggesting a sense of action, war and urgency.

Pride wells inside me, not from watching our armed forces constantly working, but from seeing the side of Guy's life I don't ever get involved in.

The Officers' Mess car park has a great big hole burnt in it from the antics at the last Squadron dinner. I wonder about the old piano that met its fate here, played by some smart nutter while it blazed away.

Return to find out Guy has to go away on a short 'there and back' trip to Turkey tonight (or rather the early hours of this morning) and, not wanting to miss out on a party I've heard of, I invite Will and Eve over to dinner.

Spend the meal trying to avoid bottom jokes (after the loo-paper incident at their house). Guy leaves us to drink coffee in the lounge at eight o'clock, saying goodnight as he has to be up for the crew bus at 'Oh god early' hours.

Will and Eve have no idea that we haven't been invited to this party, and in fact I don't even know the people throwing it. But that shouldn't stop us from going (the general consensus on the Patch is that everyone's welcome), so off we go in search of a boogie.

We walk into a brightly lit house with people talking quietly and music playing softly in the background. Latin beautifully stencilled on curtain pelmets around the living room declares 'Visitors are always welcome'. Being totally juvenile and not the kind of party I'm used to at all, I wonder about going back home. However, the night is still young – Will chats to mutual friends met years ago at training school while Eve and I sample desserts lined up in the kitchen.

After an hour, I can't bear it any longer and switch a few lights off to increase the atmosphere. Wandering into the dining room, I watch the computer screensaver proclaim 'Happy Birthday Tom' and, being drunk, change it to 'The Latin in the lounge means I love bonking'.

"Great. All we need now is some good music," I tell Eve,

heading towards the hi-fi. Soon, ABBA blares into the room and we dance on chairs to 'Waterloo'. Everyone starts to party like idiots to cheesy hits from the seventies and eighties (excellent). The music is a bit loud but not nearly loud enough for me and I pump up the volume even more, until five minutes later one of the speakers blows up.

Lucy, the hostess, looks furious and shouts at me, "You! You've broken my stereo."

"Oops. Sorry 'bout that," I whimper.

We manage with one speaker for a bit longer until I have a brainwave. Remembering we took delivery earlier of a king-sized, handmade, wrought-iron bed, and completely forgetting that Guy's tucked up fast asleep in it, I decide to show it off. Only four girls are interested to see my huge purchase, so, giggling all the way home, we tiptoe upstairs, saying "Sshhh!" too loudly and tripping up over each other. As I approach our bedroom and place my hand on the door handle, I hear a very stern voice say, "Katie…get out." (It's Guy, and he's not too pleased to be woken up.)

"Is he cross?" someone whispers.

"Yes I am. Sod off."

We turn around and go back to the party as quietly as we arrived.

At half past midnight, when 'Wheels' (the minibus) comes to collect Guy, everyone from the party walks over to our house to wave him off and make sure he isn't too angry with me.

*

Samantha and the kids leave today to settle into their new base, while George is staying behind to prepare for the dreaded march out. He repaints the whole kitchen rather than face a fine for steam marks and stays up until 4am cleaning the cooker. I keep him replenished with fizzy drinks and sandwiches, vowing that when we move house, we'll pay for a cleaner. George offers me some of the frozen food he can't take with him and wants to know how much space we have in our freezer, laughing at our lonely bottle of Schnapps on the shelf with not much else.

I'll miss the Longcroft family; even though I hardly know them, they have made me feel so welcome.

Living on the Patch is like living in a goldfish bowl – curtains twitch and the wives know more about your husband's position than you do. And I'm just as guilty…My kitchen window overlooks the street where I watch the comings and goings of neighbours.

"Next door got a new bed today," I tell Guy, who's home from Turkey in time for supper. "Megan Simpson sold Jim's car, and then a fire engine came and blocked the road for hours."

Guy looks at me amazed – I know so many people (and so much trivia already).

"Well, what else can I do when you're away all the time?" I plead.

Guy's also becoming aware that I know an awful lot more people on the base than he does just because I'm the one left behind. He knows the men from the Squadron because he works with them, whereas I know how many children they have, where they live, what their wives are called and frequently receive dinner invites.

To some, rank is more important than one's personality. For me, ignorance is bliss and I recognise people by their names, not status, founding friendships on merit, unlike some obsessed spouses. (I haven't got a clue about rank anyway, so it means nothing when people name-drop.)

Later that evening, Guy tells me about a blonde Flying Officer who was sunbathing on the tarmac next to his aircraft with the other passengers (waiting for the crew to arrive). "Hello, Guy," she says, as he walks past. It was Gwen!

Once airborne, he invited her into the cockpit for a look around and she kept asking why some red lights were flashing – was anything wrong? True to form, the crew took great delight in winding her up to the point of her becoming panic-stricken.

During the final descent, Guy told her to stand behind his seat while they brought the plane in to land. Gwen screamed, terrified but exhilarated, all the way through their descent until touchdown, and then declared what fabulous people they were for getting her home in one piece.

Another female passenger on the aircraft bitched about her, saying she gave women in the forces a bad name, behaving like a schoolgirl (poor Gwen; apparently she's shocked and very hurt). I'm sure she was just innocently enjoying herself with nothing to prove, unaware that her bubbly nature was giving this insipid and evidently jealous creature something to complain about. (Don't ever change, Gwen!)

SIX

Guy's very happy because he's landed a placement as Co-pilot to the RAF Falcons (a parachute display team who go around doing their stuff raising the profile of the Royal Air Force). After one minute of free-fall, the team deploy their parachutes and begin a twelve-man canopy (parachute) stack. These boys are Parachute Jump Instructors (PJIs) from the Royal Air Force's Physical Education Specialisation.

"Sounds tasty. Hope I get to meet them," I tell him.

Guy and Rory Spinner share the role of Co-pilot, so that one 'flies' while the other rests. The bonus is that wherever the 'Falcs' appear, Guy will have to go too, so not only can he enjoy working on his ego, posing at air shows throughout the UK and abroad, but he gets to take part in precision flying – which he loves most and has told me umpteen times exactly what they do (funny, he's never that interested in my temping jobs).

They're going to California (San Diego) next week for a month, as they need perfect weather to carry out an intensive training schedule. I did ask why they couldn't practise in the UK, and Guy said it was mainly because it would be a waste of time and money keeping an aircraft ready here, waiting for good enough weather.

He's due up at the Squadron in an hour to meet the crew before take-off, which gives us just enough time for a quickie. As we're about to rush upstairs and rip all our clothes off, Pippa arrives on the doorstep, saying she diverted her route to Devon specially to see us. Guy jokes we're the best motorway service station in Wiltshire, and kisses me goodbye before cycling off to work.

Pippa says the role of Mrs RAF suits me and laughs at the changes she sees. "You've gone from wild child to serious social standing," she observes.

"I haven't married the job, I've married Guy," I correct (but agree that some see the pilot rather than the man). "At least I didn't marry a house, like Arabella Vancelette," I snap. "Her husband's surplus to requirements – mere puppetry." (Pippa nods; Arabella is the greatest social climber of all time, who hooked a Panache client for his property.)

Guy rings up ten minutes later to say he'll be flying over the Squadron at exactly 1.30pm if we want to come up and see the Falcons' display. Pippa makes two quick calls and delays her meeting, saying she wouldn't miss it for anything.

"Obviously you aren't impressed by his job either," I tease her.

Around lunchtime, bright blue skies are replaced by dark clouds, and at one o'clock the heavens open. We drive up to the Squadron to avoid getting completely wet and notice visiting veterans have the same idea, staying inside their cars to watch. A coach-load of old boys peer out through steamy windows in the comfort of their nice dry bus as ground crew shiver together outside, trying to light marker flares.

Pippa seeks refuge under the umbrella of one of the crew (who is extremely good-looking) and we swoon as he explains what's happening. "Once airborne, the crew plan to arrive overhead at the DZ, or Drop Zone, fifteen minutes prior to the display. This gives everyone a chance to assess the weather conditions and confirm the drop height," he says. "On command from their Team Leader, the Falcons take up positions on the ramp at the back of the Hercules, ready to jump out." (Neither Pippa nor I are listening, but we let him continue.) "Red on then green on signals time to exit the aircraft."

As he's speaking, Guy establishes radio contact with our man on the ground, the Drop Zone Safety Officer (DZSO), and we get really excited hearing him say, "Falcons Drop Zone, this is Falcons Hercules aircraft. We are running in for live drop in two minutes. Request ground flare indicator."

Our hunky interpreter replies, "Falcons Hercules, this is Falcons Drop Zone – you are clear for live drop. Surface wind is three-zero-five degrees, fourteen knots."

"Oh my God, shag me now you beast," Pippa mouths at him, as the deafening roar of the aircraft passes overhead and he can't hear a word she's saying.

Sad that there aren't many spectators outside, we run into the middle of the field (can't let Guy and the crew fly over an empty show). As we watch Guy's colourful cargo free-fall, amazed they can see where to aim for through driving rain, they deploy their parachutes and begin their trademark mid-air stack, eventually landing on target. Hearing the drone of Albert approaching for the low-level finale has us running about like mad things, waving umbrellas as Guy flies over. The Hercules descends low and accelerates to 300mph, flying right over the DZ to execute a spectacular fly-past in time with the Falcon Team Leader's salute.

"Wow, that is so sexy," shouts Pippa. "I've suddenly become very patriotic."

"That's my husband," I shout to her, bursting with pride.

"I'm soaking wet, you daft mare," she shouts back over the deafening roar of engines above us.

Convinced he's seen us, we're gutted to hear that all he could see through the weather was a coach next to the field and that he presumed everyone was sensible enough to watch from there.

*

Guy's due home tonight, so I painstakingly prepare a huge meal for him (throwing away warm slops after trying to mash potatoes in the food processor). He never eats vegetables or anything vaguely healthy when away, just curry and beer, so I slog away trying to roast anything that'll fit into our poxy second-hand oven.

The Squadron calls at 7.30pm informing me of a one-day delay to Guy's trip. Apparently, it's too foggy to land at

Lyneham, so he's stuck in Cardiff for a night. I stare at my two roast dinners.

The Navigator he's gone with lives two doors up and I ring his wife to ask if she's already eaten.

"Not had a chance yet," she yawns. "Been putting the kids to bed."

I offer to bring the meals over and walk across the Patch in the dark carrying two plates of roast lamb, boiled potatoes and carrots topped with gravy – delicious! Meet TLSP out for an evening stroll with his black Labrador (he got promoted) and nod as he walks past, saying, "Evening," as if it's perfectly normal to be out walking roast dinners instead of a dog.

Guy creeps in at 10pm (so much for the delay) and makes himself a peanut butter sandwich, occasionally glancing at the two empty plates.

Since most public air shows are held at weekends, Guy's new job will play havoc with our social life – I already stand out like a single sore thumb at family events, and Guy's going to have to book leave for the Officers' Mess Summer Ball in August because I'm not going to miss out on that one.

In bed, he tells me a 'Falc' came up onto the flight deck today and told him they wanted to be the ones who decide when to jump out, not the pilots.

"I told them it would end in tears but he was adamant," he sighs.

"And? Well, what happened?"

"Two in a tree and one on a roof – I did warn 'em..." he smirks, and then moans, "Did I tell you that we're known as the 'burger slot'?"

"The what?" I ask.

"When it's our turn to display at the air show, some families go for a burger, totally ignoring the parachutes overhead."

"That's awful," I say, making all the right noises.

"So I 'bomb' them during our fly-past and descend to three hundred feet, going straight over the top of the food tent," he laughs. "You ask any kid about their favourite part of the show; they always say the fly-past!"

*

I start yet another job today, and wonder how long it will last. At lunchtime, a huge bouquet of flowers arrives for me and I go into reception to collect them.

"Bet they're from my husband – he went to California last Sunday for a month," I explain to the receptionist.

However, they're not from Guy – they're from the agency: I've won temp of the month! Still, it's only temping, and temps get all the boring jobs. The ethos seems to be, 'pile of mundane work which no one wants to do, better get a temp in'.

So here I am amongst a bunch of faceless wonders, bored silly, and I realise how spoilt I was in Yorkshire, working amongst vibrant people with a sense of humour. We had deadlines causing tears and tensions every day, women bitching one minute and being best friends the next, laughing about weight obsession and workloads, all working together to get the job done. Colleagues became good friends and they mattered to me.

I want to work with people who have style and high standards. The types that are driven by creativity and, most of all…care about their appearance. This lot smell of stale laundry, look undernourished and couldn't network a jamboree.

Now I find myself tidying shelves to pass the time and deflect accusations that I'm obsessed with weight loss by explaining I used to be in PR.

Start to worry I'm going mad with boredom when Guy phones from California.

"Hi, babe. I'm due some time off next week so why don't you come out here and join me? I'll call again on Friday and confirm everything."

I'm so excited I feel sick. An hour later, the Captain's wife, Emily, rings my mobile and says her husband has said the same thing to her but she's going to book her flight regardless.

I hesitate. "What if they don't get the time off?" I ask, thinking we'll be stuck in deepest America without a husband.

"For goodness' sake, book it, woman – you're too long dead," she laughs.

*

Oh, the agonies of waiting for that phone call. But he rang – yippee!

Thrilled to be leaving the filing and shelf-tidying behind, I go to see my boss. "I'm bored silly, so I'm off to see my hubby in Californ-i-a," I tell him, knowing the only good deal about being a temp is you can leave if you want to. (I work to alleviate the boredom of living apart from Guy, but if I can be with him instead, then stuff temping – I'm off.)

"Call us when you get back if you need another job," he says kindly.

Not fucking likely mate, I think, glancing at the office-block mausoleum before driving home.

Bags packed, I drive to Heathrow and get the next flight to Los Angeles, feeling liberated travelling alone.

I've got neck ache, backache and cramp from sitting in the cheap seats for ten hours, but Guy and the crew are waiting for me at my connecting airport in San Diego and I feel just like a girlfriend again, going all silly at the knees.

We drive up to the accommodation, an American naval base like the one in the movie *Top Gun* (it just gets better and better), and I realise I haven't got any valid ID, so I show them my Wiltshire library card to gain entry. Unbelievably, it works.

*

Wake up to hear chanting in true USA style. Troops are marching past, singing, "I don't know but I've been told…"

"Guy! Guy!" I shout. "They really do chant – I thought it was just in films."

"Yes, but they're still spams," he mutters, unimpressed.

I watch from our window as the USA's version of the SAS (known as the Navy SEALs) return from a sea exercise in black dinghies, waving at onlookers.

Everyone on the base is so friendly and I can't believe the facilities these guys have. Uncle Sam really does look after his boys – each room has air conditioning, satellite TV and an en suite bathroom. The base boasts a burger bar, cinema, laundry and a parade of shops. Ross (the Navigator) tells me he was ashamed to be British some time ago when an American pilot came to stay in the Officers' Mess and a bath towel couldn't be provided for him to go and freshen up. Imagine the poor bloke's shock at the meagre state of British forces' hospitality compared to how well looked after they are in the USA.

We drive a few miles north to a shopping mall dedicated exclusively to military personnel and their families. I find it weird to shop amongst people wearing full uniform and medals – the yanks are given medals for flying over hostile countries, and that includes Ireland. (My mum tells me stories of when she worked in a gentlemen's outfitters in Leeds. Old tramps used to come into the shop asking for a 'Desert Rat' tie – now there's valour without vanity.)

Adam Williams is the Captain of Guy's crew on this San Diego trip and I've got to know his wife, Emily, quite well over the telephone, but we've still not managed to meet up. She arrives tonight, so we hang out in the mall to kill time before collecting her. Adam says he wants to spend the afternoon in a strip club, and amazingly no one but me finds this surprising.

"Are you mad? The shops are open," I say.

We arrange to meet up with him again at the airport in time for Emily's arrival. But as her flight lands and her bags are being checked through, there's no sign of Adam.

The lads have already decided his life will not be worth living if he doesn't make it in time to meet her. Emily is spotted in the arrivals lounge and Guy dashes over, saying, "Hello there," giving her a big hug. "Adam's off, er…sightseeing," he stumbles.

"You mean he's at a strip joint," she corrects.

Just at that moment, Adam saunters around the corner wearing a big grin on his face, and Emily thumps him sharply in the ribs.

"I knew it, you git," she says.

*

All the crew decide to stick together and do the tourist thing as a big bunch of mates. I try not to be too lovey-dovey with Guy, realising the lads could be missing their wives and girlfriends.

Adam and Emily, on the other hand, are like a pair of love-struck teenagers and don't give a hoot, constantly snogging and taking banter from the rest of us about missing breakfast.

I envy Guy's lifestyle, being able to travel and see the world with his mates. The camaraderie is so strong that it's almost impossible to feel lonely. Banter is the name of the game, though, and I notice that my quiet, sensitive husband is not going to show. I'm down route with the lads and have to muck in and drink like one of them.

The international call sign for an RAF multi-engine aircraft is ASCOT (Allied Support Command Operational Transport). If a crew staying in a hotel needs to receive correspondence, it's always sent to 'Mr Ascot'. Even civilian aircraft use different identities – Concord uses 'Speedbird' – followed by the flight number (each call sign is unique to its own organisation).

So, Hercules crews away on exercise always refer to themselves as 'Ascoteers'. A typical evening out with the Ascoteers is to meet up after debrief and start looking for a suitable place for dinner, i.e. commence the Ascot Shuffle. This involves wandering up and down a busy street lined with restaurants and bars until someone finds the cheapest beer before anyone can eat (often, they end up back at the first restaurant). Also, a true Ascoteer will always manage to out-bargain the last man on any souvenir, the tackier the better.

Surprisingly (but only for me), the crew never want to eat – just drink. Dinner means a quick bite before the bar opens and then more drinking. However, I demand to be taken for a civilised meal in a restaurant (some of the other chaps think it a refreshingly good idea and come along with us).

We meet in a bar called Hooters, which would be instantly condemned in Britain by political pressure groups for its sexist attitude (amazing – the Loadie tells me one has managed to open in the UK). I'm still shocked at how a country as politically correct as the USA doesn't see what they're promoting – every waitress is gorgeous, thin, tall and tanned, wearing the shortest shorts and the tightest tops (now I realise why the lads meet here at every available opportunity). But the place does have a real family atmosphere and everyone is visibly friendly, typically American. I can't decide if this is because the local customers are stupid and ignore the fact that their waitresses are waving their enormous breasts ('hooters') in their faces or because this is their idea of family fun. Our lads, of course, love every minute and conspicuously all sit together on the same side of the table to get a better view.

One mechanical waitress introduces herself as Charity and uses the word 'yip' to answer each query. She's obviously dead from the neck up and a silent joke goes around the crew to make her 'yip' as often as possible by asking ridiculously obvious questions. They soon have her 'yipping' at everything and are in fits of giggles (without her knowledge, of course; that would be out of order).

What amazes me most about the States, supposedly land of the free, is the total lack of freedom. Here in San Diego, we're not allowed to take an alcoholic drink out into the street and so can't relax outside a café to enjoy a cold beer while watching the world go by. Smoking is banned inside a bar or restaurant except in designated areas. So, no chance of having a beer and a fag on the terrace at sunset while eating dinner, then. Doesn't sound like freedom to me!

We go for a late drink in a bar called The Last Resort, and only after about an hour do we realise it's an insult bar, where all the staff throw rude comments at customers (being British, we think it's normal). Some of the Falcons are enjoying a drink or ten in the same bar. I laugh at what a bunch of twats they look like, all wearing identical clothes: chinos and yellow Hawaiian shirt. Makes it easier for the girlies to identify them, no doubt.

*

One sad revelation during my idyllic break is that not all the guys are faithful to their wives while away. Being 'down route' often leads to loneliness and temptation; I was so naive to think it doesn't happen. We bump into another crew and I recognise one lad who lives on the Patch, out for the evening with someone who's not his wife. It still comes as a shock to think that not everyone's happily married like me.

If one of the boys has a fling (or even keeps an affair going), the incident is never mentioned by any of the crew when they return to British soil. This is known as 'detachment rules' (that way, no one gets hurt). I suppose it's a form of damage limitation, because once a spouse gets 'found out', the injured party realises a whole crew knew it was going on, and they must feel so desperately crushed.

Guy abhors gossip and will never discuss the infidelity of the crews he flies with – I sometimes hear about a failing marriage only to find out that Guy was aware of it long before the wife was.

Frequent periods of absence at short notice can wreck already precarious marriages.

My friend once told me marriage is like a bed of roses – because it's full of thorns. I'm seeing into a part of Guy's life which I would never be privy to normally, and have to behave accordingly.

*

Return home to the rat race and job hunting. I miss Guy and being part of the group, but he's not due home for ages.

I feel like I've been given a chance to see what happens to him once he leaves Lyneham. The Squadron sometimes hosts a families' day to give us an insight into the working world of our loved ones. But I've been at the sharp end – one of the lads, a fly on the wall – and that isn't going to happen very often. Mooching about the house before sunrise, struggling to combat the jet lag, I stare at his favourite poem (written by a Second World War pilot) on the door of his study:

High Flight

Oh, I have slipped the surly bonds of earth
And danced the skies on laughter-silvered wings
Sunward I've climbed and joined the tumbling mirth
Of sun-split clouds and done a hundred things
You have not dreamed of – wheeled and soared

And swung high in the sunlit silence
Hovering there, I've chased the shouting wind along
And flung my eager craft through footless halls of air
Up, up the long delirious, burning blue
I've topped the windswept heights with easy grace
Where never a lark or even eagle flew
And while with silent, lifting mind I've trod
The high-untrespassed sanctity of space
Put out my hand and touched the face of God.

John Gillespie Magee Jr

Like a lonely child, I watch out of my bedroom window as people walk across the Patch to a party in the Mess. A full moon illuminates the evening and soft light from street lamps is reflected in the faces of handsome gents. Looking at their full dress uniform makes it easy to daydream I'm somewhere in the mid-nineteenth century. Elegant women in sparkling gowns smile tenderly at their escorts, anticipating the evening ahead, and, fancying myself as Jane Austen (longing for the days of manners gone by), I feel a thrill as these delightful scenes pass our window. Then my silly, sentimental bubble bursts when they wave to me and I notice that they only just fit into those immaculately tight outfits. Shiny gold buttons threaten to explode and hit some poor sod in the eye after one aperitif too many!

Uniforms are fitted during initial Officer training, when recruits are young, fit and extremely slender. Guy tells me he was just nineteen years old when he visited the tailor for his Mess attire. After finishing a cold-weather survival exercise involving a week's starvation, even his shoes had got too big for him. The tailor measured Guy up telling him to breathe out until he went blue in the face to allow for extra growth. Years later, he's still squeezing into the same uniform, mainly because a new pair of 'dress' trousers cost around £600.

*

No work from the agency today. Still feeling lonely when Bernadette invites me to join her in the HIVE, explaining, "It's another meeting place – HIVE stands for Help, Information, Volunteer, and Exchange."

Help – questions or queries regarding any aspect of service life.
Information – job vacancies; what's on locally; school information.
Volunteer – dependants keep it running.
Exchange – new ideas for the future.

I refuse, pontificating on the abbreviation of HIVE, and invent my own capital letter-studded group – POALMA (Piss Off And Leave Me Alone).

"Oh come on, Kate, just for half an hour – we can have a coffee, and there'll be cake…"

I can't resist cake and she knows it. "Well, only for half an hour, then," I say.

We walk over to a large crèche/refugee camp. Husbands join wives for lunch in the aptly named Honey Pot Café. A mother and toddler group meets here once a week, as does the Slimming Club. All sorts of things go on, from first-aid courses to employment agency advice (there are even shelves of children's books to buy). The Bizzie Bee craft shop sells birthday presents and there's a beauty salon for pampered wives. Bernadette points out the next CAMEO afternoon (Come And Meet EveryOne) for new arrivals, which I promise unfaithfully to attend. (Aaargh! It's another saddo acronym!)

She tells me they regularly get a solicitor to give free legal advice and a representative from the Defence Housing Executive helps families solve problems with quarters. Sometimes the Station Commander holds briefing sessions here to inform worried wives about any 'situations' that are developing around the world.

I meet lots of young mums with whom I have absolutely nothing in common except the fact that my husband wears the same colour clothes to work.

(Nice cake, though.)

Late afternoon, Eve comes over to see how I'm settling in and finds me pulling on my ball gown while trying to breathe in as far as I can, wheezing, "It's no good, I've got fat. Now I'll have to lick the toilet bowl for a quick bout of dysentery – how can three months make such a difference?"

"But Kate, it's your wedding dress," Eve laughs, sitting on my bed with her foot between my shoulder blades, trying to make the seams meet and fasten twenty tiny buttons.

She comforts me by saying how mad I am turning my wedding dress into a ball gown in the first place – everyone knows wedding nerves act as an appetite suppressant, so I've probably just returned to my pre-wedding weight.

"Only a couple of weeks to the ball – extreme circumstances call for drastic action – the cabbage soup diet…" I exclaim.

Eve, Gwen and Jude are my allies, and just knowing that a few others are coping with the same pitfalls of Air Force life helps me to counteract the isolation that obviously goes with the territory. I feel more married to these girlfriends than to Guy. The base is my surrogate family, a crutch I support myself with in his absence.

Looking through the only photograph album of us before we married, I remind myself how lucky I am to be home alone and miserable (at least this way he'll come back to me at some point).

*

Guy walks in looking tanned and heroic, wearing full camouflage kit. His slightly unzipped flying suit exposes a green T-shirt showing a small print of Albert on his chest (this is how everyone knows what you fly), but a comical panama hat on his head spoils the whole image. "Did you miss your steely eyed killer, then?" he smiles.

"Guy, I don't know how to tell you this, but I've been unfaithful."

"What are you saying, Kate?"

"Well, last night Paddy from *Emmerdale* took me out and we ended up in bed together. I couldn't help myself – he paid for dinner and everything."

The relief on Guy's face is a picture. "Oh Kate, I'm so glad to hear it's another bloody dream – don't worry, darling, I have Kylie every night of the year and she always begs for more."

After soup, bananas and a large glass of water, Guy states, "It stinks in here," moving two cabbages off the kitchen windowsill to open a window.

*

Pippa, Maggie and Beth arrive late evening, excited about the ball tomorrow. Guy takes them onto camp to sort out security passes, and they love it when a guard salutes him as he drives past, thinking it ever so sexy. Pippa wants to know if Guy has any single mates and would he please reverse so that they can see it all again, chanting, "Men in uniform here we come!"

I choke on my cabbage soup as a familiar car pulls up outside and I realise it's Danny getting out.

Guy takes two suitcases from Siobhan (she's only here for one night) and chats away like old friends to Danny. I avoid looking in his eyes, feeling a knot of apprehension in my stomach, and instead hug Siobhan tightly, pleased to have my madcap friend with me again.

Danny says he's in a rush but Guy ignores his protest and invites him in for a beer, commenting, "Nice car, mister."

Everyone returns inside and I hang around behind waiting for Danny to park up, and with no other option but to be polite, I nervously ask, "How come you're here?"

"My company's running a bunch of office workers into the ground in Devon," he replies.

I look stupidly at him until he explains, "Outward Bound programme – I'm going to assess them tomorrow. Siobhan hitched a lift as I'm passing your way." Walking through the doorway out of earshot from the others, he adds, "And I wanted to know – have to know – that you're happy."

I daren't look round to answer him. Of course I'm happy, but the hairs on the back of my neck are charged with electricity and I dismiss the feeling as illicit magnetism, thinking, oh God, he really did like me and now I'm nervous.

Siobhan throws her suitcases onto the spare bed and

immediately holds her hands up in surrender. "I had no choice but to get a lift with him. Sorry, babe, but I'm broke," she apologises (confessing after one silent stare that she preferred to spend her train ticket money on a dress instead).

Returning to the kitchen, Beth hands me a coffee, explaining that Danny's phone rang and he left quickly afterwards. So much for the non-toxic diet, I think, gulping the black nectar down in one to calm my shredded nerves.

I need to get an early night before tomorrow but can't stop discussing beauty routines, world politics and Panache gossip with the girls. We're trying on each other's outfits while Guy watches television downstairs, regularly supplying us with more red wine. I don't understand their attraction to his jungle kit piled up in the bedroom corner (I must be used to seeing it lying there), but Siobhan puts on the headphones and camouflage jacket, shrieking with delight.

Beth lights up a cigarette (illegal in quarters), opens a battered old book on his desk and announces, "I hate to tell you this, sweetie, but you're not his first."

I take the small, dusty book from her and look closely at a handwritten list of women's names. It's obviously his old girlfriends but I never dreamt he'd be the type who kept a record! Giggling at our 'find', she picks up a red pen and adds my name (in capitals) at the bottom.

*

I can't stop farting and my aura smells of cabbage but the diet has worked: 5lb off – yippee!

Pippa suffered a similar ordeal trying to find a suitable dress and tells us about keeping Selfridges in London open, long after closing time, while searching for something to wear.

She says, "Eventually, I found the perfect emerald silk number but couldn't buy it because Kate's dress is green, so I bought it in red."

"Good girl. I'd have sent you back to Yorkshire," I laugh.

At two o'clock, we negotiate a washing line full of old hand towels before finding the entrance to a local hairdressing salon.

"Who?" my stylist asks when I request a Jane Austen look (getting bad feelings – this doesn't bode well). Pippa and Maggie frown at me and then sit for ages, saying, "Thanks, that's great," as tangled locks are pulled into place, and we hurry straight home to wash it out (why do women always do that?).

I produce a bathroom rota for all of us, of which Beth takes no notice and spends ages getting ready. Luckily, Siobhan manages to speed up her hourly routine to fifty-five minutes, leaving me just ten (aaargh!).

Guy pours himself into his Mess kit. I always fancy him rotten in his uniform and start to see him as a prime sperm donor (Bernadette's idea of babies might not be that absurd…).

We've all been invited to the Wing Commander's for pre-ball drinks. As we make our way there, we call in for aperitifs at various houses along the route. Before long, a crowd of us gathers going house-to-house, collecting people as we go.

I walk into one front room and receive a round of applause for getting into my wedding dress – something that even I thought unfeasible. Little do they know it's impossible to sit down, and yes, I may look stunning, but after that cabbage soup diet, I'm being propelled along like a human hovercraft!

"Kate, I have never seen you look so beautiful," Jim compliments, as I try unsuccessfully to control my trapped wind.

Lifting up my silk gown and net skirts, I reveal 'sensible' shoes and grin widely at him.

"Unfortunately, the bubble has now burst," he sighs.

Fergus McLeish pours massive brandy sours for us all in his back garden and Pippa accepts tasteless comments from Guy regarding her fantastic cleavage.

"Those tits…I mean, they're just there, aren't they," he applauds.

Maggie notices that Pippa's had more brandy sours than anyone else, and after three large ones, Pippa offers her glass for yet another, giggling to Fergus, "I must admit, they are show-stoppers aren't they." Fergus just smiles at her cleavage and meanders off, leaving us to stagger towards the ball an hour late.

The Summer Ball is excellent: dodgems, Ferris wheel, speedway, laser clay pigeon shooting and even a tethered hot-air balloon.

We go straight to the main marquee for 'inspection of puddings', Guy buys champagne and I decide to wave from the balcony overlooking the ballroom. Draping ourselves 'up' the banister in spectacular Marilyn Monroe style, I lose my balance completely, miss the rail and end up in a heap on the floor. People dancing to the band below cheer and, undeterred, I take a drunken bow.

Spend half an hour having professional photographs taken to remember this fabulous evening and then go off in search of more food. Each room holds a different cuisine: seafood in one, Mexican in another – the list of gastronomic delights is impressive. A string quartet serenades those drinking coffee in the ladies room (not a loo).

We're dancing like mad to 'YMCA' when I notice Guy doing some strange moves.

"What are you doing?" I ask.

"The 'HILTON'," he sings loudly, forming each letter with his arms to the music.

"What for?" I shout.

"Because I can't stand YMCAs. Herc crews always try and stay in a decent hotel."

Standing at the bar, he explains why (when not in theatre) they book into four-star hotels. "Because good hotels are the only places we can sleep without interruption and get a meal after flying for often over ten hours. Sometimes after sorties we only get twelve hours off before 'wheels' again, and cheap hotels have staff vacuuming outside your door when you're trying to sleep. This is bad news if you're tired and expected to fly a plane. Also, meals in cheap hotels are only available at certain times of the day. Better quality places are not glamorous, just functional – we need quiet rooms, laundry service and twenty-four hour food available, 'cos a lot of the time we land in a country in the morning but for us it's still night-time. So we order beer to drink during debrief, with breakfast, then go to bed. Staff look at us as if we're mad having a beer in the morning, but really it's our evening."

Siobhan flirts outrageously with an Officer and Guy tries to warn her that he's only interested in his own carnal pleasure, and without one iota of tact suggests she stops acting like a tart and behaves herself for once. The change in her is instant; losing all exuberance, she visibly deflates like a pricked balloon. Clearly disgusted at Guy's 'advice', she flounces out of the marquee declaring that she is no tart and is totally aware of what she's doing, thank you very much! I watch her storming away as tears pour down her cheeks.

Beth suggests we go after her, saying, "Leave her to me," and follows her into the powder room (the loo). "Siobhan? Are you in here?" she asks (I stand quietly behind).

"Go away," Siobhan snivels, sobbing behind a cubicle.

Quite a few women take the hint and do as she asks, leaving Beth and me alone with a very upset Siobhan.

Beth fathoms out which cubicle she's in and proceeds to pick the lock with her eyeliner. Fantastic!

"How on earth did you learn that?" I whisper.

"It's amazing what a girl can do when she has to," she winks. "You go – I'll sort her out."

I leave them to it and try to tear Guy and Pippa away from the fairground but they're being big kids and refuse, so I wander into the casino for a while (that is until I smell a barbecue outside and change my mind).

Ladies wearing high heels hanker after my gorgeous orthopaedic shoes and I lend them to one girl for a blissful respite.

Craig Murphy-Jones (the world's most fantastic foot masseur) gives agonisingly good foot rubs in the pudding tent to a queue of waiting women.

Pricey comes over, kisses me on both cheeks and says in a first-class accent, "Mrs Willesley, I think it's time…"

"Oh no, Pricey, it's far too early," I giggle.

He raises one eyebrow and I succumb. Reaching into my handbag, I pull out the tiara worn on my wedding day (and any other on which I'm drunk).

"Excellent, bloody excellent," he mumbles, wandering off.

I walk past a group of people next to the bouncy castle, when one bitchy girl comments that I look like a bride-to-be (totally missing the joke). That's the whole point, you tart, I want to shout, but glare at her instead.

I find Siobhan and Beth in the ballroom. Siobhan looks much happier and gives me a hug to convince me she's okay. "I've arranged to meet that bloke at midnight, but don't tell Guy," she says quietly.

"Oh Shiv," I say, hoping the bloke realises it's him who's in peril.

Some people are starting to leave, wanting home and a warm bed, but we still party like idiots. In the Mess, I follow Pricey through reception just as a dear old couple are about to leave.

"Ooh, look – Scottish Widows!" I exclaim, pointing at the lady's black velvet cloak and deep wizard hood.

The startled woman is stunned by my observation, obviously not her intended image, and 'sucks a lemon' as I rush past to link arms with Pricey.

Dancing until the early hours, we all manage to make it through to the champagne breakfast at five o'clock in the morning and then wander home arm in arm, watching the sun come up. There's something terribly civilised about walking home at sunrise in full Mess kit and ball gowns (even if we are dishevelled).

After hot chocolate, we all crash out, setting the alarm for midday when the 'survivor's barbecue' starts.

*

Late afternoon, Guy joins me and the girls for a walk, strolling across the Patch towards open fields, when I notice there's no getting away from it: I'm constantly reminded of the fact that we live at his work, and living with your spouse's colleagues is incestuous. People are obliged to speak to me and everyone looks the same in uniform.

I tell Beth, "Even strangers know my name, which makes a trip to the corner shop for a pint of milk daunting until I recognise a face."

"That's because in York you were 'someone' but here you cling to the 'Mrs' tag."

"That's true. I must get a life."

However, I'm quite in awe of my exciting new world and commit faux pas wherever I go. I tell Maggie and Siobhan of my latest blunder..."I said hello to a few mums from the Sergeant's Patch walking their children to school across the Officer's Patch yesterday, only to be greeted with blank stares – the sense of being ignored was overwhelming."

"Well of course they won't answer you, darling," says Guy. "You're an Officer's wife."

Although he means it mischievously, I do realise that there's a lot of truth in this – some wives married to higher and even lower ranks really do have chips on their shoulders about status; I've noticed that. Pride and power or inverse snobbery, call it what you like, but it would be ignorant of me to deny it (sad, I suppose, but it happens in all walks of life).

*

A Russian Antonov (huge aeroplane) was meant to leave yesterday but the crew can't afford fuel to get home and are staying in the Mess, enjoying hot showers and food. It must be sheer luxury for them, as one told Guy that their wages are normally paid in cabbages (are they on the soup diet too?).

Isobel phones to inform me about her latest disaster on the Internet. "Only meant to spend a few pounds but some berk kept raising the price and out-bidding me. I became possessed – had to beat him."

"Izzy, how do you know it was a 'him'? And what was the auction over?" I ask.

"Of course it was a 'him'. No woman would push the price of a wicker horse up to eighty pounds," she states, adding, "Stupid webshite."

"You mean website," I correct.

"No, I was right the first time. I'm never, ever going on-line again."

*

Guy's away at another air show, the last one this season. Thank goodness someone else will get the job next time and I can have him back on a weekend instead of being Norma no-mates, clinging on to happy families next door. Decide to comfort eat for an hour and hit the fridge before lying on the sofa to read magazines that have been pushed through my letterbox. I flick through *Corridors*, the official magazine of Airwaves, an RAF families magazine and *RAF Wives Quarterly* to see what happens on other stations.

I like the *Lyneham Globe*, a monthly journal, mainly because I recognise some faces and it's another way of understanding what the boys get up to on exercise (Squadrons write articles each month and the Station Commander outlines future tasks).

I also read the home-made 'Officers' Wives Newsletter', which lists all sorts of gatherings: the regular flower-arranging team are appealing for volunteers and a local artist is offering an evening on the art of painting traditional narrow-boat roses (hmm…); the Wing Commander's wife has even organised trips to the theatre and welding lessons at a local foundry.

I can empathise with the flower arrangers; it's so easy to dismiss floristry as stereotypical of a wives club. Volunteers work hard for not much recognition and I admit I haven't offered my services yet from fear of sarcastic ridicule from Guy, but I suspect I am missing out on a few good laughs judging by the amount of booze drunk when 'arranging' rooms for functions in the Mess.

*

The Russians take off at dusk. Their aircraft is so loud I can't hear my favourite TV programme start in my own front room, and I strain to pick up each drastic event on *Emmerdale*.

Funnily enough, I know exactly what stage an aircraft is at when starting up or winding down because I have no choice but to listen to engines constantly drone outside my window. Even Guy's amazed when I say over the noise, "Hang on, that's a test run – wait twenty seconds until it stops," and twenty seconds later the engine shuts down.

When I lived at home, I knew dad would walk in the door

after hearing his car pull up on the driveway. Now, when Guy's due home and the Squadron informs me of his landing time, I hear his plane go over and half an hour later he walks in the back door (it's a peculiar feeling).

*

Yvonne, a female civilian pilot Guy knows through his mate Seb (or "Sebastian, darling", as she calls him), phones to invite us to join her at the Henley Music Festival because Seb's away down route. The invite states 'Black Tie' so I dig out my old faithful Burns Night ball gown and Guy buys a dinner jacket (four hours before the festival).

We make a mental note to call Seb 'Sebastian' all evening and set off for a good time. Yvonne lives in a stunning location just outside Henley-upon-Thames, and Guy pulls up on the drive next to "daddy's" Porsche at the same time as her tremendously posh friend, Tilly, emerges out of a BMW Z3.

Guy travels with Yvonne's posh friend in her sports car, because he's a big kid and wants a ride. Unfortunately, the ticket collectors think they're married and make comments to them such as, "Allowing the missus to drive tonight, sir?" (Tilly doesn't appreciate Guy's reply: "Yes, but just the once.")

I can't believe the effort people go to with their picnics; full dining-room tables set up for three-course dinners are placed by the river, and some even have butlers on hand to open Range Rovers packed high with food. We unload our foldaway table and chairs and set up camp, trying to compete with the people beside us. It's terribly sophisticated, much more than I imagined. Yvonne brings out a full dressed salmon complete with butterfly tiger prawns and salad. Tilly offers champagne and oysters – and I, being a total ignoramus, open up my carrier bag of provisions.

"Anyone for crisps or a cheese straw?" I offer, thinking a picnic meant exactly that, but no way – not at Henley, darling!

When they stop laughing at me, we enjoy the salmon *avec tortillas*, washed down with plenty of bubbly.

Guy leans over and whispers, "Never mind, babe, I love you," before eating a cheese straw with a wink. (But I've learnt my lesson and will never take convenience finger food to Henley again.)

We wander past people still dining to find our seats in time for the concert. Tilly's tipsy and I'm blissfully happy, watching a crimson sky melt into the Thames behind a floating stage. The London Philharmonic Orchestra plays to a crowd of beautifully dressed people and I drift into another of my Austen fantasies looking at all the immaculate gentlemen and flowing ball gowns.

People sail boats behind the musicians and I particularly like the 'slipper launch', a sort of gliding walnut boat big enough for two. Everyone cheers when one sailor peddles past on a home-made craft, lounging in a wooden bath chair supported by a sort of makeshift raft. He's wearing a full dinner jacket and monocle, smoking a cigar and holding a black umbrella.

One hour later, we applaud until our hands hurt and make our way out of the stand to explore the other areas of the festival. Alongside the riverbank are different exhibitions: paintings, and wood, stone and hedge sculptures. We hunt for more champagne and I tell myself to stop, look around for a moment and appreciate what a magical evening this is as we sit by the water's edge at midnight and watch a firework finale.

Life is good.

*

Switch on the TV to catch the evening news. The staid-looking reporter describes worsening situations in a number of trouble spots around the world; the UN 'volunteers' British troops. Predictably, the broadcast shows a Hercules arriving (always the first in and last out) at a camp. The rush of emotions is confusing – I could know those men on board. It ceases to become a broadcast.

British military presence in the Gulf increases as things hot up out there again and Guy checks his equipment (gas mask etc.) ready for the inevitable call-out. He nicks stock cubes out of the kitchen cupboard, which I don't mind, but I get confused by his request for tampons.

"They make brilliant fire lighters," he explains, rolling up a hammock into a very small bag.

Because supplies of such basic items like mess tins and cups are so low in the Air Force, Guy went shopping this afternoon and bought his own titanium set, costing over fifty pounds.

"Yes I'm disgusted at being forced to buy my own kit, but it's either that or manage without when I get to the desert," he tells me.

We watch each broadcast with increasing concern (often, the first time our lads get to hear about a mission is from television news reports showing deployment or rescue exercises).

"Looks like we're off again," says Guy, heading upstairs to start packing. "Nothing would please me more than to say we're not needed, but there'll never be a world-wide outbreak of peace." Hunting through the drawers upstairs, he shouts, "Darling, have you seen my desert DPMs?"

"Might have, if I knew what they were."

"The same as my dark-green combat clothes, only sandy-coloured."

"What's DPM short for?"

"Disrupted Pattern Material."

"That is so British," I laugh. "Can't you go to war in light or dark combats – does it have to be so pompous?"

His flack jacket looks the same as a camouflage coat but it weighs a tonne, and when I try to hand it to him I can hardly lift it off the ground.

"At least you'll be safe in this," I observe, thinking he's completely bulletproof (until Guy shows me that the only Kevlar on him is a small square which just about covers his heart).

"More government cuts," he mutters.

Civilian friends call to ask Guy what the situation is and presume his lack of knowledge means he's bound to silence, believing his life to be full of excitement and danger. Far from it; he and everyone else on camp are the last to know (because Air Force communication is much slower than the more informative BBC).

Never noticed a Hercules on telly before but now I can spot

one a mile off. Guy tells me he recently watched live footage of a Hercules under sniper fire touch down briefly in Albania to rescue refugees before taking off again. People were literally fleeing for their lives, running alongside the moving aircraft, jumping up onto the lowered ramp, grasping at outstretched hands trying to pull them inside to safety.

*

Troops and equipment destined for Operation Desert Fox in Kuwait leave Lyneham on a massive scale. I lie on the bed, wondering if I could fit into his suitcase. Reading out the night-stop kit list (cheque book, NATO travel order, wash kit, shades, etc.), I write on the bottom 'pants?' since he's omitted to list them with everything else. "That's everything," I smile, handing back the list.

"Don't know when I'll be home but it shouldn't be long," Guy says as the crew bus pulls up outside our house to take him and the others away.

I sit about indoors wondering what to do with myself. Should I worry or should I just keep occupied? The noise outside my back door has become deafening with the starting of aeroplane engines.

Beth phones to say hello but really it's to ask where the Wetlands Trust exhibition panels are stored. "How are you enjoying married life?" she probes kindly.

"How would I know? Ask his wife," I snap, caught off guard, and then immediately apologise, telling her about the war situation. "He's married to Fat Albert much more than to me," I say miserably. "Can't believe I play second fiddle to forty tonnes of metal."

"Honey, the first year of marriage is always the hardest," she comforts, adding, "I found that with both of mine." And then she shouts, "Genevieve! Come down from upstairs! I hope you're not watching daytime television – it's totally unsuitable."

I giggle as she justifies her guilt to me.

"Well, so they say, but I disagree that nothing can be learnt from TV after the age of three – there's relationship counselling at ten o'clock, cookery at eleven and what to wear in a dilemma straight after. She'll be armed with all the necessary life skills."

Beth talks life into my bones, reminding me of home, and I pump information out of her about each and every one of my old colleagues. Eventually, she tells me the caterers have arrived to prepare tonight's dinner party.

"Our guests have a little boy the same age as Genevieve and I'm always looking for prospective suitors."

"Beth, Evie's only three years old!"

"So...?" she asks. "That doesn't stop the royals grooming someone for William, does it. Mark my words, there's a tomboy out there desperately wanting to climb trees and play football but the poor thing's being forced into having a leg wax and manicure because her pedigree fits. One should never miss an opportunity, Kate," she warns me, and hurriedly says goodbye.

Trying to take my mind off things, I go shopping and come back with fabric to make bathroom curtains but haven't a clue how. My material shows three fat fishes swimming along blowing bubbles (I want to give the plain-white bathroom a nautical feel). Busying myself for hours pretending I can sew really does take my mind off the activity going on outside, but I pause frequently to think how futile making curtains is compared to war.

As I proudly hang up my new blind, the phone rings: it's Jude. "Pryce's been sent to the Gulf," she says, sniffing tears away.

"So has Guy and everyone else," I reply.

"Well, I'm unsure of how I should feel. This is the first time he's gone into a hostile place. Do you fancy coming over and getting drunk?"

"Sounds great. I'm on my way."

We manage to forget our sorrows (and our loved ones) on a pub crawl, even crashing a wedding reception in the town hall so Jude can show me where she's holding her own reception in April.

*

The following morning, we wake to hear HRH The Princess of Wales making her wedding vows on Radio 4.

"They're talking about her in the past tense – she must be dead," Jude observes.

We sit glued to the TV for the rest of the morning. What a heartbreaking day! I drive home in torrential rain, unable to see more than a few feet in front of my car (convinced it's Diana venting sadness over her country home not so many miles away).

Supergluing large plastic tiles onto the bathroom wall, I whinge at myself in the mirror. "Should've listened to Hattie and married a builder."

Guy can find his way out of a jungle and fly an aeroplane, but he hates DIY. Well, I want, need, demand a shower in the bathroom and it hasn't happened, so stuff him – I'll do it myself (with some plastic tubing fashioned into a shower hose thing…). Eventually, after much swearing, I congratulate myself on another botch job – "Way to go, girl!" – and wander downstairs to celebrate with chocolate.

I sound like Princess Diana when speaking to dad later on. "Well, there are three of us in this marriage, you see – me, him and Albert."

"How's he getting on with the new Squadron?" dad queries.

"Oh, he's away a lot and always comes home stressed out from a heavy workload or the sheer number of hours he's been flying," I say. "But dad, I've never seen him so alive; he lives for flying, especially the low-level stuff. Landing on grass-strip runways in volatile countries with surface-to-air missile threats is quite normal. Albert's always the first in and last out of any war zone, so the crews take off at short notice and often end up at destinations with a hostile reception. They average sixteen hours a day and are offered Red Bull to drink in the cockpit. Snipers take shots at them coming in to land and sometimes sorties are flown in aircraft with patched-up wings.

"And he's constantly at the beck and call of a ringing telephone, disappearing at a moment's notice to attend briefings or meetings before packing a suitcase and going away for days on end, leaving me on my own."

"Er, well make sure you look after yourself, sweetheart," dad advises, unable to put things instantly right like he used to. "Sad news about Diana, eh?" he adds, changing the subject. "Suppose you'll be watching the wedding?"

"You mean funeral?"

"Whatever, love, whatever. By the time you get to my age they're all the same."

*

I feel a shiver of envy as a minibus pulls up next door to return Gerry, just back from exercise, and I hear his sleepy children cheering "Daddy!" a few minutes later as the bus pulls away. I can't believe I get jealous of little children.

And I never realised just how much hard work it is to love someone – before marriage, I was totally selfish with my time, coming and going when I pleased, and now I have to make an effort and constantly think about someone else.

Remembering to say "I love you" to Guy or just giving him a cuddle to let him know I'm there for him takes a lot of effort when rushing through a busy lifestyle. (But if I don't do it, I'm worried we'll turn into housemates, not soul mates.) However, saying that, working full-time does mean we're often too tired to get excited about anything, and I sometimes get home to find Guy fast asleep on the sofa. Instead of cooking dinner, I fall asleep next to him until it's too late to prepare a meal. So we grab some cereal an hour before bedtime, then go upstairs saying something like:

"Fancy a bonk?"

"Go on, then. But it's your turn to go on top."

"Aww, do I have to do all the work? I'm too tired."

"Me too. Night night."

SEVEN

Time ticks on. I hate temping and I'm stuck with different 'placements' every few days at the moment.

Just realised I have two worlds: the first one is in Yorkshire, where friends who know me live, and the second one is here, the Patch, where friends who don't really know me live (and still won't when we leave).

I check my e-mail – there's one from Guy in the Gulf. It reads:

Popped over to the American BX yesterday (shopping mall). It's quite small but they've got some useful things, so I bought a little compass to go on my watchstrap (the one I already have is quite safe in the bedside drawer near to where you are now). Went back to the US camp later on to go to their bar. They're limited to three drinks per person per day (poor spams) but you can always trust the Americans to bring good music to war – had one of those 'this is odd' moments as we stood outside in the desert drinking beer listening to Pink Floyd on the tannoy, surrounded by aeroplanes, trucks, tents and troops with guns (we have one pistol), looking at the only Portakabin they've got, which is a Pizza Express. It was quiet (1930hrs), and the spams, being not quite as thick as we all think they are, normally do their bar at around 2300hrs so that at midnight they can get another three drinks…

Left there after we'd had our three and went to the Brit bar in our camp. It's only open from 1900–2200hrs, but drinks are unlimited. Not the best of plans from our lords and masters, as it just makes everyone power-drink while they can get served. Left the bar when it shut, and went back to my room with some of the

*boys for an illegal drinking party. Woke up this morning with a
hangover and some empty bottles I've got to try and get rid of.*

*Anyway, we're off on a trip tonight so I'm going to get some
more rest now. Love and miss you – always, your Guy.*

The doorbell rings and I leave the computer whirring away
to find my neighbour holding a hat full of paper.

"Pick a country," says Bernadette, holding the hat under my
nose.

"Why?" I ask.

"I'm having a pot-luck supper. Each card has the name of a
country on it. You pick one and then cook a dish typical of that
country. Everyone gets to eat something different – it's pot luck.
Just bake a cake if you can't do anything else," she suggests.

"But home-made cakes are never as good as shop-bought," I
say, taking a card from the hat. I pick France. "Oh no, I can't
cook French. Can't I have Italy? Pleeease?" I beg.

After much persuasion, Bernadette lets me have what I want
– pasta (easy-peasy). However, working full-time means I can't
spare a minute to cook anything; also, being culinarily inept
means I don't know where to start preparing anything. I want
to order a pizza from the local takeaway and have it delivered
on my arrival, but decide this might be slightly insensitive.
Instead, I choose a large pepperoni deep-pan from the
supermarket and take along a chilled bottle of Chianti.

"Bernadette, can I put this in your oven? It's still frozen in the
middle," I shout through the kitchen door, thinking I'm the first
to arrive.

A hush descends on the room as Bernadette smiles and takes
my half-baked meal from me (it's suddenly obvious everyone
else went to great efforts to make their delicious dishes).

Introduce myself to everyone and drool over a dining-room
table simply groaning with sumptuous and lovingly prepared
food (lose all desire to eat any of my paltry offering but
eventually try a bit, just to look willing). I don't think I've made
a lasting gastronomic impression with this lot, but at least Rex
the dog likes my leftovers (three of the four pieces I didn't eat).

*

Excitement bubbles up inside me when 'Wheels' finally pulls up at our door – Guy's home! Contemplate running outside to kiss him passionately, but instead dash to the loo for a wee.

One hour later the phone rings. "Hello, Mrs Willesley. It's the Squadron here. Just keeping up with 'kinforming' and thought you should know that Guy's delayed for three days."

"Well, would you like to tell him yourself as he's standing next to me?" I ask the duty exec.

Guy takes hold of the receiver to hear, "Oh shit, who's down route then?"

His suitcase is full of combs, shower caps and cakes of smelly soap nicked from hotel bathrooms. Relaxing in the bath together, Guy grudgingly compliments my tiling job, then asks, "Nice new blinds, but are we on the *Titanic*?" My three fat fishes are swimming upside down – I've muddled up the material on the sewing machine!

Ordering him to take a turn at the tap end, I comment on the unusual coincidence of children's ages on the base. "They seem to have been born just after a war," I note.

"You're not wrong, Kate," he answers. "Nature, or needing to leave something of yourself behind. Flying over dodgy countries sitting on your flak jacket makes you want to procreate – or shit yourself."

After our soak, I forgive his suitcase for stubbing my toe (and Guy for dumping crates of beer, fake watches and kit everywhere) because I'm desperate for sex again (yes, of course we did it in the bath). During orgasm, the thought flashes through my mind of how I'd cope if he did die in action. I deserve an Oscar nomination for my carnal acting, intensified as it was by imaginary grief. However, nanoseconds afterwards, I remove my rose-tinted love goggles to see dirty washing, jack boots, dog tags and flight bags everywhere. I begin to imagine a small, neat widow's cottage with full wine rack and king-sized vibrator by the bed.

Guy interrupts my thoughts, asking, "Kate, can you do me a favour and stop wearing those padded, push-up bras? It's so confusing – I put my hand on your tits and keep going for four minutes until I meet flesh."

"Poor you," I say to him while staring at my breasts, which are pointing at my knees, then vehemently answer, "Never."

*

Guy's been advised to attend an administration course called Individual Studies School (ISS) to stand him in good stead for when he goes before the Captain's board. But he hates admin and curses the air blue moaning about the pedantic rules of memo-writing. The course is intensive: a written communication programme designed to enlighten pupils in all aspects of Air Force administration, including the spacing of margins in letters, correct grammar usage and organising VIP visits.

Aircrew very rarely organise royal visits or get involved in station operations unless they've been given a 'secondary duty' such as writing the Squadron history or running the Squadron shop.

It's ironic that those willing to be Officer Commanding Niff Naff and Trivia (paperwork) or in charge of bogs and drains, as Guy refers to secondary duties, find promotion comes sooner than those only wanting to fly aeroplanes.

"Guy, shall we have a baby?" I ask.

"I joined to fly aeroplanes, not desks," he snaps at me from the computer, ignoring my dramatic request, and offers to do the weekly shop just to escape the latest task (and discussing parenthood with me). I jump at the chance of him fetching and carrying groceries, so send him off with a list for:

milk
bread
coffee
something for dinner
baby

He returns far too moody to talk to, grumbling about the fictitious scenario they've set him, but I hang around, trying to thin the atmosphere a bit, and read his latest assignment:

United Kingdom Command (UKC) is responsible for all front-line AC in the UK. HQ 101 Group is responsible for strike/attack. The

> Station Commander is Group Captain B Boss and you are Flight
> Lieutenant J Bloggs. It is 0900 hours on (-date-). As Officer
> Commanding Financial Management and Plans Flight (FMPF)
> you are responsible for co-ordinating the arrangements for visits
> to the Station. On this occasion for the forthcoming visit of His
> Majesty King Samad of Narem to 306 Squadron on (-date-). You
> are to advise on the security implications of His Majesty's visit.
>
> Candidates need to supply a full procedural account for the royal
> visitor including guard of honour inspection, fly-past and police
> movement with all correspondence shown in minute form.

No wonder he's pissed off (and producing a few more grey
hairs, I suddenly see). Also notice he's worried we won't be
able to afford a house of our own because prices are rising so
fast (he's started house-hunting so that as soon as he makes
Captain we can move).

Phone Isobel and confide in her about being broody. She
comforts me, saying, "Military marriages are lonely, sis – it's
only natural to want someone else around." She reminds me
that babies, husbands and contentment come at the high price
of three in a marriage – "You, him and work…Either that or
have an affair," she suggests.

*

Guy's volunteered to host the 47 Squadron Co-pilots section
barbecue in our back garden.

"*How* many?" I gasp when he tells me the numbers.

Lucky we've put a beer fridge in the shed (giving meaning
to the expression 'a shed load of beer'). After visiting family in
Bristol, Matt and Dawn call in to see us and get roped into
party preparations. Updating me with the latest office gossip,
Dawn makes all the food as I potter uselessly around tidying
up. Matt happily invites everyone else in the street to join us.

Someone carries in two demijohns of Kokkineai (pronounced
'kock-in-elly') and starts pouring glasses for people. Kokkineai
is definitely an acquired taste (helps to drink it shortly after
consuming lots of beer when all sense of taste has gone). It's a
Cypriot drink, similar to sherry. One large plastic jug costs two

pounds (surely that says it all?). I don't fancy any myself and stick with gin and tonic.

Later, as I'm taking some big, white, empty jugs to our rubbish bin, some bloke yells at me, "What on earth are you doing with those empties, wench?"

"Tidying up, Pete. Why?" I reply, without looking up, instantly recognising the rogue.

"Well, stop immediately and give them to Guy. He'll take them back on his next Cyprus trip to get the deposit back." (I can't believe it – they take the empties all the way back to Cyprus!)

By now, the party's really going with a swing, and I notice lots of new babies being happily bounced up and down on their fathers' knees (funny how they seem to be everywhere I look at the moment). Someone comments on how ugly our garden is, mainly because the Irish Navigator who lived in the house before us decided to 'weed by four star' and poured petrol up and down the borders before setting them alight to save himself some backache. Desolate is a good description. When Samantha and George left, they told us to help ourselves to any plants and shrubs we fancied before the next family moves in. Now seems like the perfect opportunity, so Matt borrows a spade and starts digging.

He shouts over next-door's fence, "Do you like this, Kate?" holding up a holly bush.

Everyone shouts back "Yes", laughing as he attempts to pull up their apple tree, but his endeavours are not fruitful and the tree remains standing (at 45 degrees).

Guy sprints across the road to see an old colleague walking past, saying they flew wet dreams (Jet Streams) together at RAF Finningly in Doncaster. His wife's friendly enough and they accept our invitation to join us in the garden. Introducing myself to them both, I'm stunned to find out she's called Marina and admire her fat, contented baby gurgling away in the pram.

"Not Danny's Marina?" I think aloud, amazed at such a small world.

Guy laughs as Tony tells him that just before they left

Finningly, they watched fitters install a state-of-the-art fire-detection system and then the government closed the station down, leaving it to fester and decay.

"Why couldn't they use it for something – like a hotel?" I ask, and he replies that suggestions were made that it should be turned into a prison but officials told the council that the barracks were unfit for human habitation and inmates would more than likely start a riot.

I take the chance of offering Marina some food and she asks, ashen-faced, how come I know Danny (aha, I think – so it is her…). Explaining the Siobhan connection to her, she interrupts, saying, "Sometimes, I wish I'd never left him, but I took a chance."

I envy her past relationship with Danny, imagining her with him, seeing him smile. I realise these feelings are wrong, but I can't work out why I'm slightly jealous.

The boys are talking shop as usual and weigh up the pros and cons of base life. Pete points out that one perk of living on a military camp is that not far away from the main gates are all the takeaway establishments you could ever want.

Guy thinks the reason many of these places thrive is because after a long day of flying (be it an aeroplane or a desk), people who 'live in' the Officers' Mess are required to change into a suit and tie for dinner. And the dining room is only open between 6pm and 8pm, so crews returning late can't get a decent hot meal because there's no one to cook it for them.

"Air Force caterers came under the government axe and got contracted out," he moans, "which is a load of crap because the civvies disappear after their contractual hours. Crews returning late ask for a sandwich but get told, 'Sorry mate, I'm not paid to work after eight o'clock at night.'"

I nod and look suitably appalled as he explains that many of the lads want to leave the Mess and enjoy life without the restrictions of outdated rules and conduct.

"If the Mess offered a proper home everyone would stay, but lack of funds means it's a poor imitation of the old days and the boys live off Pot Noodles in their rooms."

Pricey says that when he lived in the Mess, the Station

Commander (or Staish) made a rule that no one was allowed in the bar wearing a flying suit after 7pm. This killed the bar instantly.

"Well, that's just fine for the Staish," he says, "who can leave the Mess, go back to his house and wear jeans, but the Officers' Mess bar is my front room. I want to have a beer over debrief in my work clothes before going to bed and now I can't because he lost the plot. Bring back the Scruffs Bar, when we could have a pint in peace – those who wanted to be smart went into the Mess and those who 'lived in' relaxed with a pint in everyday clothes in the Scruffs Bar."

Collapse into bed after everyone's left, saying, "Guy, please can we start a family?" knowing it would alleviate the loneliness I feel when he's away and give me someone to concentrate on.

Guy wants to know why the interest in babies all of a sudden, saying, "It'll cost a fortune, deprive us of sleep and put us through hell before growing up into a miserable teenager who crashes my car and then says he hates me."

"Aww, go on, darling," I beg. "You're going to need a new liver soon with all this partying. Please...we could grow one for spares."

*

Torture myself reading *Period Living* and *Country Homes* magazines knowing we can only afford a pokey little house. I only want the simple things in life – it's not like I want to be hugely rich and famous or anything. I just want to buy good organic food, not extra-value butter (or wine at £10 a bottle, not £2.99), a husband that loves me, a baby, a big house and a flash car...

Start work in yet another office near Swindon and drive through villages to get there, drooling at mansions flashing past. Leave the car in a town-centre car park and study estate agent windows on my way to the latest office. How many earth pounds do they want for that shed? I think aloud, staring at a four-bedroomed, detached squat in the middle of a field carpet-bombed with executive boxes.

Suddenly have an urge to say my prayers. "Dear God, I thought I'd be in a big house by now but I'll be dead soon – so please sort it out otherwise it'll be too late to enjoy it. Oh yes, and can you make Guy help around the house – or at least empty the kitchen bin occasionally – and talk to me without being prompted, and give Caroline an easy birth. Thanks a lot…Yours faithfully."

On dangerous ground; try to take myself in hand – at lunchtime in a bakery, I heard myself saying, "Cheese and onion for Lisa, tuna for me, banana muffin for Jo and a packet of crisps, please," before going to a local park and scoffing the lot. It's because temping is boring, tedious work, although I've met some fairly friendly staff. I'm shocked to see that I can never get away from judgmental people ready to jump in feet-first with misconceptions. Chatting away to one girl, she asks where I live and I find out her husband is also AF (Air Force) and that she lives on the base.

"Whereabouts are you?" she asks.

"Daffy. And you?"

"Oh, not far away," she mumbles, showing less interest in me by the second because in one word I've informed her that I'm an Officer's wife.

Tried to get hold of Guy via 'the system' but no luck. He's at the Squadron, and normally I'm put straight through to him, but the government's made a few 'improvements' (cuts) to the telephone system. I usually just phone up the relevant office and if he's not there then someone in the same room shouts, "Phone call for Willesley," or, knowing his whereabouts, takes a message.

Now that the telephone exchange is centralised, we must go through a civilian operator based on the other side of the country and they don't understand military jargon (it seems the government are trying to turn an armed force into a business call centre). So, if Guy's in 'flight planning' before going on a trip code-named 314 Bravo, I have to know the exact extension number or end up having a conversation along the lines of:

"Hello, MOD telephone exchange. Can I help you?"

"Yes please. I'm trying to get in touch with my husband, Flight Lieutenant Willesley on 47 Squadron." (I'd usually be connected straight away because Lyneham's exchange knew every inch of the base, but those days are gone.)

"Where is 47 Squadron, please?"

"You tell me, you're the operator! Sorry, I'm just amazed you don't know. It's at RAF Lyneham."

"Please hold."

So I hold for five long minutes before getting cut off – aaargh!

And that's just me, a wife trying to find out which day my husband would be home. Imagine service personnel needing to contact other military stations to organise sorties, missions and VIP visits. The whole system is a nightmare.

Pete had a similar conversation with an operator when he tried to get through to the Air Force's only parachute training school, RAF Brize Norton. The operator insisted there was no such place as RAF Brize Norton near Oxford (it's been there since before the Second World War). Unbelievably, these changes are meant to improve communications, but instead they haven't a clue; no wonder those trying to follow procedure complain.

Guy agrees with my anger and explains that the only answer is irony. Each crew has a mobile phone held by the Captain.

"One engineer programmed our voice-activated phone to dial Ops, operations, when 'Tosser' is shouted, and yelling 'Wanker' autodials Ascot Ops. No matter how many times the phone gets wiped, it always comes back reprogrammed."

I tell him I'm not really hungry (but don't mention my lunchtime sandwich frenzy) so we make a light supper of toast on the log fire. He's initiated a sex ban until I stop nagging for babies. I agree eagerly, seeing the fatal flaw in his plan.

*

New neighbours, Harry and Grace Barker plus baby, move in next door, complaining (quite rightly) about the poor state of their garden. At least we had the decency to blush after Matt dug it up.

Guy walks in from work and starts to empty the overflowing kitchen bin. I stare at him in shock until he demands to know what's so wrong.

"I'm witnessing divine intervention," I mutter, and explain my prayers.

"Kate, just because I'm emptying a stinking, over-stuffed, dirty bin does not mean it's an act of God," he snaps (but I know better).

He's off to a dining-in night tonight, so I'm going to spend a few hours on the phone. I'm learning fast – dining-in nights are functions hosted by each Squadron or section, served in honour of historical events and sometimes just to thank people for their services (people get 'dined-in' or 'dined-out' depending on if they're coming or going). Ladies guest nights are held frequently to show appreciation to us wives for all the crap we put up with: partners being away, holidays cancelled, birthdays missed, etc. And it's a good way of keeping up morale. Tonight is SODS – Station Officers' Dining Society.

Guy comes home blind drunk but I carry on reading in the lounge, pretending not to notice his giggling. He declares an immense love for me but then confesses of a deeper love for his bed before stumbling upstairs.

I watch a film until I think it's safe to follow, knowing he'll be fast asleep, and find his immaculate uniform neatly laid out under the covers (including shoes) and him stark naked on the floor, snoring. He's put his Mess kit to bed (and tucked it in) instead of himself.

I watch my freezing-cold Peter Pan sleep and silently scream at him to grow up. "Give me something I crave – a family of our own."

*

Listen intently to Guy recite last night's events and tenderly nurse his hangover with a bacon sandwich.

The Wing Commander told Pete to spice up the evening, so he followed his orders to the letter. Underneath each tablemat, he placed a somewhat saucy picture (complaining dignitaries said it was porn, but Pete insists it was harmless fun) for guests to discover throughout dinner. During the speeches, he attached a blow-up doll to a remote-control car, driving her up and down behind the top table. The Wing Commander, oblivious to the hilarious distraction for a few seconds, thought they were laughing at his jokes.

Try more nagging about parenthood, hoping he'll say yes out of boredom. He says he can't stand babies and if we are ever unfortunate enough to have them he would want nothing to do with 'it' until two years old (aha – signs of a crack). He sighs with relief when the phone rings, and goes upstairs to prepare for a sim (simulator) check.

"This abstaining lark can't continue for ever," I argue. "Bet you're having a tug every day with left-handed websites or wank mags – I know you're cheating!"

*

Have taken to phoning my sister on an evening while watching television. We can sit through a whole episode of *Heartbeat* without saying a word but sometimes comment about the storyline in appropriate places.

"You do what?" Guy asks amazed when I tell him why the phone bill's so high.

"Well, she's on her own for a month as Hugh's away again and you're away too, so we phone each other up and watch telly together. We manage to um and ah now and again to let each other know we're still there."

Guy starts to slowly hit the wall with his forehead and declares he's off to Happy Hour. Any service personnel (not civilian) can attend Happy Hour in the Officers' Mess at five o'clock on a Friday afternoon. Sometimes a family Happy Hour gets organised and everyone, including kids, turns up (Guy reckons more issues get sorted out in Happy Hour than in a whole day of work time).

An unwritten rule for military wives is that you never, ever telephone the Officers' Mess bar and ask to speak to your husband while he's having a drink with the boys – unless you're in the later stages of childbirth or about to suffer some sort of gruesome fate. Anyone who answers the telephone to 'the missus' is in for a serious ribbing about being under the thumb. So the bar becomes the equivalent of assumed male territory, a kind of gentlemen's club.

"You act like a pack of rutting stags with your self-opinionated bravado," I say, amazed at the gall he has telling me not to phone.

I join him late evening (I'm a civilian, not allowed in any earlier, remember) and find a bunch of guys wearing flying suits and blues around the piano singing, "Bye, bye Miss American pie!" out of tune at the tops of their voices.

"Catch up!" they order, handing me three gin and tonics.

A butch-looking woman wearing a large ID badge walks into the room shouting "Selrink" over and over again.

Recognising the name, I wave at her and nudge the drunken bloke beside me, saying, "Wake up, mate, I think your taxi's arrived."

Sitting up, he replies, "That's no taxi driver – that's my wife."

"Oh…sorry," I mutter, and notice on closer inspection that her name badge reads 'Dr Selrink, Royal United Hospital, Bath'.

At midnight, we stagger home and are passed by a bloke on a bicycle with ten pizzas balanced on the handlebars, secured by his chin. He's going in the vague direction of the Mess but is never gonna make it…

*

I come home to find Guy packing again.

"Please will you leave a wash kit in the bathroom so it looks like you live here," I beg, watching him repack his un-emptied suitcase. This time he's taking part in Exercise Cossack Steppe, a tactical operation involving non-NATO troops from the Ukraine and Poland. He starts to act excited, pretending to be Dr Zhivago – apparently, it's the first joint airborne exercise in years between a former Soviet bloc country and us, little old Blighty!

"I can tell you, but zen I would 'ave to kill you," he purrs in a Russian accent when I ask what's going on.

"Well, take some vitamin tablets and don't go over any nuclear plants," I suggest. "And bring me back a vibrator – I'm going mad."

After much messing around, I find out that over the next week, he'll fly a three-ship formation direct from England to a DZ at low-level in the Ukraine and from there to Krakow in Poland. The most public part of the exercise involves a multinational, demonstration drop of troops and equipment in front of a VIP audience, with our three Hercules being sandwiched between Polish and Ukranian Ilyushin 76s.

He leaves on the crew bus; I watch TV. At least one of us has job satisfaction, I think to myself, amused by his excitement.

Gwen and Jude phone to ask if I fancy going out for a drink and, with it being a school night, I offer to drive. Halfway to the pub, my car breaks down, and reluctantly we call the fourth emergency service. A mechanic checks my car thoroughly, then politely informs us that we've run out of petrol! (How stupid – I nearly die of embarrassment. But even worse, how will I tell Guy?)

*

Join another temping agency and change the notice in our kitchen headed 'Where is Kate this week?' (a list of work details in case of emergency) – the note changes as frequently as my assignments. I hate temping and have learnt to be nondescript in order to keep assignments. However, I made a new friend today: I met a lovely lady called Amber, who was exceptionally kind and bothered about me (Annabel would say, "If she were a horse, you'd buy her"). Turns out both our men work for 'Auntie Betty' (HRH) and we have a lot in common; the more we chat, the firmer our friendship becomes. Funny, it feels like I have a confidant – someone who's already been through it (a forces marriage) and is still with her husband years later despite all the shit.

Getting home early, I hit play on the answering machine to hear Caroline announce her exciting news. My legs give way and I fall onto the sofa, pressing erase before she says the word 'pregnant' (so that's why she kept throwing up during fashion show rehearsals). Why is everyone else having babies and not me?

Guy manages to make a quick phone call home tonight.

"Hi, darling. Guess where I am – and be quick, this line's a bit unpredictable." He sounds muffled.

"Well just tell me, then," I reply, uninterested, and quickly think fast about how to tell him I've wasted one roadside recovery with an empty petrol tank (premiums go up after three call-outs).

"Seventy miles north-east of Odessa," he says.

"Yeah, and?" I ask, wondering what the big deal is.

"I'm in the home of the Black Sea Fleet. Bloody hell, woman, ten years ago I'd have to be James Bond to get in here!" he yells.

"Cool." I suddenly appreciate the enormity of his statement and am grateful he doesn't have time to hear about my petrol escapade.

Russia is so basic for a massive world power. He tells me that the crew have been to a variety of destinations, including one airfield where air traffic control flatly refused to believe that three RAF Hercules aeroplanes had arrived and where a second crew was stranded after another aircraft had consumed the airfield's entire fuel stock. Guy couldn't believe they'd run out of fuel – these things just don't happen in Britain…

*

Receive an e-mail from Guy telling me that due to the speed differences and fuel considerations of the various aircraft taking part, all crews attended a detailed mass brief – held in Russian and then translated into another dialect so that the Polish interpreter could translate it into English!

Understandably, the brief took longer than anticipated, but the crews are happy with the sortie. Thankfully, they made it to the DZ safely and on time, which was fortunate, mainly because the UK defence minister and his Polish and Ukranian counterparts (as well as several television crews) were watching in the audience.

Later, during another quick phone call, Guy tells me that a member of the 'intelligence' branch has joined them on the trip.

"That all sounds rather cloak-and-dagger," I reply.

"Not at all," Guy explains. "It's just another branch, darling, nothing special. These people are statisticians, observing operations, data-gathering for future reference. Obviously, with a job title of 'intelligence', the poor bloke has to put up with endless banter, and yes – we label him a spy."

Checking into the hotel, Guy had to give a verbal headcount to the less-than-fluent receptionist…"Six crew," he says, looking for the booking details. "Captain, Co, Nav, Eng, Loadie, and Spy."

"Can you please stop calling me that," the Intelligence Officer complains. "I am not – repeat, not – a spy."

"You, sir, lie like cheap Shanghai watch," the crew all chant together.

"Okay, okay, sorry to offend you, 007," Guy chuckles, trying to placate the man.

It tickles him that everywhere they go, an entourage of surreptitious, non-English speaking 'guides' follow. If the crew happen to mention they want to go for a beer, a taxi suddenly pulls up offering a lift to the nearest bar. The same thing happens when they want to return to barracks.

"It feels a bit sinister," he says.

*

Every time Guy goes away with the boys he comes home a different person, I think, sorting through the usual heap of dirty green kit.

I hate waiting for this gung-ho, chauvinistic oaf to leave and for the gentle, loving Guy to show up again (normally happens after a couple of days, when he realises I am Kate, his wife, a female, and not some doll to grope immediately on walking through the door).

I even heard him say to the crew bus driver, "Thanks for the lift, mate. The next 'bang' you hear will be my suitcase hitting the floor." Ugh!

Banter is a way of life in the Air Force, and unless serious work issues are being discussed, humorous insults become par for the course. Women must be sharper than their male counterparts or immune to taking insults.

Guy boasts, "We're cruising at twenty thousand feet and had been airborne for around two hours when a girlie Loadie called Pang comes onto the flight deck, asking, 'Are we nearly there yet?' And I said, 'Yeah, off you get.'"

"Why is she called Pang?" I ask, totally missing the joke.

"She's so ugly – 'pang' is the noise an imaginary spade made when it hit her face."

"That's so mean," I think aloud, repulsed by him.

Met Amber's husband 'Titch' this evening at aerobics. Being a bit thick, I thought 'Titch' meant just that, so when Amber walks into the gym, I presume the short, squat bloke following behind is her husband.

"Hello there, I'm Kate. Nice to meet you," I say to the little man.

"Nice to meet you too, Kate," the giant behind him bellows, giving me a bear-hug.

*

Today, I am incredibly aware that Guy comes first and that I'm not 'me' anymore. I'm an appendage; even our house is just a storeroom for Guy's kit – some of it is still in the hall from the day we moved in. I don't want to live in a palace; I only ask not to run an assault course every time I walk through the front door (I know he's busy with Air Force life, but for goodness' sake, I'm not his mother). And why does he always walk past things on the stairs, leaving me to run up and down after him? Aaargh!

I can't believe how he takes it all for granted and expects daily blow jobs in return. Time to read the small print on that wedding certificate, matey: respect me or lose me. Does he want a wife or a waitress?

I rant away on the phone to mum. "He dumps books, bags and boots in the hall, and I decide what's for dinner every night," I moan, angry that marriage is a rude awakening and not at all how I dreamt it would be.

"Your father's just the same, love," she sighs.

With Guy away on duty so much, I'm left to take care of the more mundane tasks, like washing and ironing. He always returns home from 'route' treating the house as a hotel (which annoys me immensely), and today I've had enough.

"Or you could just clean the toilet with his toothbrush."

"Bye, mum."

Headset bags, maps, jackboots and green kit are spewed around for days on end. I find myself jumping to attention when he addresses me because it takes a while for him to get out of 'lads on tour' mode, and then he's off away yet again. And, I wrote 150 wedding thank-you letters (he managed two). Oh God, I miss my old life. I long for the good old days of being a girlfriend, when he devoted time just to me, being thoughtful, attentive, and could fix anything.

What 'they' don't tell you when you get married is that the witty, gorgeous, sensitive boyfriend you fell madly in love with is a closet slob, still hoards old beer mats, leaves wet towels on the bed after showering, has old suitcases full of junk, dumps 'important' bits of paper everywhere for weeks, complains his shoes go 'missing' from the lounge because you've moved them into the porch – and that's just the tip of the iceberg.

This morning he asked, "Kate, have you seen my quarterly report?"

"No, where did you leave it last?"

"On the coffee table."

"When?"

"About four months ago."

So I throw a blue fit. I need him to understand I'm not going to be taken for granted and intend to drive home the point (with a wedgie). As he cycles off to the Squadron, bin bags get filled with coats, bags, piles of unopened envelopes – in fact everything I can see dumped in the middle of a room or fast becoming an obstruction. My toes can't take being hit with his suitcase anymore (kept at the foot of our bed). Once it's all bagged up, I decide that the garage is going to be Guy's overflowing storeroom. To help it on it's way, I chuck it all out of the bedroom window onto the grass in front of the house.

Returning at lunchtime, he instantly bursts into a rage on the lawn, furious with me for moving precious kit, and I scream back at him from an upstairs window to sort it out – he's a slob and should put it away.

"You couldn't wait to marry me," he yells, picking up items of clothing and black bags.

"Marry, yes," I yell, aiming a boot at him from our bedroom window, "not clean and have to constantly clear up after."

Someone in uniform cycles past and calls out cheerily, "What-oh," narrowly avoiding Guy's other airborne boot.

Crying is such a relief; tears frighten him, as the crew don't cry openly (it's just not cricket to show you're upset in front of the chaps).

"Your next wife won't look after you as well as I do, you slob," I yell at him. "If you don't make an effort, I'm leaving."

"Promises, promises…" he replies, and continues dodging his kit as it lands all over our garden.

But this anger goes deeper than him being untidy, and through my sobs I insist he pulls his weight with the housework (but he just tells me to work a sixteen-hour day like he does and then complain). I only want small things, like him to make a decision on what's for dinner instead of asking me every night, and generally to start playing a part in this two-man team. I cook, clean, make beds up ready for guests and rush around organising dinner parties while working full-time without an acknowledgement from him – I feel like just another piece of his kit to pick up or discard whenever it suits him.

Why does the woman end up as a dumping ground for work stress and domestic chores? (I'm playing the role of his mother, not his lover.) Well, enough is enough; learning to live together is like walking through a minefield. (I think he was actually annoyed when he noticed that bins had to be physically emptied otherwise they overflowed and that his Mess 'bin fairy' had long gone.) I'm convinced there are two breeds of men – the first is an alien struggling to integrate properly (helpful), and the other had his mum to cook, clean and wash for him, moulding a domestic degenerate incapable of thoughtfulness.

He's been used to living in the Officers' Mess: to being served and waited on, to having his bed made for him every day, to bins being emptied, to sinks being cleaned, and generally to being doted on by his 'batty'. ('Batty' is modern slang for cleaner. Back in the days of the world wars, each Officer had a batman who would shine shoes, prepare uniforms and take on a role no different to that of a secretary or butler. Nowadays, modern messes employ groups of cleaners but still call them batties.)

"Why aren't you listening to me?"

Throwing the black sacks into the car, he snarls, "I came home to tell you I'm off on route again tonight and now I'm late for flight planning."

"Good," I scream. "Next time, stop dumping things everywhere and you might be early."

*

Alone again. Phone rings. It's Siobhan. "Going clubbing in an hour, so thought I'd ring and see how you are."

"Clubbing," I say wistfully. "I haven't been out on the town for ages. Every party we go to is with Guy's work; in fact, everything we do involves Guy's work."

"Yes, but you're happily married and I'm destined to walk this earth alone watching couples kiss, before dying a spinster – I go out partying and devour twenty-year-olds to help pass the time."

"But Shiv, your life is magical – you spend hours putting make-up on, and have no domestic ties and total freedom to do whatever you want. I have to iron a stack of clothes, run around after a tired, impatient husband and worry what's for dinner."

"You okay?" Siobhan suddenly asks.

"Oh yeah, fine. I just never realised how hard this marriage lark would be – a tremendous amount of emotional give for not a lot of response in return. Guy only ever speaks when spoken to."

"He's a bloke, dear," Siobhan offers in explanation.

Thankful for an understanding ear, I carry on. "I know, but a 'Mrs' will always covet the lifestyle of a 'Miss' because you get to be selfish instead of chief ego masseur to a weary spouse. I'm telling you, Shiv, don't be so quick to give it all up – the hidden cost is paradise."

"Ooh, you have got it bad. How long is he away for this time?" she asks.

"A week, a day, a month, who cares – he's always away. I'm fed up. I sacrificed my independence for a knight who ain't so shiny. Sorry, Shiv, I shouldn't go on like this, but it's just so lonely living with over two thousand people. I wish I'd known the day we moved here that his job took priority, even to the point of owning our home. But being besotted, I chose to ignore his work until it was too late – I've become his mistress."

Siobhan thinks for a while and says, "But your wedding was the stuff dreams are made of. How dare you ruin my perception of happiness – if you're not happy then I've got nothing to hope for."

"Eh?"

"Because it doesn't exist," she continues. "Life is crap, men are shits and I'm better off on my own."

"Yup, that's about it," I say.

Pouring myself a gin, I confess to her, "I've thought about leaving him, just to shake him up, but since he's never home I don't think he'd notice. Anyway, I married him...I'm stuck with him. If I do leave and find someone else I'll only have to go to the bother of breaking the next one in. Most men are genetically lazy."

"Danny's not," Siobhan adds, and I remember his immaculate house.

"Oh why didn't I marry him – why did I have to fall for Guy – what am I going to do?" I mutter.

"Get a cleaner."

"What a fantastic idea! I should've thought of that hours ago. Shiv, you've just answered my prayers. Thanks for listening."

"No problem," she says. "Any time. And believe me, I'm sticking with spinsterhood rather than sign on the marital dotted line."

*

Wake to the sound of gunfire and remember it's shooting practice on the range at weekends. Guy's away so I spend a bit of time in Amber's pottery studio making terrible clay figures, drinking wine while watching her produce works of art. Her two gorgeous sons are home from boarding school (much to my delight) and I meet Robbie, a tall, silent nineteen-year-old, and Curt, who's seriously smooth for his seventeen years.

"Hello boys," I drool in true Joanna Lumley, *Ab Fab* style, trying to refrain from hugging them too tightly. (I want to immerse myself in Amber and her family, as they bridge the gap left by my own relatives miles away. As soon as I leave, I crave more.)

Amber puts me in touch with a cleaner and I arrange to meet her tonight.

The minute we meet I know she's magic. Stephanie actually interviewed me! Apparently, she doesn't do cookers (well done; neither would I) and I think this is going to be the beginning of a beautiful friendship – I name her my 'fairy godmother' (my rocky, short-lived marriage could be saved and I might start to love Guy again).

*

Guy returns from a trip to Bosnia with less respect for a few 'top brass' politicians who insist on arriving in theatre with all the trappings of a celebrity. Bringing our boys home from long periods away, he listens in amazement as they tell him of one highbrow Cabinet minister who travelled to the war zone accompanied by paparazzi on board a VC10 jet, enjoying a flight and sumptuous lunch at the taxpayers' expense. The minister left the aircraft and sauntered across the tarmac, completely ignoring soldiers standing to attention. Little did he know that the SAS were surrounding the airfield on sniper alert and that two of them were having the following conversation:

Soldier one: "Isn't that the idiot…"

Soldier two: "Yup. Arrived in style. Did you see him walk straight past our lads?"

Soldier one: "Yeah, wanker."

Soldier two: "You got your sights trained on him?"

Soldier one: "Yup."

Soldier two: "So you could take him out now?"

Soldier one: "If I wanted to."

Soldier two: "Hmm."

I bet that if the minister in question had known that this conversation was taking place, he might've made a bit more of an effort to acknowledge those who give up family life and comfort to serve in hostile situations. During the first Gulf conflict, people in America wore T-shirts exclaiming 'We support our boys in the Gulf', yet this kind of ignorance from British senior Cabinet ministers speaks volumes about how badly supported our own lads are. However, mustn't grumble and all that. We Brits just vote with our feet, and nowadays a career in the Air Force means getting out before it's too late to join an airline and 'fly a pub' for twice as much salary without getting shot at.

I listen amazed as Guy continues, "What other job in the world requires you to hand in your wristwatch when you leave? Usually it's the other way round, but it's true – whenever air crew give notice to leave the Air Force, they have to return the aviator's watch they were issued with when they joined."

However, his faith in human kindness was slightly restored on the way home when he had a high-powered passenger of his own. 'King Marine' (aka the boss of the Royal Marines) was sitting unobtrusively amongst the regular soldiers in the hold.

Quickly realising who he was, Guy asked, "Why didn't you say you were on board, sir? We'd have shown you around the cockpit."

The modest chap replies, "Just wanted to see how my lads get out here, thanks very much." (That's unpretentiousness for you, Mr Politician, and it reaps immeasurable respect from the lads.)

"Life's never dull for you, is it?" I comment. "Are you in danger, going there?"

"Not really, except when the stupid Loadie came into the cockpit and asked us what to do with the pins taken from the bombs we were transporting."

"He what?" I stutter.

"Yup. It says 'Remove before loading' on the side, so he did." Guy shakes his head in disbelief. "I told him to put them back again...carefully."

I tell him about Stephanie and he hits the roof, refusing to pay for a stranger to clean our house (aaargh!).

"Tough – she starts tomorrow," I snarl.

*

Happier than I've been for ages today because Siobhan's coming to stay. She was so worried about me that she's taken some holiday. As we wait for her to arrive, I stare out of the kitchen window, noticing some incredibly plump sparrows clinging to our bird feeder.

"Look at those fat bastards, Guy. I'm not giving them any more nuts."

He gets up from the table and looks over to see what I'm banging on about before turning around and walking away.

"Guy, did you hear me?" I witter at him.

"Yes, darling, I heard you...They're not fat, they're puffing up their feathers to keep warm."

"Oh," I sigh, bored silly, and start neighbour-watching instead.

Just as Guy is leaving for work, I throw five monosodium-glutamate packet sauces onto the kitchen table and ask him to "Pick dinner". Amazingly, he offers to cook.

Siobhan arrives as I leaf through the morning's post and open a package from a local water filter company. The letter requests that we (the occupier) fill up the enclosed empty phial with a sample of our water so that they can test it for purity. She does exactly as instructed and goes to the loo to wee in the little bottle. Suspecting they might realise it's wee from the obvious colour, we water it down and place everything back in the envelope.

"I don't fit in here," I tell Siobhan over lunch.

"Yes you do, Kate – life's what you make it. You just need cheering up, that's all." She prescribes a massive dose of afternoon shopping in Bristol.

Tired and laden with smart, designer-label bags, we decide alcohol is needed to recharge our batteries and start looking for the nearest bar. Without warning, Siobhan drags me into a grim-looking shop without any windows and, rather confused, I ask, "I thought we were going to the pub?"

Giggling, "Stick with me, I'll show you the low life," she nods at the shelves and I realise we're inside a sex shop! "You need a stronger 'buzz' than gin," she says, and points at a row of vibrators named 'Dingdong'. "Go on, pick one."

Avoiding eye contact with other customers, we muffle snorts of laughter as we mooch around the shop, recognising Cunni-Linguists International products on every shelf.

Siobhan stretches up, standing on her tiptoes to reach a particularly large creation in the highest cabinet, when an unstable box causes the whole display to come crashing down, leaving her knee-deep in plastic penises. Everyone turns to stare at us (I want the ground to open up and swallow me), but Siobhan, calm and confident, shouts over to the shop assistant, "Do you have this in silver?"

Leaning against the wall outside, we clutch our stomachs laughing until it hurts, and Siobhan hugs me, saying, "Yer back! Kate, my old happy Kate, is back…"

In the pub, we celebrate losing our sex shop virginity with 'cock'-tails and I explain she needn't have bothered buying a dildo since I already have one. Naturally, Siobhan wants to know more, so I explain. "Guy put me on a sex ban 'cos I want a baby, so I made him buy me one – only problem is, it's remote control and it keeps going off in my drawer."

"What's the range on it?" she asks. "Could Guy switch it on while you're in the post office?"

I'm saddened to hear that Mr and Mrs Thorpe (opposite

Siobhan) have moved into a care home for the elderly but relieved to know that Siobhan's not flashing her chest at him anymore.

"They do return now and again," she says. "And I'm tempted to give him a quick flash. Sad, really. They have a bacon sandwich and then leave."

"Eh?"

"It's true. They like to come back to spend time in the house."

We toast Norman and his wife with our drinks and I wonder how they made it through decades of marriage. I find it so hard to live with Guy because he's incredibly stubborn, and it's crushing to think of us never being a family (but he hates babies).

"Bet they did argue but learnt to live with each other," Siobhan says wisely. "You have to look at the big picture – the future – not just at what's eating you up now. Give him time – Guy will come round to the idea of kids."

"Yes, but I'll be sixty…Should I harvest my eggs?"

Guy cooks us his favourite meal (curry and chips) for dinner and leans across to give Siobhan a huge bear-hug, saying, "Great to see you, Turtle. Kate needs her friends – I think she's finding this life hard."

"Turtle?" Siobhan whispers to me.

"As soon as you're on your back, you're fucked," I reply, explaining yet more Air Force code. She smiles and reaches for a bottle of wine.

After too much chicken dansak (and the earlier strawberry daiquiris), I lie on the sofa, groaning with heartburn. Guy, delighted to hear my stomach gasses, asks if we want to go with him for a drink in the Mess, but I'd rather watch TV.

"I'll go with you, Guy," Siobhan says. "Hang on a minute while I get changed into something more appropriate."

Thirty minutes later, she emerges in thigh-length boots and miniskirt, and almost supporting a plunging V-neck top.

"Told you I'd be quick. Is this smart enough?" she asks.

"Er, well you're certainly going to turn heads," Guy croaks, and they leave arm in arm.

They return way past midnight and Guy falls into bed, whispering, "I am ashamed of that woman. You do not want to know what she got up to."

"Oh yes I do," I say, instantly waking up on the promise of some juicy gossip. "Go on, tell me…please."

He lies quietly, staring at the ceiling, before slowly enlightening me on the evening's events. "One of the guys set up an impromptu disco next to the bar, and after a few vodkas, Siobhan starts strutting her stuff in the middle of twenty pissed-up blokes. She names them all 'Frank' before flirting outrageously with one of them. I didn't notice for a while and carried on drinking until the barmaid nudged me. I turned round to see her snogging and groping him against the window like a teenager. The audience grew as, one by one, people stopped talking to watch what was rapidly becoming a live sex show. When he put his hand up her skirt, I thought it was time to end her fame, and shouted, 'Siobhan! Put him down, for God's sake – he's married.'"

"What happened?" I ask (knowing Guy's got high morals).

"She stormed out into the Mess foyer when I told her to get her coat. And seeing the guilty party emerge from the gents, I said, 'And you…you should know better!' So she sobs her way to the cloakroom, muttering she didn't know he was married, finds her coat and bumps into her beau, asking if he's okay. He just shrugs and walks past, ignoring the tears."

Poor Shiv, I think, worrying about her being vulnerable. Guy, meanwhile, continues with the story.

"I told her to forget him because deep down he's very superficial, but she wasn't amused. Anyway, I fetch my hat and find her about to walk back into the bar but stop her. I couldn't let her go back in there with mascara all over her face and lipstick smudged up her nose – she looked about six years old.

"'I want Kate,' she blubs.

"I placate her with a hug and say, 'Come on, let's go home,' trying not to laugh at her messy face. Then I remember that my old racing bike's behind the accommodation block and go to get it, attempting to steer it home. At the entrance gate,

Siobhan starts moaning about her high heels and wants to ride the bike. So she hitches her skirt up around her waist and climbs on, just as a crew bus full of lads drives past, whistling and clapping at her fuchsia-pink G-string. Then she falls off but just laughs and waves, with my bike strewn around her ankles."

"Is she okay?"

He nods. "She's in bed…alone."

*

Guy is sitting at the dining-room table clutching a hangover in one hand and exam notes in the other, swotting furiously for next week's Captain's board.

Siobhan stays in bed until late morning, too wary of him to come downstairs. I manage to cajole her into getting up, offering headache tablets and orange juice, constantly probing her about last night. "Was he worth it, then?"

"No he wasn't – crap kisser," she replies. "Who wants to shag a man who can't kiss?"

Eventually, she finds her way downstairs to the kitchen. Guy quickly relents and forgives last night's antics but says she'll no doubt need saving again (from herself). She starts calling him 'Scary Guy' or 'Dad'.

"What I can't understand is why you called all the men Frank," I query.

Accepting coffee, she replies, "Well, I party such a lot that I can't be expected to remember every bloke's name. Calling them Frank makes life much easier."

"But it's extremely rude, don't you think?" Guy interjects.

"Yes, but a well-timed blow job usually takes their mind off my manners," she coos.

Guy leaves the room to potter about upstairs.

"Do you want kids?" I ask out of the blue, totally throwing her off track.

"Sometimes," she replies, seeing I'm deadly serious. "I'm giving myself until the age of thirty to find Mr Right, or thirty-five for Mr Almost Right and thirty-seven for Mr Will Do. If none of them appear, then I'll go visit Terrence in San Francisco with a turkey baster. He's agreed to sponsor my baby by his wife Frank." (Terrence and Frank are Siobhan's gay friends from university). "Why? You're not broody, are you?"

"Mmm," I sigh. "I see couples everywhere looking at their children with such passionate tenderness. I really hurt in here" – I make a fist by my stomach – "and I hate them for being so happy. I want what they have…to feel the total chasm of love that babies give you. I only wish Guy had told me before we married that he can't stand kids. It never occurred to me that I might marry a man who hates babies."

"You're the only woman I know who's fantasy involves going to the supermarket with a baby in the trolley seat – you really must get out more! And won't your mobile phone fry your ovaries if you keep it there?" she says, pointing at my front pocket. I instantly panic and move it round to the back.

Siobhan suggests I shake Guy up by threatening to leave him unless he changes his mind. "Don't really go, just hide in the utility room and sort out the washing – it'll take so long he'll think you've gone for good," she says.

I consider my options and decide, "Either that or get one of those cars with a telly in the headrest, then I can sit in the garage for an hour or so, letting him sweat a bit."

Lying next to each other on the spare bed, I notice that part of her scalp (about the size of a pound coin) is clearly visible above her right ear. I'm amazed I didn't see it earlier and tell her she's going bald!

Reassuring me, she explains that reception was decorated last week and that during the commotion she dropped a pen behind the fax machine. I wince in preparation for her next words…Reaching behind the cupboard, she retrieved the pen but left most of her hair stuck to the wall in an unattractive Artex swirl. A trip to the hairdresser didn't improve things much either, leaving her with a cropped, untidy mop of hair.

"Do you think it looks like I had chemotherapy six months ago? Or slept with a Nazi officer?" she wails.

Guy walks in to tell me that Beth's left a message on the answering machine; apparently, her dinner party was a complete disaster. Genevieve's betrothed is no longer favoured since both parents holiday separately (but with the child).

He laughs and mimic's her voice perfectly. "'How very strange, don't you think? Can't possibly advocate a match. I mean, darling – can you *imagine* what their children would be like...Remind me not to let her date him in fifteen years' time.'"

We spend the rest of the day reading magazines and doing nothing much until the evening when Guy offers to get a video.

"Any requests?" he asks us both.

"Whatever you fancy, as long as it has Tom Cruise in it – I love a good clit flick," Siobhan says.

"Chick flick?" Guy starts to correct.

"Or Sean – and then it's a Bean flick..." (Guy walks away, unwilling to hear any more.)

*

Waving goodbye to Siobhan, I promise faithfully to visit Yorkshire soon – her visits are always fast and furious. Guy comments that it's a good job she came this week instead of next as the Squadron's having a strip-club dancing pole installed in the bar.

"Why?" I ask amazed.

"Why not," answers Guy, then admits it's in the hope of enticing visiting females to perform for the boys.

"That'll never happen," I state.

Later that afternoon, I ask Guy, "Am I too blunt? Is it because I'm from Yorkshire?" I have just returned from yet another failed temping job – this time I lasted an hour. "What is the matter with me? Why doesn't anyone want to employ me?"

Maybe holding down a career is not the ultimate goal. Success is having a husband who loves me, time to spend with each other and no health worries.

Stephanie (the cleaner) won't hear a word against 'her boy' when I tell her that Guy's up to his old slobbish tricks again.

He teases, "Stephanie will do it," if I suggest he irons a shirt.

She also cleans for our friends Jim and Rebecca, and over morning coffee she reveals what happened earlier that morning.

"I popped round to their house as normal and set to work in the lounge. I'm quite used to finding either of them – especially Rebecca – still in bed and so busy myself in a different room until the sleeping beauty surfaces. I could hear Jim snoring upstairs, and feeling rather proud of my hard work, I finish vacuuming and go to start on the kitchen. Next thing I know, I hear him call 'Mornin', darling' from the hallway and turn just in time to see him stark bollock naked in the doorway!

"'Aw my gawd,' he exclaims. 'I'm so sorry, Steph, I thought you were Rebecca.' And without a care in the world he saunters off to get dressed, totally unmoved by the incident."

"Oh Stephanie, what did you do?" I gasp, helping myself to a biscuit.

"I stood rooted to the spot and washed the same cup up three times."

Pete phones up to get Guy's neck and sleeve measurements before going on a trip to Turkey. As dinner jackets are worn to the Christmas Draw (Ball) instead of Mess kit (dress uniform), the 47 Squadron lads want to brighten theirs up by having shirts made in Squadron colours: yellow, red and blue. The plan is to expose a white front, cuffs and collar but reveal all when they remove their jackets at midnight. He's ordering them now and someone else will collect them on the next trip.

*

Halloween – we're ready and waiting for them, armed with a tin of weird and wonderful sweets, specially selected by Guy for kid-approval rating (he's the biggest kid I know).

"Why can't we give them something healthy like apples?" I ask.

"Because kids are programmed for sugar and spice and all things E-numbered," Guy quotes.

Only problem is, we bought these goodies a week ago and

kept sneaking into the tin for a fix. Before long, the tin was half empty. Oh well, there may just be enough time to get some more (there isn't).

My heart sinks as I look at the enormous pumpkin on my kitchen table waiting to be scooped and sliced into some sort of lantern. Remembering the sheer hard work involved in making lanterns as a child, I brace myself for finger, elbow and arm ache (Guy is very keen but disappears when I ask for help).

Incredible – the knife slices through pumpkin flesh like butter, and scooping out the inside couldn't be simpler. The whole process takes around ten minutes and I congratulate myself on a wonderfully crafted face (smiling back through wonky teeth).

"Why did I think it would be such hard work? Is it because I've grown up and all I can remember is doing this with mum as a child?" I ask Zoë on the telephone.

"No," she replies in her thick Yorkshire accent. "When we were kids, there weren't such things as pumpkins – we had turnips and they took bloody ages to do."

I laugh out loud, thinking how easy today's youth have it (then feel like I'm turning into my mother). "And we didn't have pretty little tea lights like they do now," I tell her, memories flooding back, "just thick white candles from under the stairs in case the electric went off."

By this time we're in fits, remembering how we tried for hours to scoop out the inside of a swede with a spoon, the candle burning the lantern lid so all you could smell was burnt turnip.

"At least you got a turnip," she says solemnly. "We had to jump over the fence into Stanley's field and nick beetroots 'cos my mum wouldn't buy one. Can you imagine it – beetroot! Never stood up properly, just fell over."

No knocks heard on our front door until around 6pm. Out comes our half-full tin of sweets.

"We've been so popular, they've nearly all gone," Guy and I blurt out together.

"Liar," says a dad dressed as the Phantom of the Opera, accepting a can of beer from Guy.

I notice that everyone seems to go around in a gang with their dads ever-watchful at the back, making sure their kids say "please" or "thank you" and stashing some of the sweets away in a booty bag (which doubles up as a mobile beer fridge).

The effort put into each fancy dress outfit is admirable – flashing pumpkins and more ghouls than you can shake a stick at. One little girl wearing a pink princess outfit is having a mad time with her mates, blissfully unaware of the cold weather.

"I don't like black," she answers when I ask why she isn't dressed up as a witch like her chums.

By 7pm the sweets have long run out; time to move on to the dreaded fruit bowl.

"If I were you I'd turn the light off," advises one mum.

Aha! I'd forgotten that the code is 'porch light on, get your sweets here'. Guy turns it off, along with the hall light and the kitchen light. He also wants to switch off the lounge light, but I refuse to sit and watch TV by log fire.

Still the doorbell rings.

Then Guy remembers that he's got a stash of chocolate bars in his Nav bag. Do we give 'em out? Do we heck! We sit by the fire and stuff our faces, shouting "Piss off!" every time the doorbell goes.

EIGHT

"For pity's sake, we've only been married two minutes." Guy refuses to discuss babies yet again, arguing we need more time together before starting a family. He just won't see my biological clock ticking closer to thirty.

"But soon it'll be too late and I'll despise you forever," I argue.

All the usual daggers come back out and I throw verbal classics at him: "We'll be too old to enjoy our children/you're devoid of any emotion/selfish…"

"We can't afford one," he tries.

"No one can afford them," I whine. "Oh go on, pleeease – I promise to look after it and do everything."

"Honestly, hon, listen to yourself – you sound like a nine-year-old asking for a hamster, promising to clean it out and feed it."

My phone beeps to show a text message from Siobhan. It says: *'great time last wk, gud luk with Guy (and motherhood) kisses Shiv'*. And then at the end: *'phone still in your back pocket – have I just kissed your arse?'*

Usually that would make me giggle, but I delete the message and carry on interrupting Guy's drivel about needing time to develop our own relationship before bringing another on board and seethe quietly as he fusses about finding parts of his dress uniform.

"Wish me luck," he smiles nervously.

"Huh," I say (convinced he's only bothered about himself and the Captain's board exam).

Various instructors have told him throughout his flying

career that he has a good pair of hands, which is the biggest compliment a pilot can get because it means they feel the aircraft rather than just respond to instruments, so I know he's confident but hate him for always getting what he wants.

I spend all day at work (this week as an accounts clerk) waiting for the telephone to ring. It doesn't.

Arriving home, I pour myself a large gin and tonic.

"Well?" Bernadette asks, walking in without knocking. "Has he passed?"

"Don't know yet," I say, wondering what sort of scenario he could be facing – a posting away from his beloved Hercules or re-toured as a shamed Co-pilot (not good enough to make Captain).

The phone rings and we run to answer it.

"Hello? Guy, is that you?"

A paralytic voice whispers, "Captain Willesley at your service, madam."

*

Find out Guy's going to 24 Squadron and I tease him for being a route queen. At least Pete's got the same posting, so his partner in crime will be there too.

"Not happy," he mumbles. "I'd rather stay tactical and be a Captain on 47 Squadron, but at least the new J-model Hercules is going to be on 24," he says to himself.

The current K-model Hercules is about to be replaced with the new J-model. (I don't understand this; if it was a car then surely it would be an L-model?)

"What's the difference?" I ask Guy.

"The K-model is thirty years old and still has most of its original avionics. Navigation systems are state of the ark – we even use a sextant – whereas the J-model has satellite systems, computer-based planning, electronic auto-filing of flight plans and other funky stuff. Sadly, this new-improved boil wash version doesn't have an Engineer or Navigator, only a Captain and Co-pilot."

"What will happen to them?" I ask.

He quips, "Question: what does a Nav say to you? Answer:

do you want fries with that?" Then he tells me that at one of the last fancy dress parties, a Navigator was even wearing a MacDonald's uniform.

Friends seem rather confused when I tell them Guy's been promoted, thinking he's a high-up Officer in the RAF. Wrong! His rank is that of an 'Officer', the level of rank he holds is 'Flight Lieutenant' and his job is 'Captain'. All Officers have different ranks; starting with the highest, it goes:

Marshal of the Royal Air Force
Air Chief Marshal
Air Marshal
Air Vice-marshal
Air Commodore
Group Captain
Wing Commander
Squadron Leader
Flight Lieutenant
Flying Officer
Pilot Officer

Any Officer can hold the position of Engineer, Loadmaster, Administrator or Doctor (for example, you can easily have a Wing Commander as the Captain of an aircraft or a Flight Lieutenant as the Navigator).

Guy returns from the car auctions with a black BMW and poses around the base with windows down and stereo at full blast. Shrieking with excitement at our almost-new flash car, we drive over to the Arndale's house and ring the bell to swank it up.

"Naff off, yer posh bastards," Richard shouts from the doorstep, so we zoom off to the fish and chip shop to celebrate Guy's Captaincy and our latest accessory.

Zoë phones for a chat, and I ask politely, "How's Jack?"

"Kate says 'ow are yer," she asks him.

"Why?" I hear him say.

"Why?" she asks.

"Zoë! I'm just asking how he is – normal people reply 'Fine, thanks.'"

I tell her that Guy's been made a Captain but she's suitably uninterested and starts telling me about her shopping escapade this afternoon with her Aunty Madge.

"We went to that massive shopping centre…Murder Hell on the M62."

"Meadow Hall," I correct.

"Yeah, that's the one. Anyway, Aunty Madge wanted a new outfit for Tigley Ladies Darts Club and I always need slippers, so I went along to keep her company. She hired one of those electric invalid chairs 'cos she's not very good at walking since she had her hip replaced. Although, I had to run like a bugger to keep up. I'm not kidding; after ten minutes I was sweating cobs – knackered from wearing the wrong shoes rather than being unfit – so I arranged to meet her later in the food court."

"Did you get a pair of slippers?" I ask, wondering where this conversation is going.

"No. I wanted fluffy mules with a heel but all I could see were novelty animal ones. Any road, I was walking through Willis's department store when I saw Aunty Madge in the invalid car speeding away from two security guards with a pair of leather trousers and two handbags dragging behind her. Turns out they thought she was shoplifting, but she just couldn't control the speed dial properly and had managed to hook various items of clothing onto the basket as she drove through. It took me two dry sherries and three mint imperials to calm her down."

*

A lot of work is put into making bonfire night a family affair on the Patch. Most Air Force personnel attend (I suppose it stops people burning great holes in their back lawns). No expense spared, either – out-of-date flares are used as fireworks (they're an integral part of the display) and are a source of much amusement to all.

Exhausted from the boredom of today's office work, I point the car towards home and rely on 'the force' to guide me. Wake up closer to Lyneham than Swindon, wondering how I managed to drive completely unfocused, with no memory of the journey. Turning the corner into our street, adrenaline shoots through my veins as I see Danny's car sitting on our drive – what the hell is he doing here again?

Guy and Danny are in the kitchen drinking beer, laughing at some inane male tale, but I don't see the funny side and walk past, carefully composed (but confused).

Guy kisses me hello, saying, "Bet you didn't expect to see him, did you?"

Danny looks me in the eye (my stomach lurches), explaining, "When I dropped Siobhan off last time, Guy insisted that I call in if I was passing – so here I am."

Why oh why didn't I put my new suit on today, I think, kicking my shoes off in the hall. Instead, I have old faithful on (a threadbare wool substitute hanging off my bones). Man, I must look a mess.

Pete turns up five minutes later asking if Guy can come out to play before teatime and Guy refuses to let Danny leave after having just one quick beer. He insists they go for a drink in the Mess first and phones around a few of the other Captains, asking if they want to be part of the summit meeting.

Jim informs him that there's a beer call (leaving party) going on up at 30 Squadron and that he's on his way there to show his face for half an hour because he's on standby and can't drink – but he doesn't mind giving them a lift.

Two minutes later, a car pulls up outside. Pete and Guy rush past me pulling on their cabbage (camouflage) jackets, shouting, "Bye, mum," and Danny follows behind, shrugging his shoulders in apology.

I ask them to be back in time for the bonfire and go upstairs to make a bed for Pete. There's no way he'll be in any state to find the spare room, as he usually collapses somewhere in a heap – however, I always make a bed up for him anyway.

Danny can sleep on the sofa.

Wondering what the hell Danny's playing at, turning up out of the blue like this, I try to act normal, thinking how stupid I'm being. There's no way he can be interested in me anymore

– I'm married, for goodness' sake. No harm in flirting, though, is there? And he is better-looking than I remember…

When the boys get back from their beer call, we set off wearing warm gloves in the freezing night air; the lads shiver holding cold cans of beer. The bonfire is held on the general playing field between the Sergeants' and Officers' quarters, and everyone slowly sinks into the mud as we pour through a small wooden gate.

We watch an amazing display of fireworks and listen to people exclaiming "Ooh!" and "Ah!" as the night sky lights up with stripes and bursts of vibrant colour.

Pete whispers, "Thank Christ for the Chinese." (I get the giggles.)

Tannoy speakers feebly blast out what sounds like big-band music, and on the far side of the field there's a small white vehicle (it's an old ice cream van). I watch as a little man climbs into the back of it, and then suddenly the music speeds up, sounding more like jazz. (I'm convinced this little figure in the back of the van is peddling away on some sort of contraption to keep a generator going, powering the music.)

The bonfire is a good size – quite impressive. Towards the end of the display (and to signal that we should start to leave the field), a sign lights up in pretty colours, stating 'HE END' (more giggles as the 'T' refuses to ignite).

I'm surprised to hear a few parents saying, "Lets go home now and miss the crush at the gate." How sad, I think, because they won't get to see the colourful finale.

By now, the muddy gate is fast becoming a quagmire, and one little darling starts to cry because he's dropped his leaf. His dad tries to pacify him with another, bigger, better leaf, but he's having none of it. We stand squashed together like a bottleneck traffic jam and wait patiently as they try to find it.

Danny bends down until he's the same height as the boy and picks up a large, crisp leaf, explaining quietly that it was lost and needed a new friend. The little boy promises to look after it for him and I'm enchanted by this show of compassion. All the mums swoon and I must admit there's a lump in my throat. Why can't Guy be kind to children like that? I don't think he even notices them.

All cheer loudly as the blockage is cleared and we start to move through the gate. Strolling along the Patch towards the Wing Commander's house for drinks, Pete tells us that better fires can be seen every night of the week when coming into land at Birmingham airport (he means arson). In the pitch darkness of the winter evening, children run past us waving cyalumes like flags (luminous sticks used to light the inside of the aircraft when making a 'quiet entry' into a country). Blue, green, yellow and red ones hover in the night air like multicoloured fireflies.

'The boss', as Fergus is known, dishes out warm mulled wine to freezing but hardened party-goers under the cover of a massive military-green Mess tent in his front garden while his wife hands out hot dogs. Other wives bring along home-made toffee, treacle cake and fudge. Enjoying the social niceties but freezing cold after an hour of standing outside, we leave Pete drinking and begin to wander home. Danny wants to know what it's like living in such a huge community and I tell him that it gives me a sense of belonging but that the impermanence of everything often throws me off balance.

Interested in the latest new arrivals (which we seem to get every week), I sidle my way over to the posse of new mums and smile at their offspring.

"Ooh, is this baby Jamie?" I ask one smiling, unkempt new mum. "Can I have a peep?" I look inside the pram to see a large-headed baby with huge eyes and a flat, squashed nose; it's the ugliest child I've ever seen.

Totally shocked to realise there actually are weird-looking babies in this world, I try to make the right noises (but all I can think of is "eurgh" and "yak"). My babies will be beautiful.

Jude tells us she's trying for a baby and I turn green with envy. She says life is one long, temperature-controlled sex marathon (Guy would like that, I think).

"I'm a woman possessed," she continues. "Pricey came round from the anaesthetic last week after his knee operation, and when the surgeon asked if he had any questions, he replied, 'Can I have sex?' The surgeon then promptly informs the nurse that Pete's a rampant sex maniac and tells her to stay away from him – but I'd ordered him to ask...Anyway, I managed to straddle his bandaged leg, no problem – just wanted to check it was all right to do so, what with the general and everything."

I'm amazed at the lengths a 32-year-old ovulating woman will go to and add, "How could you? The poor man was injured!"

"Yes, but only on his knee," she retorts.

Unkempt mother hands Guy her ugly baby and says, "Here, hold him a minute for me, will you? I need a pee."

Guy physically recoils and almost throws baby Jamie at Danny. Danny laughs and coos dirty Irish drinking songs to him until she returns. Suddenly, I see Danny in a different light; there's something sexy about a man holding a baby (even if it is ugly).

Back home, Guy stokes up the fire with logs and we carry on chatting, me sitting on the floor (Danny opposite) and Guy lying on the sofa. I start to think that I've got it all wrong about Danny and that I was just being paranoid (as usual). We discuss his job and how he trains people to make confident decisions and to take responsibility for their actions in extreme conditions, and then drift onto the subject of Siobhan.

"She's too vulnerable," he reflects, and I know exactly what he means – all the bravado she oozes is simply a defence mechanism to stop her getting hurt. I fetch another bottle of red wine and ask what the future holds for him. He tells me how much he wants a family of his own and the simple things in life – a house in the country, a horse (I want to yell "Stop!" at him because that's my dream, but I listen and smile occasionally).

"And someone to share it all with," he finishes.

The fire crackles and spits, making our faces glow from the heat, and I notice that Guy's snoring deeply on the sofa. My toes keep touching Danny's and I don't know where to look, trying to avoid his gaze. Placing his wine glass on the hearth, he turns and gently takes hold of my hand.

"Kate, what are you doing with him?" he asks me softly, nodding at Guy.

I try to pull my hand away but can't; it's locked into his. Passion, excitement, danger and sorrow rush over me in waves. Not answering him, I look straight into his gaze and then glance over at Guy sleeping.

What do I say? How do I answer that one? Thinking about it, I don't know what I'm doing with him – I try very hard to make it work but we're always fighting, wanting different things in life. Guy wants a fast car and flying whereas I want a family and a husband who adores me. At the moment, I fill the role of wife but hate every minute because I'm taken for granted. Pulling my hand out of Danny's grasp, I know I can't answer him because I can't face the prospect of saying "I don't know", and if I had to say anything it would be that. I really don't know – I never knew marriage would be this hard.

"Believe me, he will hurt you," Danny continues. "Leave him and live with me – please, Kate, just give me a chance."

Something in me wants to answer recklessly "Yes, Danny, let's run away – be my soul mate", but also the same emotion holds me back, knowing this is the life I've chosen and I can't hurt Guy. (Oh shit, why is everything so awkward?)

Honestly, I feel like I'm stood on the edge of a precipice about to jump off – but would Danny be there to catch me? Is he offering me a chance? Do I leave Guy?

It's all too much to bear so I stand up and leave the room. Walking past the hallway table, I accidentally knock a set of keys onto the floor and bend down to retrieve them. I pick them up and go into shock. My palms sweat, my stomach heaves somersaults – because there, hanging off Danny's bunch of keys, is my engagement ring from card 107! Oh my God, my heart feels torn to shreds – I've been such a fool.

I turn it over and look at the deep-emerald stone, knowing it's the exact one I've watched and admired in the window of Coppergate Jeweller's for years. My own copy made from memory is a weak second. So he really would've proposed...

Making my way quietly upstairs to bed, I can't believe such a dramatic event just took place in front of Guy (God, I hope he was asleep). Seeking solace under two quilts and three blankets, I cry mournfully and wish the clock could be turned back.

Guy doesn't want me; he wants a girlfriend ten years younger than me who'll dote on him until he finally grows up enough to sample the delights of fatherhood.

*

Guy gets ready for work oblivious to last night's conversation between Danny and me. I keep occupied, not wanting to talk to either of them, so inevitably the atmosphere gets thicker than treacle.

When we meet in the hallway, Danny asks me for an answer as he's still waiting. I shut the downstairs loo door in his face. Leaning against the cold, stone wall, I swallow back tears and blow my nose loudly. Guy interrupts my panic attack by telling me to hurry up and come out. "Danny's leaving and we should say goodbye."

Dutifully, I follow them outside. Patting Guy on the back and thanking him for a memorable evening in the Mess, Danny gets into the car and starts the engine, saying to him, "Look after her, won't you."

Then he smiles at me, behaving with impeccable manners, but I can see his eyes are searching mine.

"Give me a chance," he whispers into my hair as I lean into the car to say my farewells.

"Goodbye, Danny," I whisper back, knowing I mean exactly that. This is my life, I chose to be here in Lyneham and I have to be with Guy (who knows, he might improve with age). But watching Danny's car drive away leaves a dull ache and I can't help feeling I've lost a friend as well as an alternative future. Seeing him hold that baby has confirmed my belief that he does want to settle down and have a family – no one could be that good with someone else's kid if they didn't want one. (Some lucky bitch is going to get my dream!)

*

Guy's going off on some huge exercise called Leading Peace and tells me the background so I understand what's going on.

In 1990, NATO and former Warsaw Pact countries signed a joint declaration stating that they were no longer adversaries. In 1994, NATO invited NACC and SCE to continue the process of understanding and co-operation between countries. The EAPC has succeeded the NACC and at present there are twenty-seven nations involved.

"Eh?" I say, as he continues, ignoring my ignorance.

"It allows for consultation on topics ranging from political and security questions to environmental and scientific issues, offering opportunities to work together on matters like disaster and civil emergency control, search and rescue, humanitarian operations, armaments co-operation, and peace support operations."

All this goes completely over my head and I make him explain it again.

"It's a sad fact of life that the delivery of humanitarian aid is unlikely to stop," Guy continues. "One Leading Peace operation was in Bosnia. Sixteen allied countries worked together under the same rules of engagement and command structures, to assist in the military provisions of the Bosnian peace agreement."

"When do you go and how long for?" I ask, not much the wiser.

"Tomorrow for two weeks," he says.

So much for devoting myself to making this relationship work, I think. We have precious little time together as it is (and he wants more before even considering a family).

"Honey-roasted hip-widener?" he asks, offering me a bag of peanuts.

*

RAF St Mawgan is hosting an exercise known to the crews as Operation Orchestrate.

Guy packs his bags, saying, "Eighteen nations in this – it's a three-day, live-flying training exercise airdropping deliveries of aid, emphasising aero-medical evacuation. Skills like these are always tested but we can never know for certain when or under what circumstances or with which fellow nations we'll be working with. The goal is to share experiences and overcome difficulties for those taking part in future humanitarian operations," he blathers.

"It sounds like one huge party to me," I tease.

"Apparently, forty Swedish nurses are involved," Guy comments, testing my reaction.

"Well then, I bet there will be considerably more casualties than they bargain for."

"And – can you believe this – I have to pay thirty pounds to go on the trip! It comes out of my Mess bill," he says.

"What a rip off," I reply in disgust, amazed he's expected to fund his own job.

"Goodbye, darling, miss me," he says, and is gone.

*

Guy phones and I hear about the massive drinking sessions going on 'post-sortie'.

"Certainly sounds like you're making an effort towards international relations," I say.

Over the background noise, he shouts, "Each country is offering their national dish for us to taste. I think I've just eaten Uzbekistan horse's testicles!"

"Just drink beer and you'll be fine," I advise. "So, are the nurses worth thirty quid?"

"Two nurses, not forty," he yells. "One's called Hans and the other's called Luis."

I smile at the thought of two butch males dampening the hopes of our drooling men waiting for the Swedish nurses to pitch up.

"An Italian Officer told me today that the only reason we Brits are the best at everything is because we always work in chaos," he laughs.

Richard and Guy are flying together, even though they belong to different Squadrons, and I phone Gwen to see if she's okay alone, knowing she's scared of the dark. She hates being on her own at night, and when Richard's away, she goes to bed with the telephone set to call Police Flight (every department is a 'Flight', i.e. Catering Flight, Admin Flight, etc.)

in case of intruders. In fact, she calls them every night so that if anyone breaks in, all she has to do is press ring-back.

"Kate, why don't you stay here tonight?" she suggests.

*

Leave Gwen's at 7am to get a shower at home. What a fabulous arrangement; neither of us need be frightened of the dark because we have company. My neighbours think I'm completely dippy, watching me emerge from my car at sunrise in polka-dot pyjamas.

At work, my supervisor comes over to interrupt my daydream (I'm in another call centre, getting rapidly automated).

"Penny for them…" she asks.

"Oh, nothing," I answer, focusing on her grey chin-hair. "Well, if you must know…" I add, not wanting her to know I was thinking about Danny, "I was just wondering if Catwoman's clothes have disintegrated yet?"

She looks puzzled so I explain. "When I was a kid, I saw a Batman and Robin show where Catwoman fell into a bottomless pit. It was over fifteen years ago and she's still falling – surely her clothes must've disintegrated by now?"

"I hope you settle in here," chin-hair says. "…Not the kind of place for abstract minds."

Over at Gwen's after work, I whinge to her about my boring day and remark how the Patch could easily be mistaken for a lonely wives commune.

"I think it's one big Air Force harem," she muses, sipping her hot toddy. "Yup, they're all married to the job and we're concubines waiting to be picked."

"Time for bed," I suggest.

"Staying married is the hard part," she offers slowly by way of confession. "But Rich loves flying – God help us if he ever gets promoted and is made to fly a desk."

(I'm intrigued and slightly pleased that others struggle too, always thinking I'm the only one suffering tough times when everyone else is blissfully happy.)

"Our parents had it easy," she continues. "Less independence and one car. It was either get on with it and learn to live together or go back to mum and dad. No one wants to go home – marriage was a ticket out, but at least their husband came back at night-time; ours are seldom seen."

"You happy?" I ask.

"Sometimes yes and sometimes no. I just keep adjusting to whatever stage he's going through and try to fit in – Co-pilot, Captain, Instructor. But I'm sure that once we've learnt to live with each other, everything else will get easier."

"Me too," I mutter, finishing the hot whisky and water.

"The weirdest thing is accepting the package deal...them and the job," she tells me. "You marry a system – no one tells you about the odd protocol you're expected to follow or Air Force procedures, but they give you bus timetables and coffee-morning rotas."

She pauses as we laugh at the absurdity of it all.

"I bet you feel like you've been lifted out of reality and dumped into a world full of strange traditions," she continues. "At least I knew what I was letting myself in for – as a reservist. Don't worry, you'll soon come to terms with being a single wife."

We make our way to the top of the stairs and she turns to hug me goodnight.

"The worst thing is crossing off the days on the calendar until he returns," she adds. "Weekends especially."

Nodding, I return her hug (my new world is a bit more comfortable now I know she feels the same) and say, "So much for marital bliss."

"Marital abyss," she smiles, and closes her bedroom door.

*

Mum and dad come to stay for the weekend and I bite my tongue as mum hands over bags of potatoes, kitchen towels and tea bags. But I can't bear it any longer as pints of skimmed milk appear, all the way from Yorkshire.

"Mother, why on earth are you bringing this stuff – do you think I don't go shopping?"

"She needs to be needed; let her do it," dad murmurs under his breath, so I shut up and accept armfuls of bread cakes, regressing five years with every short step taken towards my house.

Dad falls asleep after the long drive and I listen to mum's updates on village life. After dad's nap, we go into Bath for a bit of relaxing shopping, and while walking around, they tell me how worried they are about me being stuck miles away from them without a husband for company.

"Oh, I manage," I say, following mum into a clothes shop.

Dad waits for us outside, sitting on a bench watching the street entertainers, and when we turn up he says, "Hattie, look at this – it's not nailed down…"

I wait, confused, until mum agrees, saying, "So it is, luv. Posh here, aren't they? Back home, that would've gone by now."

When they've finished discussing unattached street furniture, mum wanders into another shop and amazingly asks out of the blue, "I meant to ask – how's that nice boy Danny getting on?"

"Don't know," I snap, teenage hormones resurfacing.

Over supper, dad reads the plans for my trendy new flat-pack furniture (time to bin the Air Force stuff), commenting it would be far easier to build a conservatory.

Hattie sits (chewing her top lip) in the armchair knitting baby clothes.

"What are you doing, mum?" I ask, thinking she could be a little less obvious.

"Getting ready, dear – Isobel will no doubt be wanting another and you won't be long," she decides.

*

"That poor lad, he works so 'ard, and on a weekend, too," mum thinks aloud, stuffing the toilet rolls I refused to accept back into the boot of their car.

"*Guy* has never been happier mum," I reassure, emphasising his name (why do they always insist on calling him 'the lad'?). "Don't fret over him. Weekends are normal working days for the crews, so we grab a Sunday whenever we can, even if it's midweek."

Kissing them goodbye, I feel sad at the thought of my parents going home but also liberated and free from their well-meaning dominance.

Tom texts my mobile to say he's coming over tomorrow for a couple of days and I dutifully change the spare-room sheets, thinking, all I ever do is washing (second thoughts, it's only Tom – he can have a sleeping bag and pillow).

Siobhan rings and gives the goss on Megan's register-office wedding yesterday.

"The complete bag – she could've told me," I seethe, annoyed at being forgotten.

Siobhan placates me, saying no one knew anything; they just grabbed two strangers from the street and got married. Then they phoned from a local hotel bar and invited everyone to join them for drinks.

"One of the witnesses they dragged off the street was very tasty," she admits. "He hung around for the champagne and ended up staying longer than expected."

"Oh no, Shiv…Stop, please. I don't want to hear any more."

"Aw, go on. Listen, he was gorgeous – tanned with green eyes…And do you know, he could do almost as much with his tongue as he could with his dick."

I pay little attention, wishing Siobhan could find a nice boyfriend to settle down with, and then pinch myself, thinking, how stupid – it's frustrating and thankless. Stay single and carefree for as long as you can, girl!

Changing the subject, I ask, "How's your mum?"

"Barking, as usual. She thinks she's possessed by a demon, or rather she thought she was. Apparently, if you're possessed then you can't take communion because it won't let you enter church or face Christ. She hadn't been to Mass for three weeks – kept wearing black and wanting sex all the time."

I burst out laughing but Siobhan's appalled at the thought of her parents copulating.

"Er, is she all right?" I ask.

"Couldn't be better. Evidently, a quick spot of self-exorcism and a nice new lilac jumper sorted her out," she says.

*

I've booked a few days off from the agency in order to see Guy. He is tired but jubilant from playing war, bearing trophies of Latvian epaulets exchanged during social/cultural activities.

Tom arrives early evening and I'm aware that Guy and I hardly ever spend time alone together – there's always someone visiting. (I make a mental note to clear the diary for a few weekends so we can work on our relationship, just the two of us.) Anyway, we celebrate the boys' homecoming by meeting Gwen, Jude, Richard and Pricey in the Mess for drinks.

Predictably, us girls chat away on the navy-blue chesterfield sofas while the boys prop up the bar, talking shop.

Gwen says, "I went to pick Richard up this afternoon and drove towards the Officers' Mess car park, but as I passed the 'nice man with the gun', a loud bang came from behind me and I slammed on the brakes, convinced I'd been shot! I sat for three minutes holding up a queue of traffic, wondering why I wasn't dead. Then I noticed brown liquid splattered all over the seats. The shot I heard was a litre bottle of cola exploding – God, I was so embarrassed. I drove slowly away covered in sticky wet goo. Richard refused to get in, preferring to walk home instead."

We link arms coming out of the powder room, presenting a slightly drunk, emotionally unstable mob, and pause at the gallery of ex-Station Commanders on the wall in reception.

"Which one would you have, then?" asks Jude.

"1976," says Gwen, pointing to a happy-looking chap.

"What about 1982, girls," I ask. "Marks out of ten?"

"I'd give him one," they both reply, laughing.

Three bottles of wine later, Jude is keen to tell us how Pricey likes her to wear his flying helmet during sex.

Nothing surprises me anymore and I ask, "Why do we do it? We put ourselves through the most bizarre performances just to keep a perverted twit interested." The girls nod automatically.

Gwen offers us supper at her house, so after last orders at the bar, we troop out, the boys wearing their hats slightly too far back in imitation of Second World War pilots.

Richard tells us all about a short cut and, like sheep, we

follow him to a muddy garden opposite some barrack blocks instead of going along the path. Gwen's shoes sink into the earth and she refuses to walk any further, while Richard impersonates Paul Calf (Steve Coogan) and has us in fits of laughter trying to coax her across the lawn.

He squelches past and slurs, "Come on, woman, jus' do it."

Gwen is adamant that she won't go into a mud bath and tells Richard he isn't being funny. Tom, tall and broad, comes to the rescue and sweeps Gwen easily off her feet, carrying her over the muddy lawn.

Hoots of "Ooh, Tom, my hero!" come from her pathetic frame, smug that we're left behind to negotiate the quagmire.

Singing dreadfully at the top of our voices and out of tune, someone shouts out of a nearby window, "Kate Willesley and Richard Arndale, bloody well shut up – the kids are asleep." (We're stunned at how people know who we are from our awful rendition of 'Bohemian Rhapsody'.)

Arriving at Gwen's front door, I hear a painful thud behind us followed by long groans. We all turn to see Craig Murphy-Jones (Murphy) trying to cycle home but so incredibly drunk that he's unable to stay perched on his bike long enough to peddle. He keeps getting on and falling straight over the other side, hitting the floor. It's amazing how he's made it this far. We stand and applaud as, eventually, he gets going again.

"Night then, chaps," he says politely, sailing off straight into his neighbours' side gate, hitting it with surprising accuracy.

*

Mid-afternoon, we call at the Arndales' house, intent on dragging them out with us for a curry (integral part of Air Force life), and as I ring the doorbell, I find their keys still hanging in the lock!

Approaching footsteps confirm that Richard's alive, and he croaks through the letterbox that he'll be with us in a minute after he's found some keys. He opens the front door wearing Gwen's pink silk dressing gown and looking very hungover.

I hand him his keys, he thanks us graciously and then shuts the door in our faces, muttering, "Piss off, you northern bastards." (Guess he wants to go back to bed more than he wants a curry.)

Unperturbed, we drive into Wootton Bassett and, even though we're stone-cold sober, eat hot curry (that's a first) while waiting for the local chemists to develop Guy's film.

Two hours later, Guy collects his photographs and quickly flicks through them until he finds the one he's looking for, exclaiming, "This one's going on the notice board!"

I look over his shoulder to see a picture of their newly qualified Loadmaster sleeping peacefully on carefully arranged cargo, completely unaware that the rest of the crew have strewn porn magazines and strategically placed scrunched-up tissues around him.

"You bastards," Tom laughs.

*

Since I've been here, four marriages have broken up. Quite a sobering thought.

Guy's in Turkey this week and offers to collect the Squadron dress shirts as he's due some time off. He follows scrawled directions to the sweatshop where Pete left his own plain-white shirt with the Turkish tailor, instructing him to "Copy this exactly, but with these colours – we need twenty shirts altogether and here are the measurements."

Guy finds the factory and asks one of the young female machinists, "What's this?" pointing to a hole neatly stitched into every single shirt (underneath the front middle button).

"Mister told us to copy exactly," the Turkish tailor answers for her, lifting up Pete's shirt to show Guy a darned cigarette hole that Pete had obviously tried to mend after a game of Mess rugby.

"Oh shit!" Guy shakes his head in disbelief.

But really, it's not their fault; they've done exactly what was asked – every shirt is perfectly tailor-made with one yellow arm, one red arm and the back shows all three Squadron colours, red, yellow and blue, only halfway down the front of each shirt is a neatly stitched hole!

On the journey home this small, insignificant puncture becomes known as Pete's Hole.

*

The Squadron Wives Club is meeting tonight to try and decide what to perform at the festive Review. I dutifully go along to help out and drive to a massive old farmhouse belonging to one of the Squadron Leaders, six miles away from Lyneham.

It's a strange feeling, being off base in a real house – I stare at Axminster carpets and touch wallpaper, enjoying individual decor instead of uniform mediocrity. It even comes with matching children: two small faces peep through the solid-oak banisters, watching us hang our coats up.

After two gins, I suggest standing on stage and reciting my own version of the voiceover from the film *Trainspotting* using a hard Glaswegian accent. But my demonstration doesn't go down too well…"Choose life, choose a job, choose a career," I begin, true to the script. But then I get louder. "I chose something else…I chose the RAF. Choose being home alone for a fortnight every month – make sure you keep up the hard Scottish accent! – choose missing your family and friends, choose moving your kids into different schools every term, choose loneliness and–"

And that's where they stop me (admittedly, I was off on a bit of a mission – feeling bitter because Guy's away yet again). We spend the rest of the evening brainstorming for an original but inoffensive idea (count me out, then).

On the way home, Olivia McLeish starts arranging a 47 Squadron girl's night out in Bath, aptly calling it a LADS (Ladies Association Dining Society) night. This woman's commitment is amazing; she undertakes the enormous task of organising a support network for Squadron wives and doesn't get paid.

Out of the four main Squadrons, two have active Wives Clubs and the other two don't do anything, mainly because the Wing Commanders' wives in question choose not to become involved (have own careers), which is fair enough. I can quite understand why some women refuse to give up precious spare time to run a service they didn't join. They don't get paid and it's a lot of hard work.

Olivia, however, is always available for a chat (over gin) and doesn't think twice about surrendering an evening for us to meet in her front room. I'm only too aware of the reaction from friends when I explain about a wives club – some flee from the idea, afraid it's 'twee', referring to pompous notions of bygone eras. Little do they know we have a great time drinking wine, making lasting friendships and combating the loneliness into the bargain. All right, it does tend to be the same bunch every time, but that doesn't stop Olivia inviting everyone (everyone being the whole hierarchy, not just Officers' wives).

*

Suffer pangs of missing Guy and put a message on the answering machine to cheer me up: "We're not in at the moment so leave a message and, if I like you, I'll call you back – if that's you, Guy, I miss you babe. Hope you have clean pants and are enjoying whichever war you're at, kiss kiss."

Walking in from a long day at work, I press play, and, after a slight pause, the caller stutters, "Er, hello…Mrs Willesley? It's Bob Fletcher on the Squadron calling to inform you that Guy is due home today."

Feeling partied-out (tired and bored of forever meeting new acquaintances) so decide to keep a low profile for a while. Suppose I just can't be bothered making any more effort and want more out of life than just socialising – something is missing; the baby issue won't go away.

*

Guy came home at 11pm last night and slept most of today before collecting his old Scottish pal, Dougie, from Bristol airport. I don't really know many of Guy's friends (met some at my wedding) so it helps to piece together Guy's life before I knew him. Charlotte, Dougie's wife, is lovely, an instant friend, and funnily enough we find we have a lot in common.

A few of the chaps are holding a Squadron mini-Masterchef competition and Pete volunteers to cook for the select few first, as long as he can use our kitchen. We borrow crockery and silverware from the Mess and he sets to work chopping vegetables, leaving us free to go shopping in Bath for the afternoon – great!

Returning home to a dinner party for seven people prepared by someone else is marvellous. I don't lift a finger, preferring to get pissed instead, and as more friends arrive, Pete creates delicious Stilton and bacon stuffed mushrooms, beef bourguignon and sticky toffee pudding. Charlotte and I award him a tall, white chef's hat (and lots of girlie praise).

Trying to be helpful but managing to get in his way, I load the dishwasher between courses, amazed at the amount of utensils Pete's managed to use. Short on dishwasher tablets, I substitute non-biological washing powder and set the machine going. Does the same thing (clothes/dishes), I think to myself, and I return to my guests.

Unloading the clean dishes an hour later, we notice they seem slightly whiter than the unused Mess plates.

"It's a bluey whiteness I quite like," I giggle.

"Oh fuck," Pete mutters when I tell him about the washing powder. "You'd better do the whole lot, then."

Dougie comes through to the kitchen with a message. "Hey, listen up. We've heard there's a party going on up at the Wessex tonight, so get your coats on."

The Wessex restaurant is where personnel who don't have a Mess go to relax and enjoy a meal. Tonight it's hosting a massive post-operation party.

"Exercise Stratagem," Jim tells us. "It's an annual airdrop competition that finished earlier this week, and the Canadians, New Zealanders and Australians are going home tomorrow. Come on, let's go – it should be a massive piss-up!"

Walking up to the party, Pete tells Dougie and Charlotte exactly what Stratagem involves and I listen in. The Canadian and New Zealand Air Forces started it in 1977. Not wanting to miss out, the Australians joined up in the eighties and we Brits came along in 1994, with each nation taking it in turn to host the competition. It's all low-level navigation, a succession of airdrops, precision, timed turning points, and tactical spot landings. But mostly it's drinking lots of Commonwealth beer. Guy mentions how much he misses the tactical job but then decides not to complain too much – at least he's not flying a desk.

We walk into the vast hall and someone holding a large, purple spacegun fires vodka into our readily opened mouths. A huge maple leaf hangs from the ceiling, competing with the decoration from the other nations involved. Charlotte and I dance the night away, rather too full of Pete's cooking to eat any of the gorgeous food on offer.

We crawl home to our beds in the wee hours and I dream I can hear the telephone ringing.

*

It wasn't a dream. I listen to the answering machine and find that we missed out on yet another party. Jim's message shouts out at us, "Where are you? Come round here now or we'll burn your house down!"

Charlotte works as a psychologist and decides (after knowing me for twenty-four hours) that I'm idiosyncratic. In her opinion, I'll never be an Air Force wife (I thank her for that). She thinks I'm an anti-establishment anthropologist enjoying watching Lyneham women try to belong to an organisation they would never associate with, were it not for their husbands.

I tell her the biggest hardship is trying to be a couple without any spare time. Life is a work treadmill directly connected to a party treadmill. Our short marriage is quantity, not quality; we cram in passion, gossip and arguments before another separation.

"Isn't that called life?" she suggests. "Dougie's exactly the same. He's devoted to his work in order to give me a comfortable lifestyle, so I just have to live with it."

I wonder if I'm expecting too much from Guy. I think I'll take a back seat and try to ease up on him for a while.

*

Guy returns from work just as I place his supper on the table.

I greet him with a long, seductive kiss and lift the lid on his plate, exposing lasagne vindaloo (his favourite).

"What's going on?" he asks. "Kate, you're scaring me – why are you being so nice?"

"Sit down and shut up," I order, pouring a beer for him. "I want us to be happy, that's all. I'm just trying to make an effort."

Guy starts eating, muttering something about women and never understanding them, and I leave him confused but pleased he's got out of doing dinner again.

I'm off to a Station Wives Club meeting at 8pm, this time in the Sergeants' Mess. We're having a charity quiz night for all the wives on base and last Thursday I signed Amber and me up for 47's team. Someone (can't remember who) told me that everyone wears hats the same colour as their husband's Squadron in order to show which team they represent, so I called into a party shop on my way home from work to find something suitable for both of us.

Amber looks dejectedly at the Red Indian headdress presented to her but I explain that it was all I could find with red, blue and yellow in it. She eventually succumbs when I beg her to enter into the spirit of things and remind her it's for charity.

"Now I remember why I stopped going to these events," she grumbles, straightening her feathers.

We walk into a noisy room full of women talking and laughing. Chinking wine glasses echo through the smoky atmosphere, which is already charged with competitiveness from teams representing every part of the base. Our entrance is greeted by stunned silence followed by stifled laughter as we stand gawping, looking like a couple of squaws. Olivia bounds over to welcome us.

"Shouldn't you all be wearing hats?" I choke at her.

"Oh, we haven't done that for at least two years," she says, indifferent to our embarrassment, and suggests we keep them on. I can feel Amber's eyes burning into the back of my neck as we walk around the tables, ignoring the sniggers, and take our seats. I'm positive I hear someone say, "Who's the twat in the hat?" so decide to keep it on all night.

Three glasses of cheap Chardonnay later, I forget about my crowning plume and manage to contribute four correct answers, resulting in our team getting an overall win in the first round.

One squaddie's wife complains to Olivia that the posse of women at her weekly meeting is getting too cliquey, and goes on to say that she feels it's top-heavy.

Not understanding her comment, I ask the person next to me for an explanation. She smiles and whispers, "Well, Kate, we'll never attract her type, because apart from you, we're all Squadron Leaders' wives" (meaning I'm just a Flight Lieutenant's wife and obviously not as high up as her).

I visibly double-take at her arrogance. I am Kate Willesley, a tall, dark-haired, friendly 26-year-old, not a Flight Lieutenant's wife or a cloned extension of my husband. How are they ever going to get partners of other ranks to attend the Wives Club with jumped-up little social climbers like her, I think to myself?

I have never been impressed by status, and even when I meet the most senior people in my various temping jobs, I always remind myself that he's still someone's dad or she's still someone's daughter. I address them as 'Bill' or 'Jill', not Station Commander so-and-so, trying to find some common ground or something they want to discuss. I'm interested in them as people, not their poxy job.

I come to these wives clubs to meet like-minded women in the same boat as me (with their husbands away) and to beat the boredom. I don't want to hear some rank-wearing wife patronise me when it wasn't her who worked hard for years to pass exams and fly aeroplanes. No, she just married a bloke who did and thinks this entitles her to his status.

And anyway, Guy would leave if they promoted him to Squadron Leader – he just won't fly a desk.

*

Haven't got anyone to escort me to the Christmas Draw (Guy's off again) and I don't want to go alone. So I ring up little brother and get him to join me (Tom agrees – anything for a party).

244

Fergus McLeish really is a nice guy who bothers about all his boys (including their spouses) and he phones me offering to send transport for tonight as it's forecast to rain. What a thoughtful chap, I think, sending a driver so our dresses won't get wet through. I decline, explaining that Tom is with me.

No point putting stockings or any other uncomfortable sexy lingerie on as Guy is not here. I opt instead for my favourite, old-faithful underwear and smile at the mirror, feeling 'plump and comfy' instead of 'hot sex siren'.

"If I die, go to a spiritualist with this bra and you'll get me loud and clear," I shout to Tom downstairs. (He ignores me.)

"I'm home alone – this is my brother," I inform everyone when they stare suspiciously at Tom, and console myself with far too many puddings. Tom makes me laugh and forget my loneliness, dragging me onto the dance floor to boogie away with Richard and Gwen.

Making light chit-chat with Olivia, I tactfully tell her about last night's patronising COW (Complete Officer's Wife) and her rank-obsessed conversation.

"Oh, ignore her, dear. I do all the time – she was a beauty-counter assistant before she met her husband," she says, adding, "People who have no status crave it most."

(This just makes my day – knowledge is power, and the next time I speak to that silly cow I'm going to smile and ask for advice on foundation!)

Apparently, the transport Fergus sent around the Patch to collect the wives in was his horsebox sporting a clean sheet on the floor! Damsels had to hold on very tight but nonetheless arrived at the ball dry, if a little shaken.

*

Guy is still stranded in Gander (Canada). Apparently, his aircraft has suffered a broken booster pump (whatever that is). With Christmas approaching fast, I fret he'll miss my birthday on Christmas Day. The rescue aircraft has also got problems and has had to abandon its trip home too, so Guy and the crew have no choice but to sit and wait.

Mum and dad are spending Christmas abroad, Tom will be with his friends in Bristol and my sister has her in-laws staying. As the days pass, I start thinking about just who I can spend Christmas with. Siobhan invites me to her family get-together in Cork, but I don't think I can face their festive ritual of watching Boxing Day wrestling with Granny Kilroy (and, of course, Danny would be there).

Guy phones me at work, saying the aircraft is working again but they've been rev-itined (given a reversed itinerary) and sent to the west coast of America, due home in four days.

"We land at twenty-three hundred hours," he shouts over a very bad line.

"Is that Wootton Bassett time?" I ask, always getting confused by GMT and local time.

Aaargh! He's now due home on Christmas Eve, but that's only if they don't break down again. I burst into tears, convinced he isn't going to make it in time. My current boss leaves the room and comes back with a massive chocolate bar – I scoff the lot in between sobs. Seems like I'm always consoling myself with food.

After work, I listen to the answering machine inform me that Guy will be home tomorrow and rant in reply, "What a load of toss – he's gone the other way, you stupid Duty Officer man." Even so, I decide to rush out and buy a Christmas tree. Then, halfway through decorating the house, I receive another phone call telling me that he's actually delayed for eight days.

Pour gin, start sobbing, then finish the tree. Oh well, as long as he's home in time for New Year…

*

The presents have been bought and sent – I've organised Christmas alone; my first married Christmas and Guy hasn't been involved at all – and only last-minute grocery shopping left to do. I feel sorry for him; he's missed out on Guinness and Mince Pies, a Squadron Ladies Guest Night and the Officers' Mess Christmas Draw.

Guinness and Mince Pies is a massive stag event ('the boys'

only) on 47 Squadron. They meet in the Squadron bar to drink gallons of Guinness and about six mince pies are arranged on a plate. However, Guy does call at bedtime to tell me that someone has managed to find a box of mince pies in Halifax (Canada) and they've just shared a can of Guinness in temperatures plummeting to around minus thirty degrees Celsius.

Irony of it all is that at least he's avoiding call-out, and the later he comes home, the more chance I have of him staying. Most of the divorced dads volunteer to cover urgent trips (called Operation Deny Christmas) which happen over the holiday period, leaving most families with a good chance of being together.

*

I surf the web looking for my perfect Christmas present. Disappointed that Gucci doesn't yet have a website, I go to the United Arab Emirates Yellow Pages, and hey presto! Hundreds of jewellers instantly display exquisite items on-screen, and like a mad, crazed, psycho shopping beast, I click on every page looking for a nice new watch.

Picking up the e-mail, I find out that Guy is back on the homeward side of America waiting for clearance to leave Washington Dulles International Airport. He tells me that the Engineer was finishing doing his checks earlier today when three vans with blacked-out windows screeched to a halt in front of their aircraft, spewing out bodyguards carrying machine guns. More amused than interested, the crew watches as Air Force One taxis past to an armed escort. At the same time, a pizza delivery van drives straight through the barricade and up to our boys on the Herc, handing out seven pizzas to ease their monotonous delay.

As Mr Clinton passes by all, Guy's crew salute him with slices of pepperoni and extra cheese!

*

Christmas Eve – hope he makes it home in time, I think, driving through the Patch. Signs have appeared on family homes exclaiming 'Santa stop here', and it occurs to me that

Santa is an anagram of Satan (quite befitting for this secular time of excess).

Write my presents wish-list, saying how much of a good girl I've been and promising to be naughtier next year. Then settle down to watch a repeat of James Bond, hoping the phone will ring to say that Guy has landed. Eat a shop-bought mince pie dusted with icing sugar (makes it look home-made) and am suddenly aware that after years of eating them, I don't really like mince pies – we only have them because it's Christmas.

The phone rings but it's only Olivia inviting me to festive drinks at their house, and being totally accustomed to separation, I accept. Although, getting out of my sofa clothes and into something more suitable for the Wing Commander's house takes immense effort as my off switch has gone for the year. I toy with the idea of getting completely smashed and ruining Guy's chances of promotion.

Quite a few of the wives also turn up alone, which makes me feel better, and I wonder why all the blokes are wearing checked shirts and bottle-green cords.

"Nice to be out of uniform then, lads?" I ask pointedly (few get the joke), and proceed to eat and drink too much. It is Christmas after all.

Back home and in bed after midnight, I hear the back door open and Guy shout, "Happy Christmas...I'm home!"

It's the best birthday present I could wish for – us together on our own. The front door's barely closed behind us before we've ripped each other's clothes off and banged our way upstairs.

*

We enjoy a long lie-in, getting up at lunchtime and running downstairs shouting, "He's been, he's been!" like a pair of kids. I open presents wrapped half in Christmas paper and half in birthday paper (force a smile). Mum gives me the same card every year – a cute kid sitting on her bed looking at the stars (she says it reminds her of me and Park-a-Garage). In the card, she's written that I'm ungrateful and should be happy to

248

have a birthday on such a special day. I wonder why, because I can't have a takeaway or go out for a pizza – I'm too busy cooking Christmas lunch and organising the day.

Guy gives me a case of my favourite wine for Christmas and I give him a plastic reindeer that poos chocolate drops. My birthday present from him comes out from under our bed (why didn't I look there?) and I happily rip open the enormous box to find an aerobics step and video.

"Thanks," I say, unimpressed, wondering what goes through his mind.

Two red velvet Christmas stockings hang on each side of the fireplace, one for me and one for Guy. My stocking remains empty but Guy's is full of tiny token parcels, and it dawns on me that frivolous extras like this appear because we women make an effort. Guy just didn't think to shop for silly gifts and fill mine. I look at my empty stocking and miss home (oh well, next year I'll fill the thing to the brim).

Opening his last parcel, Guy looks at the three words I've written on a card inside a shiny blue box.

"They're especially for you," I say. "Please remember them – don't just put them on the shelf and forget them."

Holding mistletoe over his head, I kiss him gently on the cheek and walk into the kitchen, leaving him sitting in the lounge slightly puzzled and staring at the card, which has 'Tact, gentle and foreplay' written on it.

After two hours of labour-intensive cooking, I realise we're having duck with cranberry sauce because I mixed up the birds when our local butcher delivered them. But we don't care (although I did wonder why the turkey looked rather flat – like it'd been run over). I just wanted a change from turkey on my birthday since I've had it for twenty-six years. Turns out that the duck is far too big for our naff oven, so Guy attempts to barbecue it.

Mum's equally eccentric friend, Aunty Val, has sent me a birthday tiara, which I wear all day, and dad (being the cultural attaché for Yorkshire) sent his present to us yesterday in typical Yorkshire style: there, outside the house, much to everyone's amusement, stands a tonne of coal. We set about

249

shifting big, heavy sacks off the drive and into the garage before lunch.

Fairy lights cover most houses in the street and healthy banter starts the usual competition for each neighbour to outdo the other. Guy sets up six luminous snowmen around the bottom of our birch tree, and not to be outdone, the neighbours light up their windows, making the whole street look merry. That's until the Canadians opposite switch on their lights and blind us all in the process!

Guy says he wanted to plan a birthday surprise for me and book flights to New York so we could spend Christmas in America and go shopping in Manhattan. But because he's been stuck out in the States for so long, he couldn't organise anything. Also, after so long out there, he was sick of hearing "Have a nice day!" spoken without sincerity. His longing to come home for a real Christmas with just the two of us is fine by me (we can go into Bath for my Gucci).

*

It's the Squadron Review tonight (panto) and Guy's preparing material like a naughty schoolboy, keeping everything secret from me so as not to spoil the jokes.

Volunteers and a few conscripts organise a shambles of a pantomime, staged by keen thespians totally devoid of any acting skills. The theme is: who can we take the piss out of this time? Pete tells me that the sketches always review what's happened throughout the year (like the time a Loadmaster lost £1,000 out of the back of an aircraft at 12,000 feet) and usually the boss suffers the worst amount of cruelty because it's unfair to aim at the lower ranks.

"Always aim higher, any good boss knows that – they can take it," Guy mutters.

The whole Squadron and their wives are squashed into the crew room, standing at the bar or sitting around tables fashioned from aircraft parts. I drink warm beer in front of the stage (made out of strong cardboard boxes taped together), watching a Loadmaster approaching retirement age work the audience with old jokes.

We wait for the first act to begin, listed in our programme as 'Shadow Q – Act One'.

Dusty curtains held up by a washing line part slowly to reveal a recreation of the Squadron crew room. Six Co-pilots dressed for action stand around a table with their hands poised over a telephone, ready to answer emergency calls. Not a word is uttered and no one moves an inch. Then the curtains close again and everyone wonders what on earth's going on.

Act Two begins before anyone can answer and Guy appears on stage dressed as Will Smith from *Men in Black*, wearing dark glasses and a flying suit. He's sitting at a desk, imitating the Wing Commander carrying out a typical welcome interview for new Co-pilots. The young chap playing the Co-pilot stands opposite him, visibly shaking in his boots.

"And of course, you understand that my door is always open," Guy snarls in a menacing voice.

A huge roar comes from the audience (this boss always shuts his door). The interview is full of in-jokes, which go totally over my head, but continues to whistled approvals from the more informed spectators. Guy finishes grilling his young apprentice, then stands up, shakes his hand and flashes a memory-erasing stick at him (another cheer). Then he turns to the audience and gives a sly, knowing grin while he memory-erases the crowd (insinuating that the boss, sitting somewhere in the audience, will forget what he just saw).

'Shadow Q – Act Three' begins with the curtains opening to show the same bunch of guys from Act One no longer poised over the telephone but sitting about the crew room reading porn magazines, smoking cigarettes and snoozing. The telephone's still in the middle of the table and one of the actors (Guy) picks up the receiver to check that it still works and carefully replaces the handset. Curtains close.

Slowly, it begins to dawn on me what the joke is all about…'Shadow Q' is a call sign for the rapid reaction crew. Whoever gets placed on Shadow Q must be ready to get airborne within two hours, and it's obvious by now that the guys are acting out a typical day on Shadow Q (they never get called).

Other sketches include one chap, impersonating Fluff, the famous radio broadcaster, running through his very own version of the Top Twenty. No one is spared. Anyone who committed the slightest faux pas this year gets included. We laugh and cheer, enjoying the fun at someone else's expense (thank goodness wives are ignored).

The Loadmasters perform their version of *The Full Monty* finale and strip down to bare bottoms. Cheering reaches deafening levels until each Loadie turns around to reveal the photocopied head of each 47 Squadron Executive covering their modesties!

Our friendly compère wears an expression of disbelief after each sketch – can they really get away with this?

Navigators act out a spoof Spice Girls' number (some of them have better figures than the Spice Girls themselves – why do men always have such good legs?).

The wives perform their version of John Travolta and Olivia Newton John's famous hit from the film *Grease*, 'You're The One That I Want', complete with revised lyrics: "I've got children, they're multiplying and I'm losing control, because the hours that you're flying...it's terrifying." (The last line goes: "Are you sure, are you sure down route you're mine...?")

'Shadow Q – Act Four' gets instant laughter because the crew are covered in cobwebs and have obviously all died of boredom. Then the telephone rings...

At the end of the show, the outgoing boss presents 47 Squadron with a double-flowering cherry tree and the new boss makes his welcome address to everyone.

A huge party follows the buffet and everyone gets down to the sound of the funky beat, with NODI doing the disco wearing his pink latex number again.

The atmosphere is hot and electric as Erasure blast their greatest hits from the speakers, keeping limbs moving and feet tapping, but the situation changes in an instant when Olivia takes to the dancing pole. Now I know why the chaps had this piece of devilment installed: they knew that the wives, when drunk, wouldn't be able to resist it, and our Wing

Commander's wife is certainly having a good time sliding up and down the silver shaft. NODI, seeing his opportunity, changes the music to 'Hot Stuff' and encourages our naughty minx to gyrate away. I sneak a glance at Fergus, who's stopped dancing through shock, and notice that he's forcing a smile as Olivia parties on.

"She's done that before," I shout in his ear over the music. Fergus just shakes his head at me, deeply traumatised. It does help that Olivia is wearing tight black trousers and a red silk shirt, which show off her great figure, and by now a few of the boys have pulled up armchairs around her small silver stage, cheering the show on. I'm quite impressed at how lithely she moves around the pole, intrigued at the seductiveness she's exuding (if it was me, I'd be fat and funny but definitely not sexy). Enjoying herself far too much, she straddles a Navigator – who then crawls around her platform on all fours – and attempts to lasso more recruits. When she sits on his face, Fergus coughs loudly a few times and says that it's time to leave. But Olivia disagrees and carries on sliding up and down. As he tries to pull her down from the stage, his smile stays fixed while the boys are told that her performance is over. Their applause is deafening as she takes a bow and jumps down. I congratulate her on her dancing, asking if she was ever on stage.

"No – just wanted to make an exit, sweetie," she laughs. "You wouldn't believe the shit we've gone through on this tour. I only wish someone would write it down."

Olivia blows kisses to the lads as Fergus steers her towards the way out, making excuses for their early departure. "Babysitter needs us," he attempts.

*

The long social stretch to New Year is well underway and standby crews are still hanging around, since Operation Deny Christmas remains redundant.

Guy tells me that the boss had his double-flowering cherry tree planted by the front entrance outside 47 Squadron this morning and then cleared his office, leaving it ready for the next Wing Commander to take over.

By lunchtime the tree is gone, disappeared from sight, but in its place are a pile of sticks and a sign saying 'Logs for Sale'. Not many military men master the art of tact.

Tonight, the cook-off championship finals give us another lame excuse to eat and drink to excess in someone else's house. This time it's Marcus Evans's turn to embark on a culinary expedition, and the usual dining-society gang all troop round to his place on Pintail – each street on the Patch has a duck's name (suppose it's because they fly). Pete rings the doorbell with his elbows, straining to hold armfuls of booze. (Why is the festive period such a gastronomic marathon? I feel so fat.)

Marcus opens the door, gratefully taking the bottles from us while gesturing towards the hall. I like his wife Lisa and we chat away over dinner. The conversation turns to religion, and it slowly begins to dawn on me that our hosts have a faith which is a lot stronger than Pete's, who, charged up with a few glasses of red wine, is liable to be a social grenade.

"Have you read the Bible?" asks Marcus firmly.

"Yes I have," replies Pete.

"Was that with a study guide?" says Lisa, brightly.

(Anyone who reads the Bible with a study guide is serious, so I try kicking Pete under the table to stop him from offending these lovely people.)

"No," he says. "It was with a bloody good shit every morning. I keep it in my toilet, along with the Koran and various other philosophical works."

He winks at me, knowing I've seen the piles of literature in his loo which include manuscripts that have as much in common with divinity as Ozzy Osbourne has with cross-stitch. Pete is actually very well read and keeps a collection of theological texts to strengthen his arguments, and he certainly knows his stuff. The discussion continues at 180 degrees, and when pudding arrives, Lisa's geniality is becoming strained. I suggest we change the subject.

Pete, now a fully-grown silverback social gorilla, waits for silence and then says, "Who's faked an orgasm, then?"

NINE

At least I'm having a busy life (no time to get a job). Being an Air Force wife is a full-time occupation, but Guy doesn't think so.

And since I missed out on stocking-filler presents, I order everything from a small, glossy houseware catalogue, and drive Guy insane showing off pictures of ingenious little devices that I can't possibly live without – neat little gadgets like crumb catchers, egg toppers, orange peelers, fluff removers and a million other useful-looking (but naff) contraptions. And they cost practically nothing! Guy takes the catalogue off me to hide it upstairs.

There's another fancy dress party going on at the Mess but I've got a terrible cold and don't feel like partying. It seems to be party after party at the moment, but I suppose it is the festive season. After much cajoling and persuasion, I finally agree to go but have no outfit organised. In the end I walk across to the Mess in my pyjamas, complete with hot toddy, handkerchief and teddy bear, explaining, "I am the flu virus" (literally).

These people go to amazing efforts for their outfits and it never ceases to impress me. Four people have come as a box of crayons, and coloured faces stick out of the top of a plywood painted box. Watching them turn and walk up the stairs is hilarious (eight legs tripping up). But the green crayon is a short guy, his lime-coloured head peeping out of a hole halfway down the box.

"What's with him?" I ask Guy.

"He's the used crayon."

The small, round anteroom next to the bar is beautifully laid out with food ready for the buffet, but I'm groaning with hunger and slip in unnoticed to nick a few nibbles (feed a cold and all that…). Sitting comfortably underneath the enormous table, hidden from view by a crisp damask tablecloth, I tuck into my picnic and choke on a cocktail sausage when a pair of feet appear and shuffle up beside me. The feet belong to a kind gentleman dressed as Charlie Chaplin.

"Mind if I join you?" he asks, and introduces himself as Teddy.

"Not at all," I mumble, stuffing a whole sausage roll into my mouth. "Just hope we don't get caught."

We continue eating and exchanging pleasantries until it's time to rejoin the fun.

"Very nice to meet you, Kate. I'll no doubt see you later," he says, shaking my hand firmly before going back to the noisy, smoke-filled lounge.

Standing at the bar, Guy surreptitiously asks a few dads (not lads) what it's like to be a parent, finding the answers surprisingly positive.

"But our life would be over and I'd lose the sports car, money and social life," he moans.

"How would your life change?" I say. "I'd be the one getting pregnant, giving up work and looking after a baby. You can still go away with the crew as normal but have two people to come home to instead of one. I don't see how your life would change at all."

I flounce off in a temper, aiming for the ladies where I can calm down and cool off a bit, but halfway there I see my new chum talking to COW.

"Hi, Kate. Have you met Edward the Station Commander?" she asks, slapping his rank in my face.

"Yes thanks," I reply happily. "Teddy and I raided the larder together," I giggle as he nods in agreement. "Nice lipstick," I say, walking off. I glance back and catch her mouthing "Teddy" in jealous surprise.

Depressed from getting nowhere discussing babies with him and feeling awful from this silly flu, I go home to bed leaving Guy to match my coma-induced sleep with alcohol.

*

Our main problem is not being around each other long enough to talk things over, and when we are together, the place is full of visitors getting pissed.

Interestingly enough, Guy has finally realised he can buy flowers from a shop for a few pounds and not over the telephone for a small fortune. This is a revelation for him and I receive a not-quite-dead bunch of red roses (he forgot about them and left them in the car overnight). However, I think it's a lovely gesture and plunge them into cold water, which sort of brings them back to life.

Celebrating New Year the Air Force way, we go out for a curry, and after popadoms, lamb pasanda and Indian beer, the waiter presents me with a perfect red rose.

At home, I say, "Another for my collection," and place it proud amongst its wilting companions. Delighted with the roses, I turn to Guy and whisper his reward for being so romantic. "Forget foreplay tonight, darling."

*

Festivities over, reality looms, and struggling to get up for work, I roll out of bed three hours after Guy, who left at 4am. Sipping Earl Grey, I look across the lounge and suddenly choke with shock, hot tea going up my nose and over my pyjamas. There, upside down in the vase, is my curry-house rose. I have to laugh – Guy's jealous! (I think I'll leave it there for the rest of the week.)

He rushes in after the sortie, late for a routine dental appointment. An hour later, he returns in a sombre mood, telling me they took an x-ray of his teeth for identification purposes. That is, in case he gets shot down or captured when flying in and out of Bosnia on supply trips.

Having Guy home for Christmas has allowed apathy to sneak into our life (almost forgot about the Air Force), but the grim reality of his job suddenly snaps back into my cosy world.

I phone mum for some familiar comfort. "How's dad?" I ask.

"Strange this week, love. I'm a bit concerned about him."

"Why? What's he been up to?"

"Well, he's started drinking at the other end of the bar in the pub."

"So?"

"But he's stood by the tap-room door for sixteen years. It's very worrying."

I change the subject. "How was Christmas in Tenerife?"

"Ooh lovely. We went to see the flamingo dancers three times."

"Flamenco dancers."

"That's what I said."

I listen to her talk about life back up north, growing more distant with each sentence. Supwell seems an idyllic place in my memory, but it's getting less painful to leave each time I visit. Of course I miss my parents, but it's their village, not mine. Wonder if I felt so anxious about Lyneham because everything was a new experience? Feel like I could live anywhere now and not be too bothered (as long as it was an Area of Outstanding Natural Beauty).

*

"We've worked for a whole month planning this," Guy curses as the Balkans exercise Blue Nemesis is cancelled in order to take troops out to Kosovo instead. He's leaving at the usual 'oh God early' hours and the Squadron still needs an immense amount of reorganising.

"And Albania is volatile, so we can't fly over them," he says to himself, pottering around the house with maps and flying bags.

"But are you home for dinner tomorrow?" I ask, not turning away from the TV.

He looks at me in disbelief. "Darling, there's a war going on and you want to know if I'll be home in time for tea?"

"Yup," I say, turning up the volume on *Emmerdale*, ignoring his panic. I'm so used to him disappearing at short notice that blasé doesn't cover it. And he still hasn't answered me regarding dinner.

*

Typical. The crew are delayed for a night because the British embassy in Split won't process dollars. Guy has a bureaucratic nightmare sorting out landing fees while trying to move the troops and equipment over to Greece from Macedonia.

I eat his dinner.

*

"I'm off again," Guy says. "This time I'm away for a week based in Germany, flying in and out of Macedonia."

"Well don't bring any souvenirs back this time," I warn, looking at the ugly, blue, glass hubbly-bubbly pipe gathering dust in the corner.

"But we have trophies from every war the Willesleys attend."

"I mean it – no more tat."

"I'll try to phone as often as I can," he promises. "Things are unstable, but don't worry – we're perfectly safe. I'm not being brave or anything!"

He always tells me that to try to stop me worrying, but it never works. And adultery is a bitter pill to swallow – especially when the third party turns out to be a sodding aeroplane!

Although annoyingly, I know life doesn't get any better than this. I keep waiting for the next stage, thinking that I'll be happy when I get a job. But the jobs are crap and I'm fed up. Then I wonder if I'll settle when we move off the Patch, but Guy will be away from home just as much then as he is now. So it's all shit and my only option is to make it bearable. I'm going to survive this battlefield of commitment by taking each day as it comes, see everyone's faults (my own included) and enjoy making the best of things. Because before I know it, my life will have flashed by and I'll be sixty (and pregnant).

*

Guy phones from Germany and tells me about the horror of whole families camped around Split airport perimeter fence having been thrown out of their homes. Thousands of Croatian refugees are living in army tents; some were given only minutes to pack and leave their homes by the invading Serbs. The alternative is certain death, and they walk for days without food, carrying children and a few belongings before finding safety in the United Nations camp.

"I can't bear to turn the plane around and leave," he says. "Just knowing I have that option is unbearable, when only four hours' flight away from here is the most sadness I've ever seen."

I let him talk; what other comfort can I offer?

"We were waiting to be refuelled this afternoon, watched by refugees on the hillside. They looked frightened and lonely, especially the children. One of our chaps threw a football over the fence and pandemonium broke out. Kids waved madly at us as they ran around – it was fantastic to see what one football can do."

*

Guy's back from another mercy mission. I know he's immensely low and that it will take time for him to relax, so I decide to leave him on his own for a while, giving him space to contemplate things. He does his job with bravado, banter and camaraderie. I think being a single working pawn in the all-consuming machine of warfare has an immense psychological effect on a person. Most couples are discussing what's for dinner of an evening, not how many orphans the husband saw scratching for food in a refugee compound. It's ages before I feel I can approach him, and all he wants is a hug.

"I want to move," he says, thinking living off base would remind him of a normal world outside, where people go to work in the morning and return home at night.

One of the wives phones to ask if Guy is on the same trip as her husband and, if so, when are they due home?

"He's home," I tell her.

"Oh, is he? Thanks. My husband told me he's not back until July – said it was some big exercise."

"What?"

"I thought it a bit odd too, but needed to confirm it with someone. Now I know he's having an affair."

"Are you sure?" I say, amazed at her composure.

"Well, why else would he tell me he's going away for a month when it's only a short trip? And he gets in from the pub on a Friday night and strips off in the hall before going for a shower, at two o'clock in the morning!"

"What do you do?"

"I smell his clothes for perfume."

Not knowing what to say, I find myself wishing her luck for the future. After explaining the conversation to Guy, he admits that some wives are kept completely in the dark by their other halves, who deliberately don't tell them schedules so as to buy some free time. I'm amazed – how can people be so deceptive? I wouldn't be able to cover my tracks.

Although, I'm in no position to judge an adulterer – who knows what is going to happen with our marriage? I have to trust Guy when he's away (no other choice), otherwise what's the point?

Must remember to let him know that I love him.

*

Guy has a brainwave. He asks friends and neighbours to do-nate their old toys so that he can take them to Split on the next aircraft. Unfortunately, while trying to arrange the logistics at the Squadron, unnamed higher powers intervene and say it's not possible.

"What about Teddy – can't he intervene?" I ask, before explaining how I came to befriend the Station Commander at the last Mess fancy dress party. Guy's amazed I'm on first-name terms with him.

"Pet-name terms," I correct.

He's still furious. "If ever there's a time these kids need something to cuddle or play with, it's now," he fumes.

My top-dog contact can't change things but does tell Guy that sometimes the loads are changed at the last minute, allowing room for 'other freight'. Then he finds out about an aircraft leaving for Kosovo in two days' time with available space. Guy puts a box by the entrance of each Squadron requesting toys – especially footballs (interesting to see how this situation is affecting him, someone who can't stand kids…).

*

Word has got out, and after only twenty-four hours, the Squadrons are bursting with toys, old and new. I retrieve the disposable camera from the glove compartment of my car, kept there in case I crash (the fact that I have a camera for this purpose worries Guy, but I'm only being prudent), and put it in one of the boxes of toys with a note attached saying, 'When issuing these toys, please take photos and return to 24 Squadron, Lyneham, UK'.

Driving between the four Squadrons, Guy collects the boxes before going over to the movers, who put them on board the aircraft as 'opportune freight'. He then phones my brother-in-law (Army), who luckily is based at Split airport, explaining that they need help distributing the toys arriving from Lyneham.

Hugh offers to impound the aircraft but settles on sending a Land Rover to meet the consignment.

*

Taking his mind off the toy situation, Guy decides to revise in preparation for the current Hercules' conversion to metric after thirty-two years of imperial measurement.

Head in his textbooks, he shouts "What's for dinner?" at me in the kitchen.

"Babies," I reply, trying his patience again.

"Can't we get a puppy instead?" he asks.

"No, Guy, we can't," I retort. "'Cos a dog's for life, and a child's for decades."

At bedtime, Hugh phones to say he sent some of his men to meet the aircraft and the toys were loaded into jeeps before being handed out around the camp. Some were even handed to children as they boarded a flight taking them to their new foster country.

Why is Guy so interested in helping these refugee children

but adamant that we can't have one of our own? Aaargh! (I could hit him.)

*

Drive to Worcester for Annabel's hen weekend. Her sister has booked an eight-berth barge for us to crash up and down the English countryside in.

I arrive late and park our black BMW next to a line of sports cars and wonder what Annabel's friends will be like. She's deliberately invited one girl from each of her various circles of friends (none of us have met).

One by one we climb aboard and I pitch the mood by hanging a naked-man ironing-board cover from the window. Annabel is disgusted but soon changes her mind when I open a bottle of champagne and attach her wrist to the tiller with pink furry handcuffs. We meet Malcolm our instructor, sign up, accept the keys and listen to his colloquial safety briefing before taking it in turns to see where the engine is (like we're interested...).

The 'man', as we call him, is unsure we're capable of driving this thing and takes us out on a test run. Annabel refuses to wear a crash helmet on the grounds of getting 'hat hair' and manages to steer the barge with one hand while drinking Bolly with the other (not illegal). Malcolm deems us worthy of taking 'her' out (why are boats always women?) and, telling me off for calling it a barge – it's a narrow boat, apparently – appoints me chief rope-thrower. Forty minutes and two locks later, we beg Malcolm to join us for the weekend as skipper. Sensibly, he refuses, so we name the narrow boat after him and wave goodbye like he's our trusting parent. Half a mile of sailing is enough for us on our first night and *Malcolm* gets moored up so that we can become better acquainted with each other (through booze) before our adventures begin. We decide to stand up to introduce ourselves and get less reserved as the wine flows.

"Paige, thirty-eight, divorcee from Knaresborough," a slender, pixie-faced brunette says.

"Hi, I'm Mia from Harrogate and almost divorced," says a

confident, strong and friendly woman (strangely, we give her a round of applause).

"Camilla, twenty-two and gay. But don't worry, you're all safe…for tonight, anyway," laughs Annabel's sister, sitting down.

"I'm Annabel, as you already know, and I'm enjoying my last week of freedom before marrying Jason," smiles our host, taking a bow.

"Kate, only just twenty-seven, from York but living in Wiltshire, married to the Air Force – and Guy," I offer.

"Gabby, thirty-one, mother of four-month-old Ben," a tall, attractive lady tells us.

"I'm Josie, and I'm not telling you my age," says the last-but-one of our group without getting up. "I work in the city but want to travel and get on Miss World."

We laugh as the formalities are almost over.

"And my name's Serena," says a tall, shy waif quietly. "I'm thirty years old and went to school with Annabel. Pleased to meet you all."

Trying to make polite conversation with Paige, I almost offend her by complimenting her on her designer watch. "Is it real?" I ask.

"Of course it is – why wouldn't it be?" she snaps (and I realise I'm so used to seeing fakes from Guy's travels).

We drink and chat until the late hours and then all eight of us try to get ready for bed in the confined space, constantly bumping into each other. I manage to take my bra off without removing an item of clothing (pulling it out of my sleeve) and remember that the last time I did that was in my sixth-form camping days. Camilla walks around stark naked without a care in the world.

"Wow," I blurt out, gawping at her tattoo.

"Do you like it?" she smiles, turning to show the full picture of a hunt cantering across her shoulder blades. Three hounds are clinging to the small of her back chasing the fox, which has disappeared up her bum (only the tail protrudes).

"I've got one, but it's not as good as that," says Paige, revealing a small sign near her nether region stating 'Coming soon'.

"I knew a girl who dyed her fanny green and had a tattoo

saying 'Keep off the grass'," says a voice from the bunk beds.

"Did she have a 'first hole' flag too?" laughs Camilla.

Unable to join in the discussion from never having had a tattoo let alone wanting one, I screw up my face in horror listening to the pain endured by Camilla for her art.

"I always wanted a kiwi on my hip," says Josie.

"Why would you want to have that small hairy thing?" I ask, oblivious she means fowl, not fruit.

"I'm planning to have one for my mid-life crisis," Mia jokes.

"Well you'd better hurry up then – you're running a bit late," Annabel quips.

Sleep is impossible because my bunk is far too short and I immediately get cramp in my right leg (at least Zoë's not here to tell them I dragged it).

Malcolm gently rocks everyone else off to sleep but I lay half awake, spending most of the night throwing up in a bucket.

*

Still nauseous from last night (but not quite bad enough to refuse a bacon sandwich) as we set sail across the knee-deep seas of Worcestershire.

Mia, Paige and Josie volunteer to take care of opening and closing the locks while I ram the boat repeatedly into the canal bank. Annabel floats about wearing high heels and a silk dress, looking totally unsuitable for seafaring.

"Thanks," I say, accepting a cup of cold, milky tea from Gabby (before throwing it over the side).

Serena yelps with delight as four ducks sail past her head by the kitchen window (Camilla tuts at her femininity).

I look at the sky and feel sunlight bathe my face. Even though the air has a bitter sting, we aren't really feeling cold. There's definitely something to be said for going away with a bunch of women you've never met before, because none of us are gossiping about work or each other (yet). Yes, we all probably have hidden secrets and problems of our own, but making an effort to enjoy new friends is enormously uplifting. And what's more, these seven women know nothing about the Air Force!

I hand out T-shirts to everyone with 'Annabel's getting married' on the front. On the back it says 'Not me', except for Annabel's, which says 'I'm Annabel'. We plough on towards Birmingham at a leisurely speed.

Camilla's much better at steering than me and takes over for a while, chattering happily about her recent travels across Australia.

"You cold?" she asks, offering me her jacket. "You've got nips like chapel hat pegs!"

Rather startled and immensely embarrassed that she's noticed I'm sporting erect nipples, I quickly slip the extra coat on and worry that I've pulled the lesbian.

Annabel joins us in the fresh air, bringing coffee and doughnuts. "What's married life like?" she asks. I want to say "Hard, hard work like you've never dreamt of", but instead throw up my bacon sandwich over the side. How can I be seasick on a bloody canal?

Mia shouts at us to move over to let another boat pass the other way. We slow down and see a group of women wearing 'Just divorced' T-shirts waving happily at us from their barge (Annabel is suddenly speechless).

The afternoon disappears too quickly as we chug slowly through lush, rural England. At sunset, Paige reads out her shower rota, allocating fifteen minutes a person (I'm last), while Josie takes directions to the nearest pub from a passing cyclist.

Getting slightly better at parking, mooring up and changing outfits in small spaces, we disembark *Malcolm*, leaving him safely locked up for the evening, and head towards the happening nightlife of the Tow Path Arms.

All of us except Serena (veggie) fill up on steak and chips and Annabel keeps ordering more champagne (Jason is in for huge housekeeping bills). We put small change in the jukebox and ask the landlord to turn the music up loud enough for us to hear while dancing on his rather tacky chairs. The locals are intrigued, but we don't care as none of them are young enough to bother impressing.

Gabby tells us (loudly) that she fell pregnant because she

stood on her head after having sex. Apparently, once her husband got over the shock of being used, he rather liked it.

"I've gone six weeks without a shag," moans Paige. "It's such a long time."

"I wouldn't know," answers Mia.

Serena (drunk) insensitively asks Camilla how come she has such a big gap between her two front teeth, and Camilla, unperturbed by her impolite observation, replies, "All the better to suck your clit with, my dear."

"You're such a bloke," retorts Annabel to her sister.

"Thank you," accepts Camilla, and adds, "Pass the shampoo, darling," before filling up her glass.

"Come on, ladies," pipes up the old barman. "Why does every generation think that they're the ones who invented sex? It isn't everything."

"Oh yes it is," we chant, laughing.

"How do you achieve orgasm, Gabby?" asks Paige.

"Tea, bath and bed."

"She's the one with the baby," Annabel reminds us.

I'm shocked and disgusted to hear that Josie's new boyfriend shaves his bollocks, while the others fall about laughing.

"But why?" I ask.

"'Cos he can, I suppose," answers Josie in fits of giggles. "It's quite nice, really. Makes a change."

"Sod his bollocks – can he kiss?" slurs Mia.

"Oh God yes, he's so sexy…My knees turn to jelly and my knickers are soaked every time we smooch. I'm foaming at the snatch just thinking about him."

"Eeeyaow!" we scream.

"That'll end soon enough," drawls Camilla, "once personal space invasion turns into routine."

Annabel writes her phone number in chalk at the bottom of the menu blackboard and puts smiley faces above every handwritten 'i'. Josie and Mia are getting more and more outrageous with each bottle of champagne, and taking a break from Gabby's Olympic dance routine, Annabel opens our third bottle, asking me what happened to Siobhan's good-looking brother, Danny.

"We need to marry him off," she shouts without waiting for an answer, deciding marriage is today's medicine.

"I have a friend who's desperate," Serena suggests.

"Never," I burst out. "He's far too good for any old scrubber. And anyway, I…that is, Siobhan and I love him dearly."

"Hmm, yes, I think you do," Camilla drawls (I ignore the insinuation), and our last two dancing queens sit down to join in with the conversation.

"I love Stuart," says Josie about her latest boyfriend.

"Aha!" Paige interrupts. "The question isn't do you love him – it's do you snog him?"

"Nope," Mia answers for herself, and giggles, "That's probably why I'm getting divorced."

(I make a mental note to snog Guy's brains out every day when he gets home to prove to myself how much I love him.)

"And my affair didn't help," Paige continues. "Take it from me, ladies, the day your knickers come off…your marriage is over."

"What absolute claptrap! Mine came off long before it ended," Mia says, finishing the bottle. "Although my lover, who shall remain nameless until after the decree absolute, is always accusing me of being unfaithful. But I argue that since I've been with him, I haven't even slept with my husband."

We all stare at her strange understanding of the word 'faithful'.

"But does Stuart love you?" Serena asks Josie.

"Yes, he told me so," she replies, defending him.

"When – before or after?"

"After, come to think of it. We were cuddled up in bed together."

"Then he doesn't."

"I don't love Jason," Annabel announces.

Paige chokes on her champagne, saying the bubbles have gone up her nose, and silence replaces our singing. Gabby orders eight black coffees and suggests we end the evening, saying, "We've said and drunk too much – let's go back. Things will look better in the morning."

Annabel walks back along the towpath alone, rejecting even

Camilla's offer of a hug, and we follow behind, a gaggle of drunken emotion. Swinging between tears and sniggering, Josie tells dirty jokes that cause Gabby to stop in her tracks, and we have to wait for her to finish laughing before we can start walking again.

"Why do you stop walking when you laugh?" I ask.

"Because I've no pelvic floor and I'll wee," she replies, which induces fits of uncontrollable hysteria all round and has us pissing ourselves with laughter.

*

Last day on the barge. None of us know what to say after Annabel's outburst of honesty and we tiptoe around, making polite conversation. Camilla nominates Serena to sit down and talk sense to her but Annabel's avoiding the issue, saying she was just joking.

"You don't joke about something like that," Paige whispers to me sitting on the steps.

"Look, she's obviously regretting telling us so lets stay out of it. If she wants to make a mistake then let her – I wouldn't have listened to anyone telling me to abandon my wedding," Mia advises us.

I think about the situation and realise that I didn't have one single doubt about marrying Guy. Yes, I was scared witless, but it felt so right – I always knew I loved him. How could Annabel say such a thing in jest?

Water laps the sides as we slowly move up the lock walls, inch by inch. Paige and Josie scream orders to each other from opposite ends of the barge. I help prepare breakfast and ask Josie to pull over when it's ready.

"Mmm," drools Mia hungrily, pouring maple syrup over two pancakes.

"I can never do this," I complain, trying to catch one neatly in the pan.

"Oh, let me have a go – I'm a great tosser," offers Serena enthusiastically.

After eating our fill, we set off again in a semi-straight line and I wash the dishes while waiting to catch Annabel alone.

Pre-empting me, Annabel says, "Jason's a good man."

"That why you're marrying him?" I ask.

"And other reasons," she says.

"You all right?" I ask.

Annabel bursts into tears and sobs on my shoulder, "Oh Kate, I don't want to snog him – does that mean I don't love him?"

Warm relief floods through me as I realise that there's nothing more serious bothering her. True to her sex, she's taken a flippant statement literally. I laugh out loud and give her a cuddle.

"You idiot, of course it doesn't," I tell her, wiping away my tears before offering her a tissue to mop up her own (I cry at anything).

We lurch forwards as Camilla steers us away from the lock into a tunnel, heading towards the boat yard.

Pleased to see his barge back in one piece after so many women drivers, we beg the real Malcolm to take heaps of photographs of us sitting on the roof before saying our goodbyes and promising to keep in touch with each other (I notice Josie giving her phone number to Camilla).

Leaving my new friends behind, I'm sad the weekend's over, because for one weekend, I was Kate, completely away from the Air Force – free, liberated (I actually feel like me again).

Pull onto our drive late into the evening and find Guy dozing on the sofa in front of a cyber, manic, murder mystery movie.

"What on earth are you watching?" I ask as he stirs.

"A weepy…you wouldn't like it," he yawns, and pulls my knickers off.

*

Snog Guy the instant I wake up.

Later, we wonder what has happened to my camera, when it appears at the Squadron with a note attached to it saying, 'This must be the most well-travelled camera in modern military history'.

270

The note explains that it left Split on a flight to Aviano (Italy) where a Tri-Star crew en route to America took it with them. They passed it to a Nimrod crew returning to Scotland and it was finally given yesterday to a Hercules crew coming back to Lyneham. Guy found it in his pigeonhole at lunchtime.

I can't wait to get the photos developed and drag Guy into Wootton Bassett to get them done. After lunch in the pub, we return to collect them and the shop owner asks us what's going on as he flicks through shots of the French military distributing toys to refugees. Guy tells him the story, and to his surprise the chap refuses any payment.

I sense that Guy feels better – useful from actually being able to do something. Seeing suffering and feeling utterly powerless, it's lucky he knew who to talk to. In total, he sent out thirty-six crates of toys. Can't stand kids indeed, I think to myself. Something touched his heart and made him do this for them. I know he'll make a good dad – but when?

*

Still feel queasy from losing my sea legs. I stretch my arms around Guy and give him a hug, ignoring his hints about me putting on weight, until eventually he uses the subtlety of a tank.

"Shagging you is like shagging a bucket of lard," he says, standing up.

I reel from shock and take a step back from him to catch my breath. I'm really hurt and try to recover my composure, to 'take it on the chin'.

Seeing my surprise, he immediately jokes, "It takes me longer to put my arms around you than it did when we first met." (I agree, blaming over indulgence at Christmas, but notice he's not smiling when criticising – he means it.) "And you haven't even looked at your birthday present, let alone used it," he adds, directing his gaze to the aerobics step that I've strategically placed in the dining room to enable me to reach the highest shelf.

"Because I didn't realise it was a statement," I answer.

"But look at you; it's so unfair. You were thin at our

271

wedding. Why have you got so fat in such a short space of time?"

"All right, Guy, that's enough," I say, ending his attack and trying not to cry.

Ignoring him for a moment by flicking through the TV channels, I stop at two children pretending to be pilots and suddenly see Guy looking back at me through the eyes of an eight-year-old.

"You know what the funny thing about this is?" he asks over my shoulder.

"What?" I grunt.

"Those two kids are pretending to be pilots," he says, laughing. "And…I am one! See you later, fatty."

I try to plead 'big-boned' but Guy is having none of it.

"There's no such thing – it's simply a case of less in here," he says, pointing to his mouth, "and more out of here," he adds, pointing to his arse. "And, if people are naturally big boned," he concludes sanctimoniously, "then why are there no fat people in Third World countries or photographs of big-boned people in Second World War concentration camps?" Lecture over, he gets on his bicycle and pedals off towards the Squadron.

Bastard! Why can't I have a husband who wants me fat and happy? What is so wrong with being a porker?

I empty out our cupboards of junk food (into my mouth) and decide to go on a starvation diet. (I last five hours.)

Food is so easily available – that's my main problem. Our shops are stuffed full of packaged, easy-to-cook and wonderfully satisfying food. We don't have to prepare anything or think about waiting for meals. Other generations had to struggle (cook) and manage with seasonal fruit and vegetables – life seemed so much simpler then.

The day before we married, I cut the labels out of my underwear so that Guy would never know my lower dimensions. Not because I didn't want him to know; it's just that I like big pants.

He comes home from work and tries to cuddle me from behind while I'm standing at the kitchen sink. I yelp with embarrassment and try to move away but get wedged between the drainer and him as he grabs hold of my belly, laughing at the welt of wobble in his hands.

"Just fuck off, will you," I sob.

"Come on, Kate, I'm only showing you what's there."

"Oh, and you're perfect, are you?"

"No, not at all, but I'm not fat either."

Guy's got new-found confidence, making exaggerated chewing noises while I'm eating. He obviously thinks I'm not that bothered. My husband, who I hero-worship and adore, is a really cruel shit and won't stop the jibes. But he must see how upset I am.

"I've had enough of this abuse – I'm off to bed."

As usual, he cuddles up to me in bed, his arm naturally falling across my tummy, and I turn blue breathing in. I slyly lift his hand away from my stomach region to a more acceptable boob, which he seems quite happy to hold. I can't sleep, and lie awake reliving the moment when he told me I'm a lard arse…My world has come crashing down and some of my love for him has died. How can I love him again?

Right now, I hate him.

*

At 5am the phone rings and I'm vaguely aware of Guy leaving. There's a note in the kitchen waiting for me when I surface saying 'Chin up. I still love you even if you are a fat bint. Back soon – short UK trip.'

Typical – he's gone off with bloody Albert again!

Can't stop thinking about him calling me fat. Will I ever cope or recover from his critical observation? He doesn't want me, doesn't fancy me. But he should love me. How can he be so cruel? I worship him. There's no way we can have sex again without me thinking I'm a bucket of lard, feeling vulnerable and unattractive.

Yes, I have put on a stone since we got married, but I was happy (at least I think I was).

The pain inside from Guy's comments chips away at my defences, making me feel as though I should do something about it. Ignorance is bliss (and the truth is very painful). He couldn't have done a better job of hurting me if he'd punched me in the stomach. I cry in the toilets at work (the boss thinks I have a migraine and sends me home).

I am fat, but so what?

I'm leaving him, I decide. I'm off to Amber's house (can't go to Yorkshire – they would lynch Guy for being so mean). We live separate lives most of the time now anyway. Let him figure this one out.

Catching up with Amber and the boys, I'm overcome by what a difference a taste of true friendship can make to the soul. I need female sympathy.

"It's Hattie's fault," I whinge. "She always made me clear my plate before filling it up again. I'm sure she's got a compulsive feeding disorder. Whenever anyone walks through the door, they get fed – it's a northern thing."

Amber listens patiently to my heartache.

"Some people do drugs or drink…I do large dinners," I say, reaching for another digestive.

She surreptitiously pushes the fruit bowl towards me and slides the biscuits away. (My God! Betrayal…Even my friend thinks I'm fat.)

Putting a brave front on my despair, I set off home to pack. Wave goodbye, wishing my upper arms wouldn't do the same.

*

The sense of being alone is overwhelming and makes everything worse. I wonder what I'm doing here, miles away from my family and friends. All I have is Guy; my life is Guy, and if he isn't here for me then I have no one.

Wallowing in my misery, I decide that I'm on my own in life and that anything nice I pick up along the way is a bonus. My heart's becoming hardened and I get through the day by being cynical about him – at least this way I won't get hurt again. Bastard.

It's so hard to love him in this state of mind – I just feel contempt and as though I could have made a much better job of my life by living alone.

In my head I can hear words meant for Guy, but it's too painful to speak. Why aren't you listening to me? Why can't you see I'm hurting? Why why why? You've been such a shit and you can't see it. Can you hear me in a parallel universe? Is that what it is – is there a place where all the things that you've left undone are done? (If so, I want to swap husbands.)

Wondering how the weight has crept on, I lie in bed and realise that every night *I* decide what we eat for dinner. But if I go on strike and make Guy decide or take a turn, we end up eating curry or some other takeaway, which is extremely fattening.

Oh, I so want to be a trophy wife.

*

I call the agency, saying I don't feel well and won't be in today. Actually, that's no lie – I feel totally numb.

Every time I look in a full-length mirror, I see a pot-bellied pig. I'm fat and unhappy today, when only a month ago I was happy (and fat). The main burden is this sickening thud I feel from knowing that Guy doesn't fancy me anymore.

I pick up the phone, hands shaking, and dial automatically. "Siobhan? Is that you?" I start, before realising it's the answering machine. "Oh shit – where are you? Listen carefully 'cos I've not got long. Guy's gone too far this time. He told me I'm *fat!*"

I stop short as Danny picks up the receiver, interrupting my babble.

"Kate? What's the matter – are you okay?"

"Er, Danny…No, I'm not okay, as you've probably guessed. What are you doing there?"

"The usual. My dear little sister had a DIY crisis and I'm sorting it out – heard your voice on the machine."

I burst into tears, saying how hard I've tried to make the loneliness work and that I love Guy but he can't see the support I need and now he thinks I'm fat.

"You're not fat, you're all woman," Danny says, trying to placate me.

"Fuck off."

"Get on a train and come home," he says quietly.

A light gets switched on in my head and suddenly everything's clear. The decision is agonising and I can't stop tears from streaming down my face. Why was I so stupid to not notice Danny? He's funny, good looking, kind, tidy, can cook, wants children…Oh to hell with Guy! If I'm not good enough for him after everything I've given up, the solitude I've endured just because he's there at the end of it, then he can just sod off. And if my only crime is to enjoy my food, then I don't want him anymore. The shallow git can find a thinner woman who will put up with this stupid, lonely lifestyle.

"Kate, are you still there?" he says.

"Danny, you were right. I should've listened that night you tried to tell me. He's done worse than hurt me; I'm crushed to the core. I'm leaving him."

I tell him I'll get the next train to York and he agrees to pick me up later this afternoon.

It's all happening too easily, I think, packing a few bags with overnight things (dad did warn me that walking away is the easy part). Squadron Leader Harry Barker from next door sees the tears pouring down my cheeks as I load up the taxi. He quickly leans his bicycle up against the wall and asks if everything's all right.

"No, it's bloody well not all right – can't you tell?" I sob. "I'm leaving Guy. This life stinks."

"But Kate, he really loves you," Harry pleads.

"He really loves that heap of metal he flies around in," I snap.

Harry tries to stop me from going, saying, "That's not true. Every time I fly with Guy, all he talks about is you and how much he loves you."

"Funny, all he ever talks to me about is *himself*. And he never tells me how much he loves me…"

I turn to face him, immensely aware of the life-changing conversation I'm having, discussing the end of my marriage with someone I vaguely know while his wife knocks on the window telling him lunch is ready. At moments of extreme stress, I notice surreal things (like how blue the sky is today and chewing gum stuck on the road). Time seems to stand still as my decision gets firmly planted in my mind.

Charged with anger and emotion, I argue, "He's never here, and when he is, he's off drinking with the lads. We never do anything together. He hates kids – I want kids. Harry, I'm two hundred miles from home with a husband who tells me I'm fat!"

"Fair enough," Harry acknowledges, holding his hands up, backing off and agreeing that he doesn't know the half of it.

I get into the taxi, hardly able to see through the blear of tears, and stare at the house I've called home for almost a year. Guy will get my note this evening telling him how I feel (wonder if I'm doing the right thing, but he won't expect this because he thinks he's such a good catch). I look at my watch: it's nearly one o'clock, and Danny will be at York station in about four hours. *Oh, why didn't I open my eyes and see him first?*

Harry overtakes the taxi on his bicycle, almost getting run over cutting across the road, and I settle back into the leather seats, totally void of any feeling.

Thirty minutes later, I arrive at the train station and stand on the platform. Hearing the guard announce a ten-minute delay, I walk into the buffet lounge and buy a large chocolate bar (sod him), unaware that people are looking strangely at my tear-stained face and runny nose. Heading back onto the platform, I find somewhere to sit and sob deeply, rocking back and forth on an iron bench, my head pounding in agony.

I eat the chocolate then rush to the toilet and throw it up, along with my breakfast and last night's carrots (now I really feel like shit).

The train pulls in and I let commuters off before fighting my way to the front and throwing my bags through an open door. I notice I've left one on the bench outside the buffet and hurry back to collect it when a familiar hand picks it up.

Looking into Guy's eyes, I see he's out of breath and obviously shaken. "Harry told me," he explains. "Came running into the Squadron saying I had a train to catch."

"I can't go on living with you," I whisper, taking the bag.

"Kate, what can I say…I've been a shit, I know. Please don't – I love you, Kate."

"I'm not your crew, I'm your *wife*! You just can't expect me to accept that you don't fancy me and then ignore me when I tell you to stop saying I'm fat."

"Sorry." Guy looks at his feet, more aware of his merciless ridicule. "Thought you could take it. I always thought you were so strong."

"But I'm still a person, with real feelings, and you've hurt me. Guy, deep down you're still a bachelor. It was hard enough leaving my old life behind and getting to grips with the Air Force but I did it because I loved you. I need your support but you keep saying how grateful I should be to have you. And you won't listen to me about anything – kids, missing home, not having a job…"

The guard is ushering people onto the train and I move towards the open door. Guy tries to hold my hand but I pull away.

"No, Kate, *wait*! I've been thinking seriously about having kids," he says.

"So whoopee. What changed your mind – did you take a 'grow up' pill?"

"I think I may have taken the whole box. Staying in the last hotel was a young family, and I watched this little girl follow her dad everywhere. He was her hero; she hid behind him constantly. At bedtime, they came into the bar to order warm milk and she sat on his knee in her pyjamas, waiting patiently…I want that. I just can't get it out of my head."

People are watching us from the train window, Guy in full flying kit and me with a handful of soggy tissues.

"Please don't go," he says. "I know I've been a bastard but I've never stopped loving you. This has been hard for me too – I've never lived with anyone before…Give me a second chance," Guy begs quietly. "After the dining-in night when I said all wives are spongers, I thought about what you lot have to put up with and realised it's an awful job – I know I couldn't handle it. Come on, Kate, let's go home – *please*."

I look at my husband and realise that the uniform and the

Air Force are nothing to do with the man I love. It's not him I hate but bloody Albert!

I bury my face in Guy's shoulder and he holds me tightly as the train slowly pulls away.

"Guy, I'm not fat," I sob into his shoulder. "I'm late…I think I might be pregnant."

His eyes open wide with shock as we stare at each other.

"Oh God!" I yell, hitting him as the carriage disappears from sight. "My fucking bags are still on the train!"

Author's Note

A friend hinted to me that "one does not bother with acknowledgements on a first book". But if I don't then I won't sleep (and I love my bed). So here goes...

I am deeply indebted to those who contributed: Pete Martin (my editor, shadow, conscience and friend), Lyndall Gibson (lawyer), James Carrier (website design), Mark Ralph (production) and David Thomas (the man from Boltneck Publications Ltd), who said yes.

Enormous gratitude for constant support from my parents and friends, Joy, Lizz and Lee, Ruth, Jo and Jan, Helen, Pod, Alex, June, PT, and Tracey. Thanks also to Jo Hobson, a modern-day fairy godmother. And Kirsty – you are my endless supply of material!

Jules, thank you for saying to me in the Officers' Mess bar, "For goodness' sake, woman, shut up talking about it and write" (without that gentle reprimand, I'd never have done it). And my big sister Lynne – three years ago when no one else thought it possible, your initial encouragement gave me enough security to believe in myself.

Those I force-fed text – Saz, Kate, Fiona, Andrea, Sandy, Jaynie, Mahala, Ali, Zara and Sally – thanks, guys.

My love and laughter goes to The Little Fishes Committee for letting me shock them in church, and to John Wright (vicar of Tetbury) for attempting to unravel my incessant life queries.

Finally, thanks to the big guy who always listens and answers my prayers.

*